C000115950

I see maths

Delivers ALL the objectives in the KS3 Framework
for Teaching Mathematics

Book 3

Sue Jennings and Richard Dunne

THOMAS TELFORD SCHOOL

ACCESSION N. WITHDRAWN

AREA OF
LEARNING

Thomas Telford School

547443

www.letts-education.com

Contents

Objectives are numbered consecutively within each topic as laid out in the Mathematics Framework, pages 6–11.

Letts I See Maths Book 3

Addition and subtraction

Essential exercises

1 Complete the following tables.

(a)

x	498	307		4091	39201	
y	579		1028			9987
$x + y$		682	3476	7804	50733	20118

(b)

x	$\frac{3}{5}$		$\frac{14}{87}$	$\frac{27}{131}$		$\frac{12}{10}$
y	$\frac{7}{5}$	$\frac{6}{7}$			$\frac{39}{100}$	
$x + y$		$\frac{23}{7}$	$\frac{65}{87}$	$\frac{95}{131}$	$\frac{257}{100}$	$\frac{18}{10}$

(c)

x	·7	2·81	43·86		19·506	
y	·8			4·038		7·3
$x + y$		5·67	72·93	9·207	27·37	15·09

(d)

x	109	241		449		
y	87		184		518	99
$x - y$		56	237	380	726	99

(e)

x	$\frac{9}{5}$	$\frac{7}{9}$		$\frac{19}{29}$	$\frac{47}{100}$	
y	$\frac{3}{5}$		$\frac{4}{13}$			$\frac{7}{1000}$
$x - y$		$\frac{2}{9}$	$\frac{6}{13}$	$\frac{7}{29}$	$\frac{18}{100}$	$\frac{16}{1000}$

(f)

x	·9	3·02		51·78		8
y	·7		4·67		4·912	
$x - y$		1·53	9·73	34·03	3·674	3·35

2 Work out the value of x in each of the following equations.

(a) $56 + x = 79$

(b) $206 - x = 97$

(c) $x + 2·7 = 8·5$

(d) $19·03 + x = 49·36$

(e) $x + \frac{5}{16} = \frac{23}{16}$

(f) $\frac{2}{3} + x = \frac{5}{6}$

Letts I See Maths Book 3

Addition and subtraction

3 Complete the pyramid below.

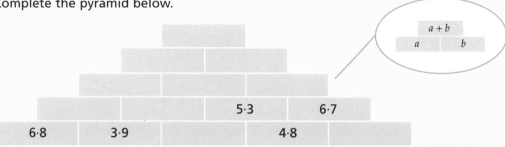

4 Complete the magic squares below.

9		
	7	6
		5

·6		·3
		·7
		·2

		$\frac{6}{15}$
	$\frac{5}{15}$	
$\frac{4}{15}$		$\frac{8}{15}$

5 Given that $p + q = r$, write down answers to the following.

(a) $r - q$ (b) $r - p$ (c) $p - r$ (d) $q - r$

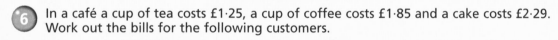

6 In a café a cup of tea costs £1·25, a cup of coffee costs £1·85 and a cake costs £2·29. Work out the bills for the following customers.

(a) two cups of tea and two cakes

(b) one cup of tea, two cups of coffee and one cake

(c) five cups of coffee, three cups of tea and eight cakes

(d) one cup of coffee, one cup of tea and four cakes

Homework

Write a real-life story for each of the maths stories below.

(a) $35 + 56 = 91$ (b) $83 - 29 = 54$ (c) $5·98 + 3·61 = 9·59$

(d) $3·71 - 1·45$ (e) $\frac{2}{5} + \frac{3}{5} = \frac{5}{5}$ (f) $\frac{8}{10} - \frac{3}{10} = \frac{5}{10}$

Multiplication and division

Essential exercises

1 Complete the following multiplication grid.

×	8	3	5	9	7	6	4	2
7								
4								
6								
8								
2								
9								
5								
3								

2 Complete the following multiplication tables.

$73 \times 0 =$	$29 \times 0 =$	$82 \times 0 =$
$73 \times 1 =$	$29 \times 1 =$	$82 \times 1 =$
$73 \times 2 =$	$29 \times 2 =$	$82 \times 2 =$
$73 \times 3 =$	$29 \times 3 =$	$82 \times 3 =$
$73 \times 4 =$	$29 \times 4 =$	$82 \times 4 =$
$73 \times 5 =$	$29 \times 5 =$	$82 \times 5 =$
$73 \times 6 =$	$29 \times 6 =$	$82 \times 6 =$
$73 \times 7 =$	$29 \times 7 =$	$82 \times 7 =$
$73 \times 8 =$	$29 \times 8 =$	$82 \times 8 =$
$73 \times 9 =$	$29 \times 9 =$	$82 \times 9 =$

3 Use the tables in Exercise 2 to find the following.

(a) 73×60 (b) 290×8 (c) 82×500

(d) $584 \div 73$ (e) $87 \div 3$ (f) $574 \div 7$

(g) $2{\cdot}9 \times 4$ (h) ${\cdot}82 \times {\cdot}9$ (i) ${\cdot}73 \times 90$

4 Complete the following grid.

x	$\frac{5}{10}$	$\frac{2}{10}$	·4	·3	·02	
y	$\frac{3}{10}$		·6			·04
$x \times y$		$\frac{8}{100}$		·21	·06	·28

Letts I See Maths **Book 3**

Multiplication and division

Challenging exercises

5 Work out the answer to 69×47 by:
(a) completing the multiplication grid
(b) using the vertical method in the box.

×	60	9	Totals
40			
7			
		Answer	

$$\begin{array}{r} 69 \\ \times\ 47 \\ \hline \\ \hline \end{array}$$

6 Use your answers to Exercise 5 to write down the answers to the following.

(a) 40×69
(b) 7×69
(c) $2760 \div 69$
(d) $360 \div 9$
(e) $6·9 \times 4·7$
(f) $69 \times ·47$
(g) $3243 \div 69$
(h) $32·43 \div 4·7$
(i) $324·3 \div 6·9$

7 Given that $p \times q = r$, write down the answers to the following.

(a) $r \div q$
(b) $r \div p$
(c) $10p \times q$
(d) $p \times 100q$

Problem-solving exercises

8 Work out the costs of the following items.

(a) six bars of chocolate @ 85p each
(b) ten pairs of socks @ £2·76 a pair
(c) nine cold drinks @ £1·24 each
(d) thirty-two textbooks @ £9·34 each

9 Tickets for the cinema cost £6·45 for an adult and £4·75 for a child. Work out the costs of going to the cinema for the following families.

(a) two adults and three children
(b) one adult and four children
(c) three adults and two children

Homework

Write a real-life story for each of the maths stories below.

(a) $25 \times 68 = 1700$
(b) $67 \times 92 = 6164$
(c) $945 \div 45 = 21$
(d) $1242 \div 54 = 23$

Book 2 Review

Review Review Review

Negative numbers

Essential exercises

1 Complete the grids below.

(a)

x	⁻3	⁻7	⁻8	⁻9	⁻15	⁻14	⁻19
y	⁻6	⁻2	⁻6	⁻12	⁻23	⁻27	⁻33
$x + y$							

(b)

x	⁻18	⁻21	⁻33	⁻79	⁻101	⁻504	⁻98
y	⁻6	⁻16	⁻28	⁻61	⁻100	⁻437	⁻85
$x - y$							

(c)

x	7	10	8	13	⁻19	⁻25	⁻102
y	⁻7	⁻10	⁻5	⁻17	36	⁻15	⁻98
$x + y$							

(d)

x	29	⁻18	45	⁻37	⁻68	65	⁻100
y	⁻17	6	⁻57	46	⁻70	73	200
$x - y$							

(e)

x	9		13	11	⁻6		⁻99
y		14				⁻7	
$x + y$	⁻15	⁻5	53	2	9	2	0

(f)

x	⁻7		18	⁻9	45		101
y		⁻3				⁻17	
$x - y$	0	9	36	12	50	4	202

Letts I See Maths **Book 3**

Challenging exercises

2 Complete the multiplication grid below.

×	4	3	2	1	0	-1	-2	-3	-4
4	16								
3			6						
2							-4		
1									
0					0				0
-1									
-2									
-3								9	
-4		-12							

3 Complete the following multiplication tables.

6 × 1 =	6 × -1 =	-6 × 1 =	-6 × -1 =
6 × 2 =	6 × -2 =	-6 × 2 =	-6 × -2 =
6 × 3 =	6 × -3 =	-6 × 3 =	-6 × -3 =
6 × 4 =	6 × -4 =	-6 × 4 =	-6 × -4 =
6 × 5 =	6 × -5 =	-6 × 5 =	-6 × -5 =

4 Given that 8 × -3 = -24, complete the following equations.
(a) -3 × 8 =   (b) -24 ÷ -3 =   (c) -24 ÷ 8 =

Problem-solving exercises

5 Find the value of the number x such that the sum of the numbers situated along each line is the same. The number a is any number.

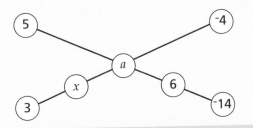

6 Find the value of the number x such that the sum of the three numbers at the vertices of each triangle is the same. The numbers a and b are any numbers.

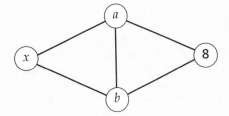

Homework

Complete these magic squares.

-9		
	-7	-6
		-5

-6		-3
		-7
		-2

		-6
	-5	
-4		-8

Percentages

Essential exercises

1 Write the following numbers as percentages.

(a) $\frac{1}{4}$ (b) ·75 (c) $\frac{5}{100}$ (d) ·63

(e) 0·08 (f) 0·003 (g) 1·25 (h) $\frac{3}{8}$

2 (a) Complete the following table.

Percentage	Sum of money						
	£1	£5	£10	£20	£50	£75	£100
1%							
5%							
10%							
20%							
50%							
75%							

(b) Use the table above to find the following.

(i) 15% of £50 (ii) 23% of £75

(iii) 65% of £10 (iv) 85% of £20

3 Complete the following, showing your workings.

(a) 32% of 50 (b) 47% of 70 (c) 6% of 90 (d) 13% of 8

4 Work out the answers to the following questions.

(a) 25% of a number is 13. What is the number?
(b) 8% of a number is 24. What is the number?
(c) 100% of a number is 2·5. What is the number?
(d) 200% of a number is 15. What is the number?
(e) 150% of a number is 18. What is the number?
(f) 400% of a number is 20. What is the number?

5 Complete the following sentences. The first one has been done for you.

(a) To increase a quantity by 34%, multiply by 1·34.
(b) To increase a quantity by 27%, multiply by ... .
(c) To increase a quantity by 5%, multiply by ... .
(d) To increase a quantity by 15%, multiply by ... .
(e) To decrease a quantity by 28%, multiply by ... .
(f) To decrease a quantity by 76%, multiply by ... .

Challenging exercises

6 Complete the following sentences by giving the single multiplier needed to work out each answer.

(a) To increase a quantity by 10%, followed by an increase of 15%, multiply by ... .

(b) To increase a quantity by 5%, followed by an increase of 20%, multiply by ... .

(c) To increase a quantity by 10%, followed by a decrease of 10%, multiply by ... .

(d) To decrease a quantity by 10%, followed by an increase of 10%, multiply by ... .

7 (a) A sum of £20 is deposited in a new savings account. Each month, for six months, the investment (the deposit plus any interest) earns interest at a rate of 3%. How much is in the savings account after six months?

(b) A sum of £50 is invested in a company. The investment loses its value at a rate of 2% a month for eight months. How much is left after eight months?

Problem-solving exercises

8 Tony received the following marks in his end-of-year tests:
English $\frac{40}{90}$; Science $\frac{57}{130}$; Maths $\frac{27}{50}$

(a) Work out Tony's test results as percentages.

(b) In which subject did Tony do best?

9 (a) In 2002 a company made profits of 4·5 million pounds. In 2003 their profits had increased by 50%. How big were their profits in 2003?

(b) Andy had a score of 18 out of 25 in a test. The next week his score had improved to 24 out of 25. What was the percentage increase in his test score?

Homework

Complete the following table.

	Fraction	Decimal	Percentage
(a)	$\frac{1}{4}$		
(b)		0·09	
(c)	$\frac{13}{20}$		
(d)			0·5%
(e)	$\frac{23}{25}$		
(f)		0·625	
(g)			57%

Essential exercises

1 Simplify the following expressions by collecting together like terms.

(a) $2x + 6x + 9x$

(b) $14x - 8x$

(c) $7x - x$

(d) $4x + 2y + 5x + 7$

(e) $4a + 6a + 5$

(f) $5a + 3b - 2a$

2 Multiply out the brackets in the following expressions.

(a) $5(x + 3)$

(b) $7(2x + 8)$

(c) $3(4x + 3y)$

(d) $2(4x - y)$

(e) $4(3x + 2y + 3z)$

(f) $6(8x - 2y - 7)$

3 Factorise the following expressions.

(a) $2x + 6y$

(b) $5x + 7xy$

(c) $\frac{1}{2}x + \frac{3}{2}y$

(d) $16xy + 8yz - 4yw$

(e) $7x + 14xy$

(f) $3 \cdot 5x^2 + 7x$

4 Simplify the following expressions.

(a) $3(4x + 2) + 2(5x + 3)$

(b) $4(x + y) + 7(2x + 3y)$

(c) $5(2x + 6) + 17$

(d) $7(2x - 3y) + 25y$

5 Work out the values of x in the following equations.

(a) $x + 7 = 15$

(b) $x + 19 = 37$

(c) $x + 98 = 121$

(d) $x + \frac{1}{2} = 5\frac{1}{2}$

(e) $x + 3 \cdot 7 = 5 \cdot 4$

(f) $x + \cdot 08 = 2 \cdot 6$

6 Work out the values of x in the following equations.

(a) $x - 8 = 3$

(b) $x - 26 = 54$

(c) $x - 76 = 76$

(d) $17 - x = 12$

(e) $49 - x = 21$

(f) $103 - x = 77$

7 Work out the values of x in the following equations.

(a) $3x = 27$

(b) $8x = 64$

(c) $15x = 60$

(d) $x \div 4 = 5$

(e) $x \div 7 = 9$

(f) $x \div 8 = 6$

Letts I See Maths **Book 3**

Book 2 Review

Challenging exercises

8 Simplify the following expressions by multiplying out the brackets and collecting like terms together.

(a) $5(2x + 4) - 3(x + 7)$

(b) $4(5x - 6) - 2(4x - 5)$

(c) $3(8 - 3x) - 7(x - 4)$

(d) $2(x - y + 4) - (x - y - 3)$

9 Factorise the following expressions.

(a) $3xy + 4xz - 2x^2$

(b) $35x^3 - 21x^2y$

(c) $51xy^2 + 21x^2y - 27xz^2$

(d) $\frac{xy}{2a} + \frac{xz}{3a}$

10 Solve the following equations to find the values for x.

(a) $4(2x + 3) + 3(5x + 2) = 156$

(b) $3(3x + 4) - 2(x - 5) = 57$

(c) $67 - 2(7 - 2x) = 81$

(d) $7(2x - 5) - 3(x - 4) = 87$

Problem-solving exercises

11 Let the mass of a tin of beans be x and the mass of a packet of biscuits be y (the mass of each is measured in the same units). Write down expressions for the mass of the following combinations.
(a) four tins of beans and three packets of biscuits
(b) ten tins of beans and two packets of biscuits
(c) five tins of beans and seven packets of biscuits

12 Let x be the cost of a cold drink and let y be the cost of a sandwich in a café (the cost of each is in the same units). Write down expressions for the cost of the following orders and simplify them.
(a) Three people ordered four drinks and three sandwiches, and five people ordered seven drinks and four sandwiches.
(b) Two people ordered two drinks and one sandwich, and ten people ordered fifteen drinks and eight sandwiches.
(c) Four people ordered seven drinks and five sandwiches, and three people ordered two drinks and one sandwich.

Homework

Look at this algebraic expression.

$$3(5x + 8y - 2z) + 7(4x - 3y + 5z) - 11(8x + 3y)$$

Explain what the instruction 'simplify this expression' means and describe what you would do.

Essential exercises

1 Solve the following equations to find the values of x.

(a) $x + 3 = 18$ (b) $x - 4 = 9$

(c) $5 + x = 21$ (d) $7 - x = 4$

(e) $5x = 35$ (f) $\frac{x}{6} = 4$

2 Solve the following equations to find the values of x.

(a) $2x + 3 = x + 7$ (b) $3x + 4 = 2x + 9$

(c) $5x + 6 = 3x + 14$ (d) $7x + 5 = 3x + 29$

(e) $9x + 23 = 7x + 57$ (f) $10x + 35 = 5x + 100$

3 Solve the following equations to find the values of x.

(a) $4x - 3 = x + 12$ (b) $7x - 16 = 5x - 6$

(c) $6x - 13 = 2x + 19$ (d) $11x - 5 = 7x + 31$

(e) $15x - 70 = 12x + 20$ (f) $37x - 99 = 25x - 51$

4 Solve the following equations to find the values of x.

(a) $5 - 4x = x - 30$ (b) $6x - 13 = 43 - 2x$

(c) $19 - 3x = 4x - 9$ (d) $2x - 11 = 5 - 6x$

(e) $20x - 121 = 11 - 2x$ (f) $14 - 2x = 4x + 11$

5 Work out the values of the following expressions when $x = 5$ and $y = 3$.

(a) $4x + 5y + 14$ (b) $6x - 3y$

(c) $10x - 4y - 21$ (d) $2x^2 + 5y$

Algebra 2

Challenging exercises

6 Solve the following equations.

(a) $3(x - 2) = 2(x - 1)$

(b) $5(2x + 3) = 3(4x - 5)$

(c) $3(x - 9) = 23 - 2(x - 5)$

(d) $5(0.5x + 2.4) = 3(1.5x - 3.6)$

7
(a) On the same axes, draw the graphs of $y = 3x - 2$ and $y = 2x + 5$.

(b) Write down the coordinates (x, y) of the point of intersection of the two graphs.

(c) Solve the equation $3x - 2 = 2x + 5$.

(d) Explain the link between your answers to (b) and (c).

(e) What graphs would you draw to solve the equation $4x - 7 = 2x + 9$?

Problem-solving exercises

8 Anita bought three packets of biscuits, each containing the same number of biscuits, and gave seven biscuits to the secretaries in the office. She now has the same number of biscuits as Jamie who has two full packets and five biscuits left from another packet. How many biscuits are there in a full packet?

9 The head of Year 9 wanted to take students to see an art exhibition. He needed to order some coaches. If he ordered five coaches there would be twenty-three empty spaces but if he ordered four coaches he would have to leave nineteen students in school. How many students would each coach seat?

Homework

Look at the following algebraic expression.
$75xy - 13x^2 + 12xy^3 + 3xyz - 2xy^2 + 18$

The expression has six different terms.

Write expressions with:

(a) four different terms

(b) seven different terms.

Letts I See Maths Book 3

Linear graphs

Essential exercises

1 Use computer software or a graphics calculator to generate the following linear graphs and write down what you notice. Sketch each set of linear graphs on the same axes.

(a) $y = x - 2$, $y = x - 1$, $y = x - 0.5$, $y = x$, $y = x + 0.5$, $y = x + 1$, $y = x + 2$

(b) $y = x$, $y = 0.5x$, $y = 2x$, $y = 3x$, $y = 3.5x$, $y = 4x$, $y = 5x$, $y = 6x$

(c) $y = {}^-x$, $y = {}^-0.5x$, $y = {}^-2x$, $y = {}^-3x$, $y = {}^-3.5x$, $y = {}^-4x$, $y = {}^-5x$, $y = {}^-6x$

(d) $y = 2x$, $y = 2x + 3$, $y = 2x - 4$, $y = 2x + 5$, $y = 2x + 3.4$, $y = 2x + 0.75$

2 Sketch the following linear graphs. Label the axes and indicate any points on each line that you can see from its equation.

(a) $y = x + 7$ (b) $y = x - 8$ (c) $y = x + \frac{1}{2}$

(d) $y = 2x + 4$ (e) $y = 3x - 9$ (f) $y = {}^-2x + 3$

3 (a) Write down the equation of a line parallel to $y = x$ with the intercept on the y-axis at (0, 5).

(b) Write down the equation of a line parallel to $y = 4x$ with the intercept on the y-axis at (0, 9).

(c) Write down the equation of a line parallel to $y = 7x$ with the intercept on the y-axis at (0, ⁻3).

(d) Write down the equation of a line parallel to $y = {}^-3x$ with the intercept on the y-axis at (0, 2).

4 $y = ax + b$ The gradient of this line is a and the intercept on the y-axis is b.

(a) Write down the equation of a line with gradient 2 and intercept 3.

(b) Write down the equation of a line with gradient ⁻6 and intercept 10.

(c) Write down the equation of a line with gradient 7 and intercept ⁻1.

(d) Write down the equation of a line with gradient 0.5 and intercept 7.6.

(e) Write down the equation of a line with gradient 1 and intercept 0.

5 Write down the gradient and intercept on the y-axis of each of the following linear graphs.

(a) $y = 3x + 4$ (b) $y = 7x - 5$ (c) $y = 10x + 0.6$

(d) $y = {}^-4x + 8$ (e) $y = {}^-3x - 2$ (f) $y = x + 1$

Letts I See Maths Book 3

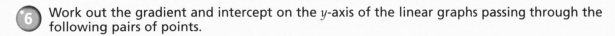
Review

Challenging exercises

6 Work out the gradient and intercept on the y-axis of the linear graphs passing through the following pairs of points.

(a) (2, 5) and (4, 9)   (b) (1, 1) and (2, 4)   (c) (1, 3) and (2, 1)

(d) (1, 1·5) and (2, 2·5)   (e) (1, 0·5) and (2, ⁻1·5)   (f) (1, 10) and (2, 20)

7 Write down the gradient and intercept of the following linear graphs.

(a) $y = 4x + 11$ (b) $y = 4 + 2x$ (c) $y = 3 - 5x$

(d) $y = ⁻6 - 3x$ (e) $x + y = 10$ (f) $2x + y = 7$

8 Rearrange the following equations in the form $y = ax + b$.

(a) $y - x = 3$ (b) $⁻3x + y = 4$ (c) $2y + 6x = 14$

Problem-solving exercise

9 The distance–time graph on the right shows four stages of a journey.

(a) Work out the gradient of each stage of the journey.

(b) Write down the average speed for each stage of the journey.

(c) Tell a story using the facts in the distance–time graph.

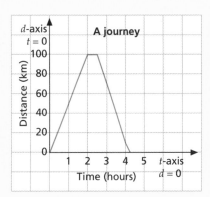

Homework

Copy and complete the following grid.

Equation of graph	Gradient	Intercept on y-axis
$y = x$		
$y = x + 3$		
$y = 3x + 7$		
$y = 7x - 4$		
$y = ⁻2x + 8$		

Letts I See Maths Book 3

Essential exercises

1 Calculate each of the angles marked with a letter, and explain how you worked it out.

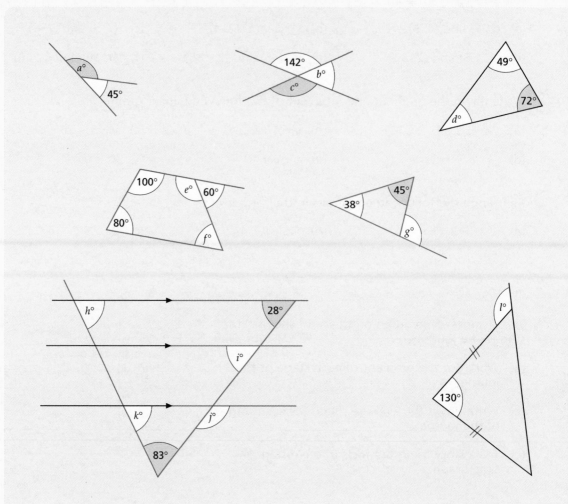

2 Complete the following sentences.

(a) The sum of the interior angles of a triangle is … .

(b) The sum of the interior angles of a quadrilateral is … .

(c) The sum of the interior angles of a pentagon is … .

(d) The sum of the interior angles of a hexagon is … .

(e) The sum of the interior angles of an n-sided polygon is … .

(f) The sum of the exterior angles of any convex polygon is … .

Letts I See Maths **Book 3**

Challenging exercise

3 Calculate each of the angles marked with a letter, and explain how you worked it out.

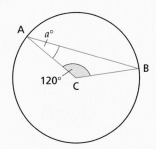

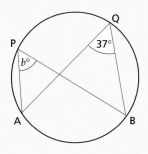

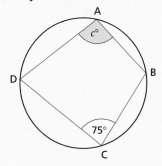

C is the centre of
the circle.

A, B, P and Q are all on
the circumference of
the circle.

A, B, C and D are all on
the circumference of
the circle.

Problem-solving exercises

4

PQRS is a parallelogram.
Copy the diagram.
(a) Mark the lines that are parallel.
(b) Mark the lines that are equal.
(c) Mark the angles that are equal.
(d) Make a statement about the opposite angles
of a parallelogram.

5

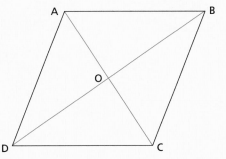

ABCD is a rhombus.
Copy the diagram.
(a) Mark the lines that are parallel.
(b) Mark the lines that are equal.
(c) Mark the angles that are equal.
(d) Work out the value of AÔB.

Homework

ABCD is an isosceles trapezium.

Inspect the isosceles trapezium ABCD.
See if you can work out the angles
marked $a°$, $b°$, $c°$ and $d°$ to discuss in
your next lesson.

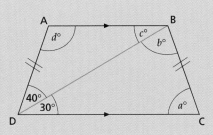

Essential exercises

1 Calculate the areas and perimeters of the figures below.

(a)

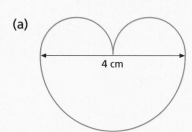

4 cm

(b)

12 cm

2 Calculate the areas and perimeters of the figures below.

(a)

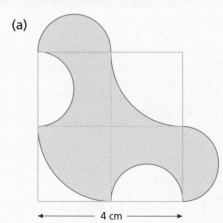

4 cm

(b)

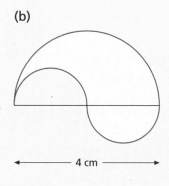

4 cm

3 In the grid below, use the approximation $\pi \approx 3\cdot14$ to work out the missing numbers.

Circle measurements	(a)	(b)	(c)	(d)	(e)
radius	5 cm			0·25 cm	
circumference		12·56 cm			
area			28·26 cm²		314 cm²

Challenging exercises

 (a) Construct the figure on the right where the outer circle has a radius of 5 cm.

(b) Calculate the perimeter and area of each coloured section. Use π ≈ 3·14.

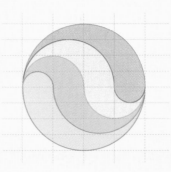

5 Calculate the perimeter and the area of each of the coloured sectors of the circles below. Use π ≈ 3·14.

(a)

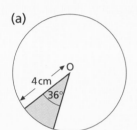

(b)

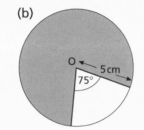

(c)

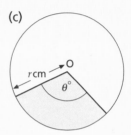

Problem-solving exercises

In the questions below, use the approximation π ≈ 3·14.

6 Catriona competes in triathlon races. She has to cycle 40 km on a bike that has wheels with diameter 70 cm. Approximately how many revolutions does the wheel make in the race?

7 Metal strips have to be cut to place around large cylinders with radius 1·5 m. The strips have to overlap by 6 cm. Calculate the length of the strips, to the nearest millimetre.

8 A conference is being organised for political leaders. Twenty-five of the participants meet around a large circular table with radius 1·66 m. If each person requires an arc of 42 cm around the edge of the table, will the table be large enough?

Homework

Draw a circle with radius 4 cm. Use a pair of compasses to construct a regular polygon with edges approximately 4 cm in length.

Essential exercises

1 The diagram shows a shaded square inside a larger square.
Calculate the area of the shaded square.

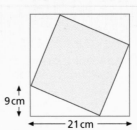

9 cm

21 cm

2 The area of the parallelogram ABCD is 108·75 cm².
Calculate its perpendicular height.

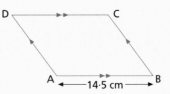

14·5 cm

3 Calculate the area of the trapezium PQRS.

8 cm

5·5 cm

12 cm

4 The shape on the right is an octagonal prism.
Its cross-section is a regular octagon with
area 121 cm².

   (a) Calculate the volume of the prism.

   (b) Calculate the total surface area of
       the prism.

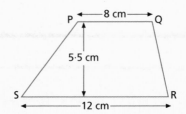

5 cm

27 cm

5 Calculate the volume of this girder.

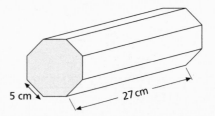

12 cm

42 cm 17 cm

16 m

12 cm   12 cm

6 A cuboid has length l, width w and height h.
   (a) Write a formula for the volume V of the cuboid.
   (b) Write a formula for the total surface area A of the cuboid.
   (c) Write a formula for the total edge length L of the cuboid.
   (d) Calculate the total surface area when $l = 9$ cm, $w = 6$ cm and $h = 15$ cm.

Challenging exercises

 7 (a) Calculate the volume of this cylinder.

(b) Calculate the total surface area of the cylinder.

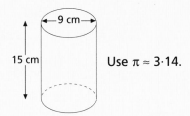

←9 cm→

15 cm

Use π ≈ 3·14.

 8 Prisms A and B have the same cross-sectional area.
Prism A is 11 cm long and has a volume of 231 cm³.
Prism B is 7 cm long. What is its volume?

Problem-solving exercises

 **9** A cylinder is cut from a wooden cuboid as shown in the diagram
on the right.

(a) Calculate the volume of the cylinder.

(b) Calculate the volume of wood wasted.

(c) The total surface of the cylinder is covered in shiny silver
paper. Draw a sketch of the paper that needs to be cut and
work out its total area.

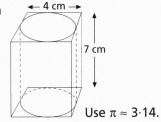

← 4 cm →

7 cm

Use π ≈ 3·14.

10 A rectangle measures 13x cm by 11x cm.

(a) Find the area of a square that has the same perimeter as that of the rectangle.

(b) Which has the larger area, the square or the rectangle, and by how much?

Homework

Design a container in the shape of

(a) a cuboid

(b) a cylinder

to hold exactly a litre of water.

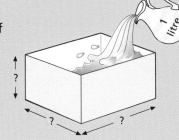

Goals

By the end of this lesson you will be able to answer questions such as these:

👁 The median of five consecutive even numbers is 32. What is the smallest number?

👁 The ratio of men to women in a sports club is 3 : 7 and there are 240 people in the club. Calculate the number of women in the club.

Starter

1 Each of the following is the final sentence in a word problem. Introduce a variable for each one, starting with the word, 'Let …'.

(a) How many cats did John buy? (b) Calculate the length of the radius.

2 Look at the explicit information in each of the following and complete the sentences.

(a) There are three consecutive whole numbers.
'Let the smallest number be … . Then the three numbers are … .'

(b) There are three consecutive whole numbers.
'Let the middle number be … . Then the three numbers are … .'

(c) There are three consecutive whole numbers.
'Let the largest number be … . Then the three numbers are … .'

(d) The difference between two numbers is 5.
'Let the smallest number be … . Then the two numbers are … .'

(e) The difference between two numbers is 5.
`Let the largest number be … . Then the two numbers are … .'

(f) The sum of two numbers is N. 'Let one number be … . Then the two numbers are … .'

Demonstration 1

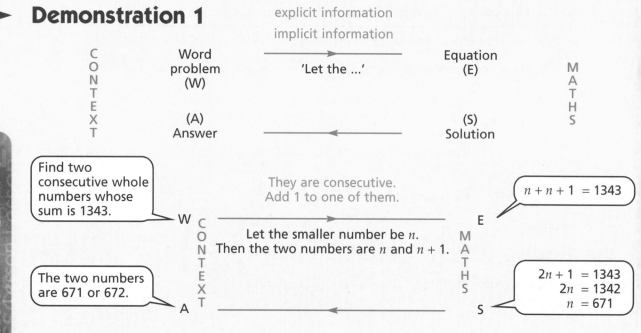

Find two consecutive whole numbers whose sum is 1343.

They are consecutive. Add 1 to one of them.

$n + n + 1 = 1343$

Let the smaller number be n.
Then the two numbers are n and $n + 1$.

The two numbers are 671 or 672.

$$2n + 1 = 1343$$
$$2n = 1342$$
$$n = 671$$

Letts I See Maths Book 3

Demonstration 2

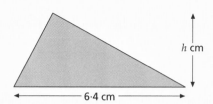

h cm

6·4 cm

$A = \frac{1}{2}bh$

> The area of a triangle is 38 cm² and its base is 6·4 cm. What is its perpendicular height?

W

$$38 = \frac{1}{2} \times 6\cdot4 \times h$$

C O N T E X T

Let the perpendicular height be h cm.

M A T H S

E

$$38 = 3\cdot2h$$

$$\frac{38}{3\cdot2} = h$$

S

$$h = 11\cdot875$$

> The height of the triangle is 11·9 cm (1 d.p.).

A

$h = 11\cdot9$ cm (1 d.p.)

Key words context equation explicit information implicit information 'Let ... ' solution unknown variable

....

Worked example

Exercise bank

1 If 120% of a number is 76·87, what is the number?

Let the number be x. Then 120% of $x = 76\cdot87$

$$1\cdot2x = 76\cdot87$$

$$x = \frac{76\cdot87}{1\cdot2}$$

$$x = 64\cdot1 \text{ (1 d.p.)}$$

The number is 64·1 (1 d.p.).

Plenary

 Discuss the Goals.

 Discuss: The square of the sum of two numbers that differ by 1·3 is 187·69. Calculate the smaller number.

 Discuss: The square of the sum of two numbers that differ by h is N. Calculate the smaller number.

Essential exercises

1 (a) Find two consecutive whole numbers whose sum is one thousand, nine hundred and seventy-nine.

(b) Find three consecutive whole numbers whose sum is two hundred and fifty-two.

(c) Find two consecutive whole numbers such that their sum is eighteen more than the square of thirteen.

(d) Find four consecutive whole numbers whose sum is six less than eighty.

2 (a) Find two numbers whose sum is nine and whose product is twenty.

(b) Find two numbers whose difference is three and whose product is fifty-four.

(c) Find two numbers whose sum is twenty and whose quotient is three.

(d) Find two numbers whose difference is twenty-four and whose quotient is nine.

3 What is the number?

(a) Three times the number then add five is thirty-two.

(b) Five times the number then take away eight is sixty-two.

(c) The number divided by ten is thirteen.

(d) The number divided by three then add seventeen is thirty-four.

4 In a sale, prices are reduced by ten per cent. Work out the original prices of goods whose sale prices are the following.

(a) £49·50   (b) £31·50   (c) £37·80   (d) £72·90

5 (a) The area of a triangle is 28 cm² and its perpendicular height is 5·6 cm. What is the length of its base?

(b) What is the length of a side of a square with area 84·64 cm²?

(c) What is the length of the radius of a circle with area 63·585 cm²? (Use $\pi \approx 3·14$.)

(d) What is the length of a side of a cube with volume 32·768 cm³?

6 (a) The mean of four consecutive whole numbers is 15·5. What are the numbers?

(b) The median of five consecutive whole numbers is 27. What are the numbers?

(c) The average speed of a car is 48 m.p.h. How far does the car travel in $1\frac{1}{2}$ hours?

(d) The average speed of a car is 64 m.p.h. How long does it take to travel 160 miles?

Challenging exercises

7 Select a pair of consecutive whole numbers. Square each number and find the difference. What do you notice? Test with different pairs of consecutive whole numbers.

Repeat with pairs of numbers whose difference is 2, or 3, or 4 etc.

Generalise.

8 A car travels from A to B for three hours at an average speed of 50 m.p.h. It then travels from B to C for another two hours. If the average speed for the whole journey from A to C is 60 m.p.h., what is the car's average speed from B to C?

Problem-solving exercises

9 Jack spent £10 on two sandwiches and four teas. Hannah spent £23 on six sandwiches and five teas. If sandwiches are all the same price, work out the cost of one sandwich and the cost of one tea.

10 Study the rectangle on the right. The numerical value of its area equals the numerical value of its perimeter.

(a) See if you can find more rectangles with this property.

(b) Investigate for different polygons.

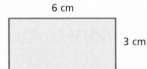

6 cm

3 cm

11 A quadrilateral ABCD has side lengths AB = 3 cm, BC = 6·2 cm, CD = 9·5 cm and DA = 10·7 cm. The quadrilateral is enlarged to A'B'C'D' and A'B' = 13·5 cm.

(a) Work out the scale factor of the enlargement.

(b) Calculate the lengths of the sides B'C', C'D' and D'A'.

12 Prove that the sum of three consecutive whole numbers is always divisible by 3.

13 The ratio of girls to boys in a class is 4 : 5. If there are fifteen boys in the class, how many girls are there?

Homework

'I am thinking of a number.'

Make up five number puzzles like those in Exercise 3 to ask students in your class.

Formalising arithmetic

Goals

By the end of this lesson you will be able to answer questions such as these:

 Complete the grid.

x		1·6
y	2·3	
$(3x - y)^2$	14·4	18·7

 Given $(3x - y)^2 = 13·5$, calculate the value of x.

Starter

1

x is a variable. x can take all values. I know that x can be, for instance, … .

y is a variable. y can take all values. I know that y can be, for instance, … .

x is a variable. x can take all values. When I am told $x > 5$, I know the values of x are restricted. I know that x can be … .

x is a variable. x can take all values. When I am told $x \geq 5$, I know the values of x are restricted. I know that x can be … .

x and y are variables. x and y can take all values. When I am told $x + y = 5$ *and* I am told $y = 3$, I know that x can be … .

Demonstration 1

Grids and equations
The grids contain implicit information about some equations.
The equations contain explicit information.

Grid 1

x	1·3		$\frac{1}{5}$	
y		4·3		‾4
$x + y$	6·4	5·7	$\frac{7}{5}$	2

Equations 1

$$1·3 + y = 6·4 \qquad x + 4·3 = 5·7$$
$$\tfrac{1}{5} + y = \tfrac{7}{5} \qquad x + {}^-4 = 2$$

Grid 2

x	1·3		$\frac{1}{5}$	
y		4·3		‾4
$x - y$	6·4	5·7	$\frac{7}{5}$	2

Equations 2

$$1·3 - y = 6·4 \qquad x - 4·3 = 5·7$$
$$\tfrac{1}{5} - y = \tfrac{7}{5} \qquad x - {}^-4 = 2$$

Grid 3

x	1·3		$\frac{1}{5}$	
y		4·3		‾4
$x \times y$	6·4	5·7	$\frac{7}{5}$	2

Equations 3

$$1·3y = 6·4 \qquad 4·3x = 5·7$$
$$\tfrac{y}{5} = \tfrac{7}{5} \qquad {}^-4x = 2$$

Grid 4

x	1·3		$\frac{1}{5}$	
y		4·3		‾4
$x \div y$	6·4	5·7	$\frac{7}{5}$	2

Equations 4

$$\frac{1·3}{y} = 6·4 \qquad \frac{x}{4·3} = 5·7$$
$$\frac{\frac{1}{5}}{y} = \tfrac{7}{5} \qquad \frac{x}{{}^-4} = 2$$

Demonstration 2

Grid 5

x			2
y	3		
$2x + y^3$	31		31

What quantity is doubled?
What quantity is cubed?
Name the two terms.

Grid 6

x			2
y	3		
$2(x + y^3)$	58		58

What quantity is doubled?
What quantity is cubed?
Name the two factors.

Grid 7

x			2
y	3		
$2(x + y)^3$	250		250

What quantity is doubled?
What quantity is cubed?
Name the numerical factor.
Name the repeated factor.
How many times is it repeated?

Grid 8

x			2
y	3		
$(2x + y)^3$	343		343

What quantity is doubled?
What quantity is cubed?
Name the repeated factor.
How many times is it repeated?

> **Key words**   factor   repeated factor   term

Worked example

Exercise bank

 Given $x^{\frac{1}{2}} + 3y^2 = 19\cdot3$, calculate x when $y = 2\cdot4$.

$$x^{\frac{1}{2}} + 3 \times 2\cdot4^2 = 19\cdot3$$
$$x^{\frac{1}{2}} + 17\cdot28 = 19\cdot3$$
$$x^{\frac{1}{2}} = 2\cdot02$$
$$x = 2\cdot02^2$$
$$x = 4\cdot1 \ (1 \text{ d.p.})$$

Plenary

👁 Discuss the Goals.

👁 Read these so that they can be written down accurately by someone listening to you:

(a) $2x + 3$ (b) $2(x + 3)$ (c) $2x + y^2$ (d) $x + y^2$ (e) $(x + y)^2$

Letts I See Maths Book 3

Formalising arithmetic

Essential exercises

1 (a) Complete the grid below.

	(i)	(ii)	(iii)	(iv)	(v)	(vi)	(vii)	(viii)
x		17·5		2·9	806		·091	
y	14		·37			423		14·2
$x + y$	35	34·9	·94	7·5	912	859	·208	69·1

(b) For each entry in the grid above, write down an equation and solve it. The first is one shown here:

$$\text{(i)} \quad x + 14 = 35$$
$$x = 21$$

2 (a) Complete the grid below.

	(i)	(ii)	(iii)	(iv)	(v)	(vi)	(vii)	(viii)
x	19·4	27·8			159	·37		
y			9·9	37·6			·04	⁻8
$x - y$	13·6	15·3	20·4	41·5	77	·09	·51	18

(b) For each entry in the grid above, write down an equation and solve it. The first one is shown here:

$$\text{(i)} \quad 19·4 - y = 13·6$$
$$y = 19·4 - 13·6$$
$$= 5·8$$

3 (a) Complete the grid below.

	(i)	(ii)	(iii)	(iv)	(v)	(vi)	(vii)	(viii)
x	3·5		2·3		82	1·4	3·8	
y		4·9		·51				·05
$x \times y$	26·6	3·92	14·72	4·59	574	1·96	0·95	3·15

(b) For each entry in the grid above, write down an equation and solve it. The first one is shown here:

$$\text{(i)} \quad 3·5y = 26·6$$
$$y = 7·6$$

4 (a) Complete the grid below.

	(i)	(ii)	(iii)	(iv)	(v)	(vi)	(vii)	(viii)
x	24	13·5			980	1326		3·5
y			17	37			0·24	
$x \div y$	8	15	13	19	28	26	0·31	0·14

(b) For each entry in the grid above, write down an equation and solve it. The first one is shown here:

$$\text{(i)} \quad 24 \div y = 8 \quad \text{or} \quad \frac{24}{y} = 8$$
$$y = 3 \qquad\qquad\quad y = 3$$

Number and Algebra

Letts I See Maths Book 3

Formalising arithmetic

Challenging exercises

5 Complete the grid below.

x		·3		1·2			⁻4	13
y	5			0·4			⁻1	
$2x$	12		14			22		
y^3		1			27	125		-8
$3(x^2 + y)$			174		156			

6 A teacher asked students to write the expression 'five x squared minus four'. The students found three different ways of writing this:

$5x^2 - 4$ $5(x^2 - 4)$ $(5x)^2 - 4$

Part of the grid on the right has been torn off. Work out which expression goes above each column and then complete the grid.

x			
-3			
-2			
-1	21		
0	⁻4	⁻4	
1		1	⁻15
2			0
3			

Problem-solving exercise

7 Complete the magic squares below.

(a)

$x - 2$	$x + 3$	$x + 2$
		$x - 3$

(b)

		$x + 1$
	$2x$	
$3x - 1$	5	

(c)

$2x + 7$	$x + 5$	3
		$x + 6$

Homework

(a) Write down all the whole number factors of the following numbers.
   (i) 8   (ii) 15   (iii) 24   (iv) 29

(b) Write down all the factors of the following expressions.
   (i) $2x$ (ii) $3xy$ (iii) $6x^3$ (iv) $3xyz$

Letts I See Maths Book 3

Goals

By the end of this lesson you will be able to answer questions such as these:

👁 Use (i) additive inverses and (ii) inverse operations to solve these equations.
(a) $x + 3 = 0$ (b) $x + {}^-2 = 0$ (c) $x + 3 = 5$ (d) $3 + x = 5$ (e) $x + {}^-2 = 5$

👁 Use (i) multiplicative inverses and (ii) inverse operations to solve these equations.
(a) $3x = 1$ (b) $^-2x = 1$ (c) $^-\frac{1}{5}x = 1$ (d) $^-2x = 5$ e) $^-\frac{1}{2}x = 5$

👁 Explain why $\frac{m}{n} \div \frac{a}{b}$ has the same value as $\frac{m}{n} \times \frac{b}{a}$.

Starter

1 **Read this:** For every real number a, there is a real number ^-a, called the additive inverse. What is the additive inverse of each of these?
(a) 4   (b) 19   (c) $\frac{1}{2}$ (d) $^-4$ (e) $^-\frac{1}{2}$

2 **Read this:** For every real number a, there is a real number $\frac{1}{a}$, called the multiplicative inverse. What is the multiplicative inverse of each of these?
(a) 4   (b) 19   (c) $\frac{1}{2}$ (d) $^-4$ (e) $^-\frac{1}{2}$

3 **Read this:** There is a real number 0, called zero, which does not change a number it is added to. It is called the identity element for addition. What do you get if you add the identity element for addition to each of these?
(a) 4   (b) 19   (c) $\frac{1}{2}$ (d) $^-4$ (e) $^-\frac{1}{2}$

4 **Read this:** There is a real number 1, called one, which does not change a number it multiplies. It is called the identity element for multiplication. What do you get if you multiply each of these by the identity element for multiplication?
(a) 4   (b) 19   (c) $\frac{1}{2}$ (d) $^-4$ (e) $^-\frac{1}{2}$

Demonstration 1

Solving equations using the additive inverse and inverse operations

(a)
$$x + 2 = 0$$
$$x + 2 + {}^-2 = 0 + {}^-2$$
$$x = {}^-2$$

(b)
$$x + 2 = 0$$
$$x + 2 - 2 = 0 - 2$$
$$x = {}^-2$$

(c)
$$x + {}^-4 = 0$$
$$x + {}^-4 + 4 = 0 + 4$$
$$x = 4$$

(d)
$$x + {}^-4 = 0$$
$$x + {}^-4 - {}^-4 = 0 - {}^-4$$
$$x = 4$$

(e)
$$x + 4 = 7$$
$$x + 4 - 4 = 7 - 4$$
$$x = 3$$

(f)
$$x + 4 = 7$$
$$x + 4 - {}^-4 = 7 - {}^-4$$
$$x = 3$$

(g)
$$x + a = b$$
$$x + a - a = b - a$$
$$x = b - a$$

(h)
$$x + a = b$$
$$x + a + {}^-a = b + {}^-a$$
$$x = b + {}^-a$$

Letts

Flexibility in arithmetic

Demonstration 2

Solving equations using the multiplicative inverse and inverse operations

(a)

$$3x = 7$$
$$\frac{3x}{3} = \frac{7}{3}$$
$$x = \frac{7}{3}$$

(b)

$$3x = 7$$
$$3x \times \frac{1}{3} = 7 \times \frac{1}{3}$$
$$x = \frac{7}{3}$$

(c)

$$ax = b$$
$$\frac{ax}{a} = \frac{b}{a}$$
$$x = \frac{b}{a}$$

(d)

$$ax = b$$
$$ax \times \frac{1}{a} = b \times \frac{1}{a}$$
$$x = \frac{b}{a}$$

Key words   additive inverse   identity element for addition
identity element for multiplication   multiplicative inverse

Worked example

Exercise bank

1 Solve $2 \cdot 5x = 17 \cdot 5$.

$$\frac{5}{2}x = \frac{35}{2}$$
$$\frac{2}{5} \times \frac{5}{2}x = \frac{2}{5} \times \frac{35}{2}$$
$$x = 7$$

or

$$2 \cdot 5x \div 2 \cdot 5 = 17 \cdot 5 \div 2 \cdot 5$$
$$x = 7$$

Plenary

👁 Discuss the Goals.

👁 What is the identity element for subtraction?

👁 What is the identity element for division?

👁 What is the multiplicative inverse of each of these?

(a) $\frac{2}{3}$ (b) $\frac{11}{7}$ (c) $\frac{1}{3}$ (d) $\frac{3}{1}$ (e) 3

(f) x (g) $\frac{1}{x}$ (h) m (i) $\frac{1}{2 \cdot 34}$ (j) $\frac{2 \cdot 34}{1}$

(k) $2 \cdot 34$ (l) $\sqrt{5}$ (m) $5^{\frac{1}{2}}$

Letts I See Maths Book 3

Number and Algebra

Flexibility in arithmetic

Essential exercises

1 Solve the following equations.

(a) $3 + x = 0$ (b) $8 + x = 0$ (c) $19 + x = 0$

(d) $53 + x = 0$ (e) $x + 89 = 0$ (f) $x + 131 = 0$

(g) $^-7 + x = 0$ (h) $x + {}^-23 = 0$ (i) $^-203 + x = 0$

2 Solve the following equations.

(a) $3 \times x = 1$ (b) $5 \times x = 1$ (c) $10 \times x = 1$

(d) $x \times 8 = 1$ (e) $x \times 23 = 1$ (f) $x \times 100 = 1$

(g) $x \times \frac{1}{11} = 1$ (h) $\frac{1}{17} \times x = 1$ (i) $x \times \frac{1}{89} = 1$

3 Solve the following equations.

(a) $\frac{2}{3} \times x = 1$ (b) $\frac{3}{5} \times x = 1$ (c) $\frac{7}{9} \times x = 1$

(d) $\frac{5}{8} \times x = 1$ (e) $x \times \frac{6}{11} = 1$ (f) $\frac{21}{47} \times x = 1$

4 Complete the following sentences. The first one has been done for you.

(a) $6 \div \frac{2}{3}$ has the same value as $6 \times \frac{3}{2} = 9$.

(b) $8 \div \frac{4}{5}$ has the same value as ... .

(c) $10 \div \frac{5}{7}$ has the same value as ... .

(d) $\frac{3}{4} \div \frac{3}{4}$ has the same value as ... .

(e) $\frac{6}{7} \div \frac{3}{7}$ has the same value as ... .

5 Complete the following sentences. The first one has been done for you.

(a) $\frac{3}{7} \times \frac{14}{5}$ has the same value as $\frac{6}{14} \times \frac{14}{5} = \frac{6}{5}$.

(b) $\frac{4}{5} \times \frac{10}{13}$ has the same value as ... .

(c) $\frac{5}{12} \times \frac{6}{7}$ has the same value as ... .

(d) $\frac{11}{15} \times \frac{3}{4}$ has the same value as ... .

(e) $\frac{5}{3} \times \frac{12}{7}$ has the same value as ... .

Challenging exercises

6 Solve the following equations.

(a) $x - {}^-7 = 0$

(b) $^-19 - x = 0$

(c) $x - \frac{^-2}{3} = 0$

(d) $^-8 \times x = 1$

(e) $\frac{^-4}{5} \times x = 1$

(f) $\frac{^-11}{23} \div x = 1$

7 Calculate each of the expressions below using a single multiplication.

(a) $31{\cdot}6 \times 17 + 31{\cdot}6 \times 9 + 26 \times 8{\cdot}4$

(b) $2{\cdot}43 \times 8 + 25 \times 0{\cdot}67 + 2{\cdot}43 \times 17$

(c) $19{\cdot}3 \times 11 + 19{\cdot}3 \times 23 - 34 \times 6{\cdot}7$

(d) $78{\cdot}9 \times 7 - 89 \times 0{\cdot}7$

(e) $64{\cdot}9 \times 3{\cdot}7 + 6{\cdot}49 \times 63$

(f) $30{\cdot}05 \times 163 - 0{\cdot}63 \times 3005$

Problem-solving exercises

8 ΔABC is an object that has been enlarged to become the image ΔA′B′C′.
ΔA′B′C′ is an object that has been enlarged to become the image ΔA″B″C″.

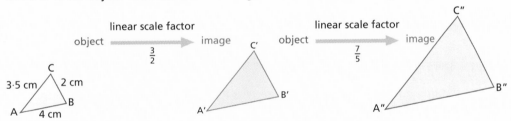

(a) Calculate the lengths of the sides of the triangles ΔA′B′C′ and ΔA″B″C″.

(b) What are the linear scale factors of the enlargements below?

(i) ΔABC to ΔA″B″C″

(ii) ΔA″B″C″ to ΔA′B′C′

(iii) ΔA′B′C′ to ΔABC

(iv) ΔA″B″C″ to ΔABC

9 An object is enlarged with linear scale factor $\frac{a}{b}$. What linear scale factor of enlargement would return the image to its original size?

Homework

Write down how you would work out the following calculations mentally.

Example $17{\cdot}3 \times 19 = 17{\cdot}3 \times (20 - 1) = 17{\cdot}3 \times 20 - 17{\cdot}3 = 346 - 17{\cdot}3 = 328{\cdot}7$

(a) 463×19

(b) 67×99

(c) 349×99

(d) 47×101

(e) $4{\cdot}67 \times 101$

(f) 48×15

Using a calculator

Goals

By the end of this lesson you will be able to answer questions such as these:

◉ Use your calculator to evaluate the following.

(a) $3 \cdot 9^{-1 \cdot 3}$

(b) $\sqrt[5]{7 \cdot 73}$

(c) $\frac{12!}{5!}$

◉ Given $f : x \longrightarrow x^{\frac{1}{4}}$, use your calculator to draw the graph of $y = f(x)$.

Starter

1 (a) Check that your calculator does this correctly: $2 + 3 \times 4 = 14$ (i.e. check that it is programmed to use algebraic logic).

(b) Check that your calculator gives the correct answer to this: $8 \div 2 \div 2 = 2$.

2 Explain why these are correct answers.

(a) $2 + 3 \times 4 = 14$

(b) $8 \div 2 \div 2 = 2$

Demonstration 1

Practice with your calculator

1 (a) $78\,945 \times 3648 = 287\,990\,000$ (5 sig. figs.)

(b) $7 \cdot 8945 \times 3 \cdot 648 = 28 \cdot 80$ (2 d.p.)

(c) $78\,945 \times 3648 = 2 \cdot 8799 \times 10^8$ (5 sig. figs.)

(d) $7 \cdot 8945 \times 3 \cdot 648 = 2 \cdot 88 \times 10^1$ (3 sig. figs.)

2 (a) $3^5 = 243$

(b) $2 \cdot 7^5 = 143 \cdot 5$ (1 d.p.)

(c) $2 \cdot 7^{1 \cdot 5} = 4 \cdot 44$ (2 d.p.)

(d) $2 \cdot 7^{-1 \cdot 5} = \cdot 23$ (2 d.p.)

3 (a) $\sqrt{7 \cdot 73} = 2 \cdot 8$ (1 d.p.)

(b) $\sqrt[3]{7 \cdot 73} = 1 \cdot 98$ (2 d.p.)

(c) $\sqrt[4]{7 \cdot 73} = 1 \cdot 67$ (2 d.p.)

(d) $7 \cdot 73^{\frac{1}{2}} = 2 \cdot 8$ (1 d.p.)

(e) $7 \cdot 73^{\frac{1}{3}} = 1 \cdot 98$ (2 d.p.)

(f) $7 \cdot 73^{\frac{1}{4}} = 1 \cdot 67$ (2 d.p.)

4 (a) $5! = 120$

(b) $45! = 1 \cdot 196 \times 10^{56}$ (4 sig. figs.)

(c) $1 \times 2 \times 3 \times 4 \times 5 = 120$

(d) $\frac{45!}{44!} = 45$

(e) $42 \times 43 \times 44 \times 45 = 3 \cdot 575\,88 \times 10^6$

Number and Algebra

Letts I See Maths **Book 3**

Demonstration 2

$$y = \frac{1}{x}$$

x	-2	-1·5	-1	-·5	0	·5	1	1·5	2	2·5	3	3·5	4	4·5	5
y	-·5	-·67	-1	-2	∞	2	1	·67	·5	·4	·33	·29	·25	·22	·2

(all to 2 d.p.)

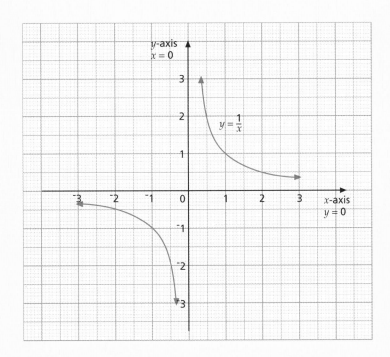

Key words   algebraic logic   cube root   factorial   fourth root
inverse   reciprocal   scientific calculator   2nd function key
square root   'to the power of'

Exercise bank

Plenary

👁 Explain how to check if a calculator uses algebraic logic.

👁 Discuss how to evaluate $5 \times 4 + 2 \times 7$ with a basic calculator (i.e. one that does not use algebraic logic).

👁 Discuss the Goals.

Number and Algebra

Using a calculator

Number and Algebra

Essential exercises

1 Use a scientific calculator to work out the following.

(a) $726 + 34 \times 29$

(b) $21 + 3 \times 13 \times 79$

(c) $41 \times 17 + 23 \times 12$

(d) $8 \cdot 5 + 7 \times \frac{4}{5}$

(e) $(16 + 29) \times 11$

(f) $240 \div (3 \times 8)$

(g) $240 \div 3 \div 8$

(h) $240 \div 3 \times 8$

(i) $240 \div \frac{3}{8}$

2 Use a scientific calculator to work out the following.

(a) $^-2 \cdot 5 \times {}^-4 \cdot 6$

(b) $^-3 \cdot 2 \times {}^-7 \times 4$

(c) $^-5 \cdot 4 \times {}^-6 \times {}^-8$

(d) $^-2 \times {}^-3 \times {}^-4 \times {}^-5$

(e) $^-6 \cdot 3 \div 9$

(f) $^-5 \cdot 6 \div {}^-0 \cdot 8$

(g) $^-3 \cdot 6 \div {}^-0 \cdot 3 \div {}^-4$

(h) $^-64 \div 2 \div 2 \div 2$

(i) $^-142 - \frac{117}{13}$

3 Use a scientific calculator to work out the following.

(a) $\dfrac{53 \cdot 42 \times 1 \cdot 5}{2 \cdot 5 \times (7 \cdot 3 - 2 \cdot 8)}$

(b) $8 \cdot 4 + (12 \cdot 4 - 3 \times 4 \cdot 5)$

(c) $\left((3 \cdot 2)^2 + (8 \cdot 6 - 2 \cdot 4)\right)^2$

(d) $\sqrt{\dfrac{3 \cdot 4^2 - 4 \times 1 \cdot 2}{10}}$

4 Write the following fractions in ascending order by first converting them to decimal fractions, using a calculator.

$\frac{2}{3}, \frac{1}{5}, \frac{3}{8}, \frac{2}{9}, \frac{3}{4}, \frac{4}{7}, \frac{5}{6}, \frac{4}{5}$

5 Use a scientific calculator to work out the following.

(a) 4^3

(b) 2^7

(c) 3^5

(d) 29^0

(e) $\sqrt{38 \cdot 44}$

(f) $\sqrt[3]{9 \cdot 261}$

(g) $\sqrt[4]{625}$

(h) $\sqrt[8]{256}$

6 Use a scientific calculator to find the function key that will return each number to the one you started with.

(a) $5 \xrightarrow{\ y^3\ } 125$

$5 \xleftarrow{\ ?\ } 125$

(b) $5 \xrightarrow{\ x^{-1}\ } 0 \cdot 2$

$\xleftarrow{\ ?\ }$

Letts I See Maths Book 3

Using a calculator

Exercise Bank Exercise Bank

Challenging exercises

7 Factorial: $n!$ $6 \times 5 \times 4 \times 3 \times 2 \times 1 = 6!$ (six factorial)
Use a scientific calculator to work out the following.

(a) 4! (b) 7! (c) 3! × 5! (d) 6! ÷ 3! (e) 0!

8 Reciprocal: $\frac{1}{n}$ or n^{-1}
Use a scientific calculator to work out the following.

(a) 2^{-1} (b) 10^{-1} (c) $0\cdot5^{-1}$ (d) $0\cdot01^{-1}$ (e) 8^{-1} (f) $2^{-1} \times 2$

9 Trigonometric functions:
sin (sine) cos (cosine) tan (tangent)
Use a scientific calculator to work out the following to 3 d.p. (Make sure that the calculator is in degree mode first.)

(a) cos 60° (b) sin 30° (c) cos 45° (d) sin 80° (e) tan 120°

10 Inverse trigonometric functions:
$\sin^{-1}$ (inverse sine) $\cos^{-1}$ (inverse cosine) $\tan^{-1}$ (inverse tangent)
Use a scientific calculator to work out the following angles to 2 d.p.

(a) $\cos^{-1} 0\cdot5$ (b) $\sin^{-1} 0\cdot8$ (c) $\tan^{-1} 0\cdot8$ (d) $\sin^{-1} 0\cdot3$

Problem-solving exercises

11 Use a scientific calculator to convert the following vulgar fractions to decimal fractions, and describe what you notice.

(a) $\frac{1}{7}, \frac{2}{7}, \frac{3}{7}, \frac{4}{7}, \frac{5}{7}, \frac{6}{7}$

(b) $\frac{1}{6}, \frac{2}{6}, \frac{3}{6}, \frac{4}{6}, \frac{5}{6}$

(c) $\frac{1}{9}, \frac{2}{9}, \frac{3}{9}, \frac{4}{9}, \frac{5}{9}, \frac{6}{9}, \frac{7}{9}, \frac{8}{9}$

(d) $\frac{1}{11}, \frac{2}{11}, \frac{3}{11}, \frac{4}{11}, \frac{5}{11}, \frac{6}{11}, \frac{7}{11}, \frac{8}{11}, \frac{9}{11}, \frac{10}{11}$

12 In a right-angled triangle, $c^2 = a^2 + b^2$.

Calculate the values of c for the following values of a and b.

(i) a cm = 3 cm, b cm = 4 cm (ii) a cm = 2·4 cm, b cm = 3·7 cm

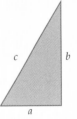

Homework

Find the 'log' key on your calculator. Work out the following.

log 1 log 10 log 100 log 1000 log 10000 log 100000 log 1000000

Goals

By the end of this lesson you will be able to answer questions such as these:

- State the base and the exponent (or index, or power) in each of the following.
  - (a) 3^2
  - (b) 5^{-4}
  - (c) $5^{\frac{1}{4}}$
  - (d) a^n

- Use a calculator to find the value of each of the following.
  - (a) $\sqrt{34}$
  - (b) $13^{\frac{1}{2}}$
  - (c) $\sqrt{3\cdot4}$
  - (d) $1\cdot3^{\frac{1}{2}}$
  - (e) 19^3

- Express each of these as surds.
  - (a) $5^{\frac{1}{2}}$
  - (b) $7^{\frac{1}{2}}$
  - (c) $3\cdot5^{\frac{1}{2}}$
  - (d) $12^{\frac{1}{2}}$
  - (e) $1000^{\frac{1}{2}}$

Starter

1 Express each of these in the form a^b.
  - (a) $7 \times 7 \times 7 \times 7 \times 7$
  - (b) $1\cdot3 \times 1\cdot3 \times 1\cdot3 \times 1\cdot3 \times 1\cdot3$
  - (c) $y \times y \times y$

2 Express each of these in the form $a^b \times c^d$.
  - (a) $7 \times 5 \times 7 \times 5 \times 5 \times 5 \times 7$
  - (b) $1\cdot3 \times 5 \times 1\cdot3 \times 5 \times 1\cdot3$
  - (c) $2\cdot1 \times 1\cdot3 \times 1\cdot3$

3 Express each of these in the form a^b.
  - (a) $2^3 \times 2^5$
  - (b) $7^2 \times 7^3$
  - (c) $7^1 \times 7^3$
  - (d) 7×7^3
  - (e) $2^1 \times 2^1 \times 2^1 \times 2^1$

4 Express each of these in index form.
  - (a) $y \times y \times y \times y$
  - (b) $x \times x \times x$
  - (c) $y \times y \times y \times y \times y \times x \times x \times x \times x$
  - (d) $y \times x \times x \times y \times y \times x \times x \times y \times x \times x$

Demonstration 1

Exponential (index) form

> x^3
> x cubed
> x to the power of three
> x to the three
> $x\text{^}3$

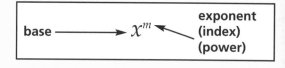

base $\longrightarrow x^m \longleftarrow$ exponent (index) (power)

$$x^3 \quad \times \quad x^2 \quad = \quad x^5$$

$$\underbrace{x \times x \times x}_{} \qquad \underbrace{x \times x}_{}$$

$$x^5 \quad \div \quad x^2 \quad = \quad x^3$$

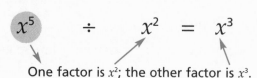

One factor is x^2; the other factor is x^3.

$$x^m \quad \times \quad x^n \quad = \quad x^{m+n}$$

$$x^m \quad \div \quad x^n \quad = \quad x^{m-n}$$

$$\frac{x^m}{x^n} \quad = \quad x^{m-n}$$

Letts I See Maths **Book 3**

Number and Algebra

Demonstration 2

Using index notation sensibly

1

$$a^{\frac{1}{2}} \times a^{\frac{1}{2}} = a^{\frac{1}{2}+\frac{1}{2}} = a^1$$

$$\sqrt{a} \times \sqrt{a} = a$$

$$a^{\frac{1}{2}} + a^{\frac{1}{2}} = 2a^{\frac{1}{2}}$$

$$\sqrt{a} + \sqrt{a} = 2\sqrt{a}$$

2 $\quad x^m \div x^n = x^{m-n}$

(a)
$$x^3 \div x^5 = x^{-2}$$
$$\frac{x^3}{x^5} = x^{-2}$$
$$\frac{1}{x^2} = x^{-2}$$

(b)
$$x^3 \div x^3 = x^0$$
$$\frac{x^3}{x^3} = x^0$$
$$1 = x^0$$

(c)
$$x^m \div x^m = x^0$$
$$\frac{x^m}{x^m} = x^0$$
$$1 = x^0$$

Key words   base   exponent   exponential   index   power

Worked example

Exercise bank

1   Write these in the form a^b.

(a) $\dfrac{5^4}{5^2}$ (b) $\dfrac{5^2}{5^4}$ (c) $\dfrac{5^4}{5^4}$ (d) $\dfrac{y^4}{y^2}$ (e) $\dfrac{y^2}{y^4}$ (f) $\dfrac{m^4}{m^4}$

$$\frac{5^4}{5^2} = 5^2 \qquad \frac{5^2}{5^4} = 5^{-2} \qquad \frac{5^4}{5^4} = 5^0 \qquad \frac{y^4}{y^2} = y^2 \qquad \frac{y^2}{y^4} = y^{-2} \qquad \frac{m^4}{m^4} = m^0$$

Plenary

👁 Explain why $3^0 = 1$.

👁 Explain why $m^0 = 1$.

👁 Explain why $3^0 = 2^0$.

👁 Discuss $\sqrt{5} \times \sqrt{5} = 5$ and $\sqrt{5} + \sqrt{5} = 2\sqrt{5}$.

👁 Discuss the Goals.

Index laws

Essential exercises

1 Complete the following table.

	Index notation	Written in full	Value
(a)	2^5	$2 \times 2 \times 2 \times 2 \times 2$	32
(b)	10^3		
(c)	3^4		
(d)	5^3		
(e)	1^9		
(f)	0^5		
(g)	$(^-1)^3$		
(h)	$(^-2)^4$		
(i)	19^1		
(j)	$2 \cdot 4^2$		

2 Simplify the following expressions using index notation.

(a) $3 \times 3 \times 3 \times 3 \times 3 \times 3 \times 3$

(b) $29 \times 29 \times 29$

(c) $87 \times 87 \times 23 \times 23 \times 23$

(d) $2 \times 2 \times 7 \times 7 \times 2 \times 2 \times 7$

(e) $10 \times 10 \times 10 \times 10 \times 5 \times 5 \times 5$

(f) $x \times x \times x \times x \times x \times x \times x \times x \times x$

(g) $a \times a \times b \times b \times b$

(h) $xy \times xy \times xy$

3 Simplify the following expressions using index notation.

(a) $5^3 \times 5^8$

(b) $8^2 \times 8^5 \times 8^7 \times 8^3$

(c) $39^3 \times 39^5 \times 45^2 \times 45^4$

(d) $2^4 \times 2^5 \times 2^3 \times 3^6 \times 3$

(e) $6^{13} \div 6^5$

(f) $10^4 \div 10^6$

(g) $78^9 \div 78$

(h) $2^3 \div 2^3$

4 Write the following numbers as vulgar fractions.

(a) 3^{-1}

(b) 10^{-2}

(c) 4^{-1}

(d) 5^{-3}

(e) 8^{-1}

(f) 10^{-4}

5 Work out the value of each of the following expressions.

(a) $\sqrt{3} \times \sqrt{3}$

(b) $\sqrt{2} \times \sqrt{2} \times \sqrt{2} \times \sqrt{2}$

(c) $5^{\frac{1}{2}} \times 5^{\frac{1}{2}}$

(d) $\sqrt{4+5}$

(e) $\sqrt{9} + \sqrt{16}$

(f) $2^{\frac{1}{3}} \times 2^{\frac{1}{3}} \times 2^{\frac{1}{3}}$

(g) $\sqrt{5} \times \sqrt{2} \times \sqrt{2} \times \sqrt{5}$

(h) $8^{\frac{1}{3}} \times 81^{\frac{1}{4}}$

(i) $169^{\frac{1}{2}} \times 64^{\frac{1}{6}}$

Challenging exercises

6 $y = 2^x$

(a) Work out the values of 2^{-2}, 2^{-1}, 2^0, 2^1, 2^2, 2^3, 2^4, 2^5 ... .

(b) Use a computer or graphics calculator to generate the exponential graph, $y = 2^x$.

(c) Study the graph of $y = 2^x$ and describe its shape. Can the variable y have any negative values?

(d) If you were given £2 on January 1st and, at the beginning of each month, you received double the amount you received the previous month, how much would you receive in December?

7 The binary number system (base 2): ... 2^4, 2^3, 2^2, 2^1, 2^0, 2^{-1}, 2^{-2} ...
Write the following decimal numbers as binary numbers.

(a) 16   (b) 13   (c) 25   (d) 15   (e) 1·5   (f) 3·75   (g) 5·875

8 Evaluate the following.

(a) $16^{\frac{3}{2}}$ (b) $27^{\frac{2}{3}}$ (c) $1000^{\frac{4}{3}}$ (d) $\frac{1}{2^{-1}}$ (e) $8^{\frac{-1}{3}}$

Problem-solving exercise

9 Centimetre cubes are joined together to make larger cubes.

(a) Imagine a 3×3 cube dipped in red paint.
   (i) How many of the smaller cubes would have no faces painted red?
   (ii) How many of the smaller cubes would have exactly one face painted red?
   (iii) How many of the smaller cubes would have exactly two faces painted red?
   (iv) How many of the smaller cubes would have exactly three faces painted red?
   (v) How many of the smaller cubes would have exactly four faces painted red?

(b) Imagine a 4×4 cube, then a 5×5 cube, ... $n \times n$ cube. Investigate how many of the faces are painted red when the cubes are dipped in red paint.

Homework

Pythagorean triples

$3^2 + 4^2 = 5^2 \longrightarrow$ (3, 4, 5) is called a Pythagorean triple.

Investigate to see if you can find other whole numbers (a, b, c) such that $a^2 + b^2 = c^2$.

Number and Algebra

Conventions for answers

Goals

By the end of this lesson you will be able to answer questions such as these:

- Express 3·492 correct to   (a) 1 d.p.   (b) 3 sig. figs.

- Express ·003492 correct to   (a) 4 d.p.   (b) 3 sig. figs.

- Express in standard index form   (a) 3·492   (b) ·003492.

- What are the least upper bound and the greatest lower bound of 7·6 (1 d.p.)?

- Each side of a square is of length 7·5 cm (2 sig. figs.). What are the least upper bound and the greatest lower bound for the area?

- Each side of a square is of length 7·5 cm (2 sig. figs.). What are the least upper bound and the greatest lower bound for the perimeter?

Starter

1 Vulgar fractions greater than unity are conventionally expressed as mixed numbers.

(a) $\frac{7}{4} =$ (b) $\frac{11}{7} =$ (c) $\frac{35}{13} =$ (d) $\frac{1003}{998} =$

2 It is conventional to state the level of accuracy of the answer. Express 34.781 to the following levels of accuracy.

(a) correct to 1 d.p.   (b) correct to 2 d.p.
(c) correct to 4 sig.figs.   (d) correct to 2 sig.figs.

3 One convention is to use standard index form for very large or very small answers.

(a) Express 345·6 in standard index form.   (b) Express ·03456 in standard index form.

Demonstration 1

A cube has a volume of 7300 cm³, to two significant figures. Find the length of one side and give your answer to a suitable degree of accuracy.

Let x cm be the length of each side of the cube.

$$x^3 \approx 7300$$

$$7250 \leq x^3 < 7350$$

$$19·354 \leq x < 19·443$$

$$19·4 \ (1 \ \text{d.p.}) \leq x < 19·4 \ (1 \ \text{d.p.})$$

$$x = 19·4 \ (1 \ \text{d.p.})$$

Each side of the cube is 19·4 cm long (to 1 d.p.).

Letts I See Maths Book 3

Demonstration 2

$$\longleftarrow 3{\cdot}05 \leq 3{\cdot}1 \text{ (1 d.p.)} < 3{\cdot}15 \longrightarrow$$

All these numbers are definitely less than or equal to 3·1 (1 d.p.) so they are called **lower bounds** of 3·1.

You can see **3·05** is the greatest lower bound.

All these numbers are definitely greater than or equal to 3·1 (1 d.p.) so they are called **upper bounds** of 3·1.

You can see **3·15** is the least upper bound.

Key words decimal places   greatest lower bound   least upper bound
lower bound   significant figures   standard index form   upper bound

Worked example

Exercise bank

1. A rectangle has sides measured as 3·2 m (1 d.p.) and 5·9 m (1 d.p.). Calculate the greatest lower bound and least upper bound for the area of the rectangle.

   The largest area is 3·25 × 5·95 = 19·3375 m²
   The smallest area is 3·15 × 5·85 = 18·4275 m²

Plenary

◉ Discuss the Goals.

◉ Explain what is meant by 'the upper bounds' and 'the least upper bound' of 4.3 (1 d.p.).

◉ Explain what is meant by 'the lower bounds' and 'the greatest lower bound' of 4.3 (1 d.p.).

Number and Algebra

Conventions for answers

> **Essential exercises**

1 Work out the areas of the following shapes. Give your answers to two decimal places (2 d.p.).

(a)

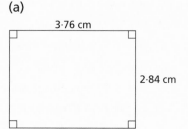

3·76 cm

2·84 cm

(b)

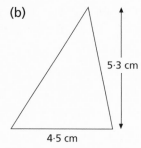

5·3 cm

4·5 cm

(c)

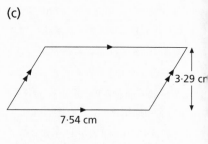

7·54 cm

3·29 cm

(d)

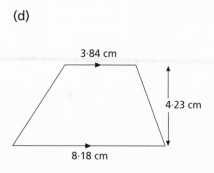

3·84 cm

4·23 cm

8·18 cm

(e)

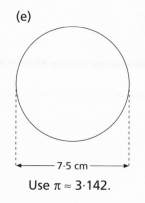

7·5 cm

Use $\pi \approx 3\cdot142$.

(f)

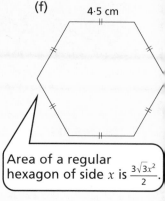

4·5 cm

Area of a regular hexagon of side x is $\frac{3\sqrt{3}x^2}{2}$.

2 Give your answers to the following questions correct to three significant figures (3 sig. figs.).

(a) Calculate the volume of a cube with edge length 3·2 cm.

(b) Calculate the area of a circle with radius 4·7 cm. (Use $\pi \approx 3\cdot142$.)

(c) Calculate the mean of the following set of numbers:
2·56. 7·39, 5·45, 3·24, 4·33, 6·05

(d) Viewed under a microscope ($\times 10\,000$), an organism's length measures 32·87 mm. What is its actual length?

(e) The earth has a diameter of 12 756 km. Calculate its circumference. (Use $\pi \approx 3\cdot14$.)

(f) The moon has a diameter of about a quarter of that of the earth. What is its approximate circumference?

3 Write the following numbers to (a) 2 decimal places (b) 3 decimal places (c) 3 significant figures.

(i) 0·049 24

(ii) 342·162 98

(iii) 140·6377

(iv) 200·3956

(v) 0·020 463

(vi) 0·008 102

Conventions for answers

Challenging exercises

4 Write the following numbers in standard index form, $A \times 10^n$ where $1 \leq A < 10$ and n is an integer.

(a) 43 560   (b) 0·000 57   (c) 86·25   (d) 0·0721

5 Round your answers to the following calculations to three significant figures and then write them in standard index form.

(a) 294 000 × 8630   (b) 0·000 259 × 0·006 72

(c) 0·02 ÷ 0·000 45   (d) 2·364 × 102 × 1·698 × 104

6 State the upper and lower bounds, in the form $a \leq p < b$, for the following data that has been measured within certain limits.

(a) The diameter of the moon is 3000 km, to the nearest thousand kilometres.

(b) The population of Pakistan in 1977 was 75 million, to the nearest million.

(c) Wind speeds in tornados can reach 650 km per hour, to the nearest 10 km per hour.

(d) The average temperature in January in Newfoundland is ⁻5°C, to the nearest degree Celsius.

Problem-solving exercise

7 π is an infinite decimal. π is an irrational number. π does not have an exact value. We use different approximations for π depending on the degree of accuracy required.

π = 3·141 592 65 (to 8 d.p.)

Using a sophisticated measuring instrument, the diameter of the circle on the right was measured as 2·360 49 cm.

Estimate the circumference of the circle by rounding the values for π *and* the diameter to each of the accuracies stated below.

(a) one significant figure   (b) two decimal places

(c) three significant figures   (d) three decimal places

Homework

Estimate answers to the following calculations by rounding each number to one significant figure.

(a) 4·75 × 3·142   (b) 864 × 29   (c) 0·0513 × 37

(d) 62·84 ÷ 9·45   (e) $\dfrac{52·79 \times 61·4}{48·3 \times 5·94}$ (f) 41·98 ÷ 1·76

Goals

By the end of this lesson you will be able to answer questions such as these:

- Draw a graph of $y = x + 2$ using $(x + 2)$ and y as the variables.

- If y is proportional to x, write down the proportionality relationship and the associated equation (using k as the constant of proportionality).

- If y is inversely proportional to x, write down the proportionality relationship and the associated equation (using k as the constant of proportionality).

- The distance, d, moved by an object is proportional to twice the square of the time, t, for which it has moved and, when $t = 10$ s, $d = 400$ m.
  - (a) Calculate d when $t = 4$ s.
  - (b) Calculate t when $d = 720$ m.

Starter

1 y is a variable; x is a variable. Look at $y = x$ and answer these questions.
- (a) When the variable x has the value 2, what is the value of the variable y?
- (b) When the variable x has the value 0, what is the value of the variable y?

2 y is a variable; $x + 3$ is a variable. Look at $y = x + 3$ and answer these questions.
- (a) When the variable $x + 3$ has the value 2, what is the value of the variable y?
- (b) When the variable $x + 3$ has the value 0, what is the value of the variable y?

Demonstration 1

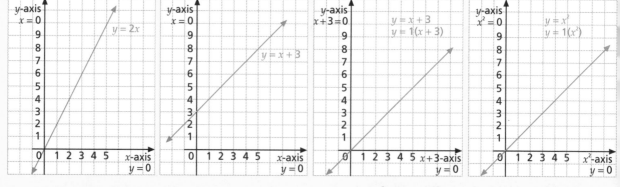

y is proportional to x $y \propto x$ $y = kx$

$y \propto x$
$y = kx$

$y \not\propto x$
$y \neq kx$

$y \propto (x + 3)$
$y = k(x + 3)$

$y \propto (x^2)$
$y = k(x^2)$

Letts I See Maths **Book 3**

Number and Algebra

Demonstration 2

y is inversely proportional to x $y \propto \dfrac{1}{x}$ $y = \dfrac{k}{x}$

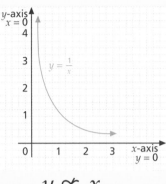

$$y \not\propto x$$
$$y \neq kx$$

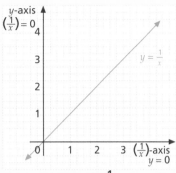

$$y \propto \dfrac{1}{x}$$
$$y = k\left(\dfrac{1}{x}\right)$$

Key words   inversely proportional   proportional

Worked example

Exercise bank

1 The distance, d, moved by an object is proportional to the square of the time, t, for which it has moved.

(a) Write down the proportionality relationship and the proportionality formula (i.e. express d in terms of t with a constant of proportionality k).

$d \propto t^2;\ d = kt^2$

(b) Given $t = 10$ s when $d = 500$ m, calculate k.

When $t = 10$, $d = 500$, so $500 = k \times 10^2$; $k = 5$; $d = 5t^2$.

(c) Calculate d when $t = 4$ s.

Using $d = 5t^2$ when $t = 4$, we obtain $d = 5 \times 4^2 = 80$; $d = 80$ m.

(d) Calculate t when $d = 720$ m.

Using $d = 5t^2$ when $d = 720$, we obtain $720 = 5t^2$; $t = (144)^{\frac{1}{2}}$; $t = 12$ s.

Plenary

👁 Discuss the Goals.

👁 Look at the equation $y = 3(x^2 - 1)$. Discuss which variables are proportional.

👁 Look at the equation $y = 3x^2 - 1$. Discuss which variables are proportional.

👁 Look at the equation $y = \dfrac{3}{x^2}$. Discuss which variables are proportional.

Letts I See Maths Book 3

Proportionality

Number and Algebra

Essential exercises

1 (a) Complete the table below for the perimeter (P) and the area (A) of a square.

x cm

x cm

Length of side (x cm)	0	0·5	1	1·5	2	2·5	3	3·5	4	4·5	5
Perimeter (P cm)											
Area (A cm²)											

(b) On the same axes, plot the points (x, P) and x, A) in different colours.

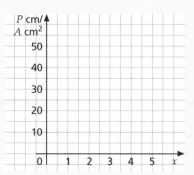

(c) Is the perimeter (P) of a square proportional to the length of its side (x)?

(d) Is the area (A) of a square proportional to the length of its side (x)?

2 The price of petrol (£P) is proportional to the quantity (Q litres).
$P \propto Q$ and so $P = kQ$.

(a) Use the graph on the right to estimate the value of k, the gradient of the graph.

(b) Estimate the price of 1 litre of petrol.

(c) Estimate how much petrol you would get for one pound.

(d) Estimate the cost of 40 litres of petrol.

(e) The price of petrol increases by 5%. Work out the new value of k.

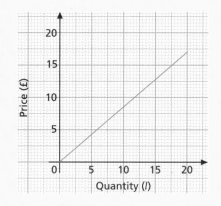

3 In the tables below, $y \propto x$ and so $y = kx$ Work out the values of k and complete the tables.

(a)

x	0	1	2	3	4	5	6	7	8	9	10
y	0			10·5				24·5			

(b)

x	0	0·5	1	1·5	2	2·5	3	3·5	4	4·5	5
y		0·85							6·8		

Challenging exercise

4 In each of the tables below, work out whether $y \propto x$, $y \propto x^2$, $y \propto x^3$, or $y \propto \frac{1}{x}$.

(a)

x	0	0·5	1	1·5	2	2·5	3	3·5
y	0	0·5	2	4·5	8	12·5	18	24·5

(b)

x	0·1	0·2	0·3	0·4	0·5	0·6	0·7	0·8
y	0·4	0·8	1·2	1·6	2·0	2·4	2·8	3·2

(c)

x	1	2	3	4	5	6	8	12
y	12	6	4	3	2·4	2	1·5	1

(d)

x	⁻2	⁻1	0	1	2	3	4	5
y	⁻2	⁻0·25	0	0·25	2	6·75	16	31·25

Problem-solving exercise

5 Study the distance (d miles)–time
(t hours) graph on the right.

(a) Is $d \propto t$?
(b) Work out the gradient of the graph.
(c) What does the gradient represent?
(d) (i) Draw the distance–time graph
using the values in the table below.

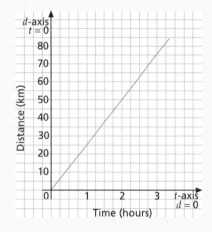

Time (t seconds)	0	2	4	6
Distance (d metres)	0	30	60	90

(ii) Write down the equation of
the graph.

Homework

On a pay-as-you-go mobile phone, the cost of
a call is proportional to the length of the call.
Use the graph on the right to estimate the
following.

(a) The cost of a one-minute call.
(b) The cost of a 45-second call.
(c) The time you can get for £1·50.

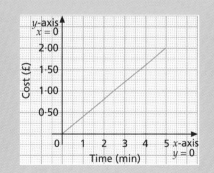

Goals

By the end of this lesson you will be able to answer questions such as these:

👁 Value added tax (VAT) at 17·5% is charged on a television set costing £275 before tax. Find the selling price.

👁 A computer costs £763 including VAT at 17·5%. Find the untaxed price of the computer.

👁 A balloon is blown up so that its volume increases from 5·7 litres to 7·3 litres. Calculate the percentage increase in volume.

Starter

1 Each of the following is the final sentence in a word problem. Introduce a variable for each one, starting with the word, 'Let …'.

(a) Calculate the original price.

(b) Calculate the final price.

(c) Calculate the percentage increase.

(d) Calculate the original length.

(e) Find the increase in area.

(f) Find the cost of production.

Demonstration 1

(a)

105% of 41·3 = 46·5

scale factor   object   image

$x\% \text{ of } P = N$

$$\frac{x}{100} \times P = N$$

(b)

$\frac{105}{100}$ of 41·3 = 46·5

scale factor   object   image

$\frac{x}{100}$ of $P = N$

$$N = \frac{x}{100} P$$

$$x = \frac{100N}{P}$$

(c)

$\frac{105}{100} \times 41\cdot3 = 46\cdot5$

scale factor   object   image

$\frac{x}{100} \times P = N$

$$P = \frac{100N}{x}$$

Letts I See Maths **Book 3**

Demonstration 2

(a) $x\%$ of $y\%$ of $z\%$ of $P = N$

(f) $x\%$ of $x\%$ of $x\%$ of $P = N$

(b) $\frac{x}{100}$ of $\frac{y}{100}$ of $\frac{z}{100}$ of $P = N$

(g) $\frac{x \times x \times x}{100^3} P = N$

(c) $\frac{x}{100} \times \frac{y}{100} \times \frac{z}{100} \times P = N$

(h) $\frac{x^3}{100^3} P = N$

(d) $\frac{x}{100} \frac{y}{100} \frac{z}{100} P = N$

(e) $\frac{xyz}{100^3} P = N$

Key words   image   'Let ...'   object   percentage decrease   percentage increase

Worked example

Exercise bank

 A car costing £14 000 depreciates by 12% during the first year; then by 18% during the second year; then by 5% in each subsequent year. Write an expression for the value of the car after five years.

Value of car at the end of five years $= \left(\frac{88}{100}\right)\left(\frac{82}{100}\right)\left(\frac{95}{100}\right)^3$ of £14 000

Plenary

👁 Do the calculations in the Goals and discuss:

   (a) the initial 'Let ...' sentence

   (b) the manipulation of the equations.

Letts I See Maths Book 3

Number and Algebra

Percentages

Essential exercises

1 (a) There was a 15% discount in a sale. Ramesh bought a pair of trainers in the sale for £55·25. What was the original price of the trainers?

(b) A metal rod at room temperature is 17 cm long. When it is heated, it expands to a length of 20·74 cm. Find the percentage change in length.

(c) Cass saved £35 when she bought a TV in a sale. What was the original price of the TV if it had been reduced by 20%?

(d) There were 60 950 people who visited an art gallery in 2002. This was an increase of 15% on 2001. How many people visited the art gallery in 2001?

(e) A house increases in price from £170 000 to £181 050. What is the percentage increase?

2 VAT at 17·5% has to be added to these prices of goods in a shop. Work out the prices with VAT, to the nearest pence.

(a) £23   (b) £45   (c) £89·99   (d) £227·89

3

Dan compared some special deals in two supermarkets. In shop A, goods were offered with a 15% discount. In shop B, the offer was 'buy one and get a second one half price'. Complete the table below and compare the two shops.

Original price for 1	Price for 1 in shop A	Price for 1 in shop B	Price for 2 in shop A	Price for 2 in shop B
45p	38p	45p	76p	68p
78p				
£1·25				
£2·50				
£3·48				
£6·10				
£10·00				
£23·00				

Number and Algebra

Percentages

 4

(a) A pensioner deposits £5500 in a savings account with an annual compound interest of 5·5%. How much will be in the account at the end of six years?

(b) The average annual rate of inflation over a four-year period was 2·5%. How much would a loaf of bread cost at the end of the four-year period that cost 75p at the beginning?

(c) From 1 May 2002 to 30 September 2002, house prices changed in the following way: May – increased by 4%; June – increased by 3%; July – increased by 6%; August – increased by 1·5%; September – decreased by 2·5%.

Complete the table below showing house price changes in this period.

	Price on 1 May	Price on 30 September
(i)	£65 000	
(ii)	£134 000	
(iii)	£228 000	
(iv)	£540 000	

Problem-solving exercises

 5 Write Alison's end-of-term test results as percentages (to the nearest whole number) and then place them in ascending order.

Art: $\frac{18}{20}$; English: $\frac{73}{84}$; Maths: $\frac{75}{100}$; Science: $\frac{78}{140}$; French: $\frac{21}{25}$; D & T: $\frac{14}{15}$

 6

(a) In a survey of a class of 35 students, twenty said they preferred the colour blue for a uniform. What percentage of the class is this? (Give your answer to the nearest whole number.)

(b) In a survey of 2500 people, 985 said they would vote for the Green Party. What percentage is this?

(c) In 2002 it was reported that 1 in 7 women over 50 smoked. What percentage is this? (Give your answer to the nearest whole number.)

Homework

True or False?
(a) If my savings increase by 9% and then decrease by 9%, the result would be an overall increase.
(b) If I add VAT of 17·5% and then deduct 10% discount, the result is greater than first deducting the 10% and then adding 17·5% VAT.
(c) A reduction of 15%, followed by a further reduction of 15%, is the same as an overall reduction of 27·75%.

The distributive law 1

Goals

By the end of this lesson you will be able to answer questions such as these:

- Discuss the relationship between the following.

  (a) $7(40 + 3)$

  and

×	40	3
7	280	21

  and

×	40	+	3
7	280	+	21

  (b) $7(50 - 7)$

  and

×	50	-7
7	350	-49

  and

×	50	–	7
7	350	–	49

- Simplify these expressions.

  (a) $7(x - 3) + 2x + 1$

  (b) $x(5 + 7y) - 2(x + 2xy)$

- Look at these strings of terms. Write each string as a product of two factors.

  (a) $5x + 15$ (b) $7x - 35$ (c) $15x + 12xy$ (d) $15x^2y - 20xyz$

Starter

1 Calculate each of these and justify your answer in each case

(a) $^-3 \times 4 =$ (b) $4 \times {}^-3 =$ (c) $^-1{\cdot}2 \times 4 =$ (d) $4 \times {}^-1{\cdot}2 =$

(e) $^-3x \times 4 =$ (f) $4 \times {}^-3x =$ (g) $^-1{\cdot}2y \times 4 =$ (h) $4 \times {}^-1{\cdot}2y =$

Demonstration 1

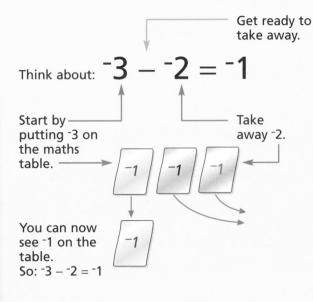

Get ready to take away.

Think about: $^-3 - {}^-2 = {}^-1$

Start by putting $^-3$ on the maths table.

Take away $^-2$.

You can now see $^-1$ on the table.

So: $^-3 - {}^-2 = {}^-1$

Get ready to add.

Think about: $^-3 + 2 = {}^-1$

Start by putting $^-3$ on the maths table.

Add 2.

You can now see $^-1$ on the table.

So: $^-3 + 2 = {}^-1$

Number and Algebra

Demonstration 2

$$x(5 + 7y) - 2(x + 2xy)$$

> Put x lots of 5 and x lots of $7y$ on the maths table.

> Get ready to take away.

> Remove 2 lots of x and 2 lots of $2xy$.

$$5x + 7xy - 2x - 4xy$$

$$3x + 3xy$$

Key words   distributive law   expression   simplify   string

Worked example

Exercise bank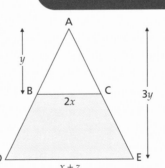

1 Calculate the area of the trapezium BCED.

Area BCED $= \frac{1}{2}(x + z) \times 3y - \frac{1}{2} \times 2xy$

$= \frac{3}{2}xy + \frac{3}{2}yz - xy$

$= \frac{3}{2}yz + \frac{1}{2}xy$

$= \frac{1}{2}y(3z + x)$

Plenary

👁 Look at this string of terms: $3x(2y + 5) + \frac{xy}{2} + y(7 - 2x) + x - 2y$

  (a) How many terms are there?
  (b) Use the distributive law and simplify the expression.
  (c) How many terms are there in the new string?

👁 Discuss the Goals.

Letts I See Maths Book 3

The distributive law 1

Essential exercises

1 Complete the grids below.

(a) $9 \times 87 = 9 \times (80 + 7)$

×	80	+	7		
9		+		=	

(b) $6 \times 79 = 6 \times (80 - 1)$

×	80	–	1		
6		–		=	

(c) $5(x + 7)$

×	x	+	7		
5		+		=	

(d) $8(x - 3)$

×	x	–	3		
8		–		=	

2 Multiply out the following brackets.

(a) $3(x + 8)$ (b) $2(x - 6)$ (c) $4(x + y)$

(d) $7(x + y + 5)$ (e) $5(2x + 8)$ (f) $3(4x + 5y)$

(g) $x(x + 2)$ (h) $x(3x + 4)$ (i) $xy(2x + 3y)$

3 Factorise the following expressions.

(a) $4x + 6$ (b) $12y + 20$ (c) $14x - 35y$

(d) $10xy + 25xz$ (e) $6x + 15y + 21z$ (f) $2 \cdot 5x + 7 \cdot 5$

(g) $26a - 65b$ (h) $51p + 34q$ (i) $45y - 90z$

4 Simplify the following expressions.

(a) $3(x + 5) + 19$ (b) $2(5x - 4) + 3(2x + 6)$

(c) $25 + 7(x - 3)$ (d) $5x + 3(x + 9)$

(e) $4(3x + 2) + 3(4x - 1)$ (f) $9(2x + 4) - 6(3x + 5)$

5 Use the distributive law to simplify the following calculations.

(a) $273 \times 37 + 273 \times 63$ (b) $43 \times 3 \cdot 5 + 6 \cdot 5 \times 43$

(c) $89 \times 125 - 89 \times 25$ (d) $15 \times 19 \cdot 5 - 15 \times 4 \cdot 5$

(e) $14 \times 3 \cdot 2 + 14 \times 2 \cdot 5 + 14 \times 4 \cdot 3$ (f) $27 \times 31 + 19 \times 27$

(g) $67 \times 2 \cdot 4 + 67 \times 11 \cdot 7 - 67 \times 4 \cdot 1$ (h) $56 \times 3 \cdot 265 + 44 \times 3 \cdot 265$

Letts I See Maths **Book 3**

Challenging exercises

6 Calculate:
(a) the perimeter (b) the area
of the shaded shape below.
(Leave your answer as a multiple of π.)

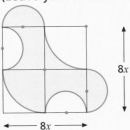

8x

8x

7 Write the area of the shaded part of the diagram below as a multiple of π.

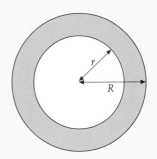

r

R

Problem-solving exercises

8 Work out the areas of the trapezia below and write the answers in their simplest form.

(a)
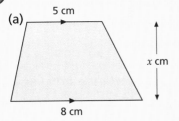
5 cm

x cm

8 cm

(b)
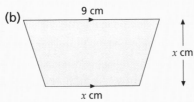
9 cm

x cm

x cm

(c)
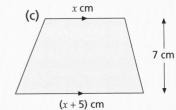
x cm

7 cm

(x + 5) cm

9 A cylindrical water container has a circular cross-section area of 120 cm² and a height of 75 cm. Work out the volume of water left in the container when the height of the water has dropped by x cm.

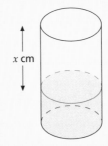

x cm

Homework

Write down the area of the shaded part of the diagram on the right.

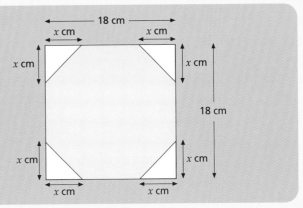

18 cm

x cm   x cm

x cm   x cm

x cm

18 cm

x cm   x cm

x cm   x cm

Negative numbers

Goals

By the end of this lesson you will be able to answer questions such as these:

👁 Calculate   (a) $^-2 \times ^-3$ (b) $^-2a \times ^-3b$.

👁 Use the distributive law to simplify the following expressions.
   (a) $5(2x - 3) - 3(2x - 1)$ (b) $5(2x - 3) - (2x - 1)$

👁 Prove $^-1 \times ^-1 = 1$.

Starter

1 Study the following.

   (a) $3 + 7 = 3 - ^-7$ (b) $15 - 9 = 15 + ^-9$ (c) $p + q = p - ^-q$ (d) $r - s = r + ^-s$

2 Look at each string of two terms. Copy the first term and then complete the string as a difference of two terms.

   (a) $7 + 6 =$ (b) $3xy + 5az =$ (c) $5 + ^-4 =$ (d) $\sin x + 2yz =$

Look at each string of two terms. Copy the first term and then complete the string as a sum of two terms.

   (a) $7 - 6 =$ (b) $3xy - 5az =$ (c) $5 - ^-4 =$ (d) $\sin x - 2yz =$

Demonstration 1

To prove: $^-1 \times ^-1 = 1$

Proof

$\times$	0	$-$	1	
$^-1$	0	$-$	$^-1$	1

Let $n = ^-1 \times ^-1$

then $n = ^-1 \times (0 - 1)$

          $n = ^-1 \times 0 - ^-1 \times 1$

          $n = 0 - ^-1$

          $n = 1$

Therefore $^-1 \times ^-1 = 1$

Letts I See Maths Book 3

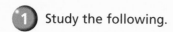
Number and Algebra

Demonstration 2

$$x(5 + 7y) - 2(x - 2xy)$$
$$x(5 + 7y) + {}^-2(x + {}^-2xy)$$

| Put x lots of 5 and x lots of $7y$ on the maths table. | Get some more. | Add $^-2$ lots of x and $^-2$ lots of ^-2xy. |

$$5x + 7xy + {}^-2x + {}^-2 \times {}^-2xy$$

$$5x + 7xy - 2x + 4xy$$

$$3x + 11xy$$

$$x(5 + 7y) - 2(x - 2xy) = 5x + 7xy - 2x + 4xy$$

Key words   distributive law   string of terms

Worked example

Exercise bank

1 Use the distributive law to simplify $^-5(2x - 3) - 3(2x - 1)$.

$^-5(2x - 3) - 3(2x - 1) = {}^-10x + 15 - 6x + 3$
$\qquad\qquad\qquad\qquad = {}^-16x + 18$

Plenary

  Look at this string of terms: $3x(2y + 5) - \frac{xy}{2} - y(7 - 2x) - (x - 2y)$

(a) How many terms are there?
(b) Use the distributive law and simplify the expression.
(c) How many terms are there in the new string?

  Discuss the Goals.

Letts | See Maths Book 3

Negative numbers

Essential exercises

1 ... $<$ $^-5$ $<$ $^-4$ $<$ $^-3$ $<$ $^-2$ $<$ $^-1$ $<$ 0 $<$ 1 $<$ 2 $<$ 3 $<$ 4 $<$ 5 $<$ ...

Insert the correct sign, $<$ or $>$.

(a) 16 ... 3 (b) 4·3 ... 4·7 (c) 2 ... $^-3$

(d) $^-4$ ... $^-1$ (e) $^-3$ ... $^-3·5$ (f) 0 ... $^-0.5$

2 Complete the following sentences.

(a) 3 − 5 has the same value as 3 + ... = ...
(b) $^-6$ − 4 has the same value as $^-6$ + ... = ...
(c) 9 − $^-3$ has the same value as 9 + ... = ...
(d) $^-4$ − $^-2$ has the same value as $^-4$ + ... = ...
(e) 0 − 8 has the same value as 0 + ... = ...
(f) 7 − x has the same value as 7 + ... = ...

3 Complete the following equations. The first one has been done for you.

(a) 1 + $^-1$ = 0 (b) 2 + ... = 0 (c) 87 + ... = 0 (d) x + ... = 0
    1 − 1 = 0   2 − ... = 0   87 − ... = 0 x − ... = 0

4 Complete the following equations.

(a) 4 + 9 + $^-7$ − 3 − $^-6$ = (b) $^-29$ + 18 + $^-6$ − $^-41$ =
(c) 96 − $^-103$ − $^-47$ + $^-36$ = (d) $^-14$ − 17 − 33 =

5 Complete the following equations.

(a) $^-2 \times 3$ = $3 \times ^-2$ = $^-3 \times 2$ = $2 \times ^-3$ =
(b) $^-7 \times 6$ = $6 \times ^-7$ = $^-6 \times 7$ = $7 \times ^-6$ =
(c) $^-5 \times x$ = $x \times ^-5$ = $^-x \times 5$ = $5 \times ^-x$ =

6 Multiply out the following brackets.

(a) $^-4(x + 3)$ (b) $^-9(x + 2)$ (c) $7(^-x + ^-5)$

7 Complete the following equations.

(a) $^-4 \times ^-6$ = (b) $^-8 \times ^-9$ = (c) $^-x \times ^-y$ =

8 Multiply out the following brackets.

(a) $^-2(x + ^-5)$ (b) $^-7(x + ^-2)$ (c) $^-6(x + ^-4)$
(d) $^-3(x − 6) = ^-3(x + ^-6)$ = (e) $^-4(x − ^-2) = ^-4(x + 2)$ =

Letts I See Maths **Book 3**

Negative numbers

Challenging exercises

9 Prove that $^-2 \times {}^-5 = 10$.

10 Work out the value of each of the terms in the following sequence.

$(^-1)^2$, $(^-1)^3$, $(^-1)^4$, $(^-1)^5$, $(^-1)^6$, ... $(^-1)^{2n}$, $(^-1)^{2n+1}$

11 (a) Work out the next three terms in the sequence: 3, $^-6$, 12, $^-24$, 48, ...

(b) Write down the nth term of the sequence in part (a).

12 Multiply out the following brackets and simplify.

(a) $3(4x + 2) - 2(3x + 4)$ (b) $17 - 5(2x - 4)$

(c) $6(x - 2) - 9(2x - 8)$ (d) $48 - 6(5 - 3x)$

Problem-solving exercise

13 Write down the areas of the shaded parts of the following shapes. Give the answers in their in their simplest form.

(a)

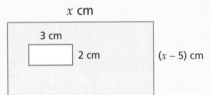

(b)

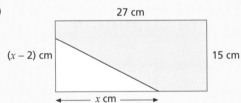

(c)

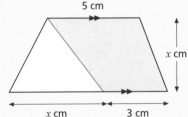

(d)

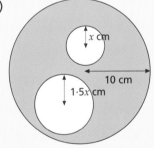

Homework

Imagine the minus key on your calculator has broken. Rewrite the following calculations so that you can use your calculator using the plus key instead.

(a) $73 - 46 - 19$ (b) $124 - {}^-93 - 111$ (c) $405 - 287 - {}^-649$

(d) $3{\cdot}27 - 0{\cdot}04 - 2{\cdot}09$ (e) $^-498 - 962 - {}^-1264$

Letts I See Maths **Book 3**

Number and Algebra

63

Simultaneous equations

Goals

By the end of this lesson you will be able to answer questions such as these:

👁 Look at these equations: (i) $y = 2x - 3$ (ii) $y = x + 2$.   Solve them simultaneously using:

(a) graphical methods   (b) elimination   (c) substitution.

Starter

1 Look at this graph.

(a) State some (x, y) solutions of $y = 2x + 3$.

(b) State some (x, y) solutions of $y = x + 2$.

(c) State the simultaneous (x, y) solution for $y = 2x + 3$ and $y = x + 2$.

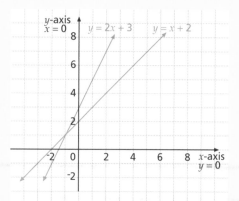

Demonstration 1

> Either equation could be used because each gives y in terms of x.

> In both equations the coefficient of y is 1.

Method of substitution

$$\begin{cases} y = 2x + 3 & (1) \\ y = x + 2 & (2) \end{cases}$$

Substitute the expression $2x + 3$ from equation (1) for y in equation (2):

$$2x + 3 = x + 2$$
$$x = {}^{-}1$$

Substitute the value $^{-}1$ for x in equation (2):

$$y = {}^{-}1 + 2$$
$$y = 1$$

When $x = {}^{-}1$, $y = 1$.

The simultaneous solution is $({}^{-}1, 1)$.

Method of elimination

$$\begin{pmatrix} y = 2x + 3 & (1) \\ y = x + 2 & (2) \end{pmatrix}$$

Equation (1) – equation (2):

$$0 = x + 1$$
$$x = {}^{-}1$$

Substitute the value $^{-}1$ for x in equation (2):

$$y = {}^{-}1 + 2$$
$$y = 1$$

When $x = {}^{-}1$, $y = 1$.

The simultaneous solution is $({}^{-}1, 1)$.

Number and Algebra

Letts I See Maths Book 3

Demonstration 2

To solve the linear simultaneous equations using the method of elimination

$$3x + 5y = 21 \quad (1)$$
$$2x + 3y = 13 \quad (2)$$

To eliminate x, the coefficient of x in each equation must be the same.

To eliminate y, the coefficient of y in each equation must be the same.

Eliminate x

Equation (1) × 2:	$6x + 10y = 42$	(3)
Equation (2) × 3:	$6x + 9y = 39$	(4)
Equation (3) – equation (4):	$0 + y = 3$	

Make the coefficient of x in each equation equal to 6.

Substitute the value 3 for y in equation (2):
$$2x + 9 = 13$$
$$x = 2$$

The simultaneous solution is (2, 3).

> **Key word**   coefficient   elimination   linear   simultaneous   substitution

---

Worked example

Exercise bank

 Solve the linear simultaneous equations $4x + 3y = 19$ and $2x - y = 7$.

$$4x + 3y = 19 \quad (1)$$
$$2x - y = 7 \quad (2)$$

(2) × 2:	$4x - 2y = 14$	(3)
(1) – (3):	$5y = 5$	
	$y = 1$	
Substitute $y = 1$ in (2):	$2x - 1 = 7$	
	$2x = 8$	
	$x = 4$	

The solution is $x = 4$ and $y = 1$.

Plenary

👁 Discuss the graphical solution of the following pairs of simultaneous equations.

(a) $y = 2x + 1$ and $y = 2x + 3$

(b) $y = 2x + 1$ and $y = 2x + 2$

(c) $y = x^2$ and $y = 1$

(d) $y = x^2$ and $y = ^-1$

👁 Discuss the Goals.

Letts I See Maths Book 3

Simultaneous equations

Essential exercises

1 Logical reasoning

(a) Three lemonades and two orange juices cost £5·30. One lemonade and three orange juice cost £4·80. Work out the cost of (i) one lemonade (ii) one orange juice.

(b) At the cinema, it cost £20·90 for two adults and three children and £33·10 for three adults and five children to watch a film. Work out the cost of (i) one adult (ii) one child to watch a film at the cinema.

2 Graphical method

Draw graphs to solve the following linear simultaneous equations.

(a) $y = 2x + 1$
$y = x + 1$

(b) $y = 3x + 2$
$y = 6x - 1$

(c) $y = 2 - x$
$y = x + 6$

(d) $y = x + 1$
$y = 3x + 5$

(e) $y = \frac{1}{2}x + 2$
$y = 3 - 2x$

(f) $y = 3x - 2$
$y = 4 - 3x$

3 Substitution

Use the method of substitution to solve the following linear simultaneous equations.

(a) $y = 3x$
$6x + 2y = 30$

(b) $y = 4x$
$2x + 7y = 36$

(c) $x = 6y$
$2x + 4y = 8$

(d) $x = 3y$
$2x + 4y = 8$

(e) $y = 5x$
$7x + 2y = 34$

(f) $y = \frac{1}{2}x$
$9x + 4y = 55$

4 Elimination

Use the method of elimination to solve the following linear simultaneous equations.

(a) $x + 2y = 8$
$x + 5y = 17$

(b) $x + 2y = 11$
$x - y = 2$

(c) $3x + 2y = 11$
$5x + 3y = 17$

(d) $2x + 6y = 10$
$3x + 7y = 12$

(e) $2x + 4y = 24$
$6x - 2y = 2$

(f) $3x + y = 7$
$6x - 3y = {}^-3$

(g) $3x + 4y = 57$
$2x + 5y = 59$

(h) $2x + 7y = 96$
$3x - 2y = 19$

Number and Algebra

Letts I See Maths **Book 3**

Challenging exercises

 5 Discuss the solutions to the following pairs of linear equations.

(a) $2x + 3y = 7$

  $4x + 6y = 14$

(b) $3x + 4y = 11$

  $5x + 3y = 11$

(c) $3x + 5y = 27$

  $9x + 15y = 83$

 6 (a) On the same pair of axes, draw the graphs of $y = x^2$ and $y = 3x - 2$.

(b) Write down the coordinates of the two points of intersection of the two graphs.

(c) Explain why these points give you the solution to $x^2 - 3x + 2 = 0$.

(d) What two graphs would you draw to solve the equation $x^2 - 7x + 12 = 0$?

Problem-solving exercise

7 Form, and solve, simultaneous equations to answer the following problems.

(a) On 1st June 2003, Jane's mum is five times Jane's age, in years. On 1st June 2010, Jane's mum will be three times Jane's age, in years.

  (i) How old is Jane on 1st June 2003?

  (ii) How old is Jane's mum on 1st June 2003?

(b) The sum of two numbers is 104 and their quotient is 7. Find the two numbers.

(c) The difference between two numbers is 22 and, when you divide the larger number by the smaller number, you get 5 remainder 2. Find the two numbers.

(d) In a farm shop, Dan buys three cabbages and two turnips for £2·64 and Josi buys two cabbages and five turnips for £2·75.

  Work out the price of (i) one cabbage (ii) one turnip.

(e) Gavin buys four widgets and seven paddles for £5·46. Neil buys three widgets and eight paddles for £5·58.

  Work out the price of (i) a widget (ii) a paddle.

Homework

(a) Write down six different equations in x and y that are satisfied by the values $x = 3$ and $y = 5$.

(b) Draw the graphs of $y = 2x - 1$ and $y = 3x - 4$, and check that they intersect at (3, 5).

Letts I See Maths **Book 3**

Number and Algebra

Goals

By the end of this lesson you will be able to answer questions such as these:

👁 Find the product of these two binomial factors: $(x + 2)(x - 5)$.

👁 Find the product of these two binomial factors: $(x + \alpha)(x + \beta)$.

👁 Factorise this quadratic expression: $x^2 + 5x + 6$.

Starter

1 (a) $^-3 \times 2 =$ (b) $2 \times {}^-3 =$ (c) $^-2 \times {}^-3 =$

2 (a) $^-3 + 2 =$ (b) $2 + {}^-3 =$ (c) $^-2 + {}^-3 =$

3 (a) $^-3 - 2 =$ (b) $2 - {}^-3 =$ (c) $^-2 - {}^-3 =$

4 (a) $^-3x + 2x =$ (b) $2x + {}^-3x =$ (c) $^-2x + {}^-3x =$

5 (a) $^-3x \times 2x =$ (b) $2x \times {}^-3x =$ (c) $^-2x \times {}^-3x =$

Demonstration 1

Calculating the product of two binomial factors: $(x + \alpha)(x + \beta)$

$(x + 3)(x + 5)$

×	x	+	3	
x	x^2	+	$3x$	$x^2 + 3x$
+				+
5	$5x$	+	15	$5x + 15$
			Answer	$x^2 + 8x + 15$

$(x + 3)(x + 5)$

×	x	3	
x	x^2	$3x$	$x^2 + 3x$
5	$5x$	15	$5x + 15$
		Answer	$x^2 + 8x + 15$

$(x - 3)(x + 5)$

×	x	−	3	
x	x^2	−	$3x$	$x^2 - 3x$
+				+
5	$5x$	−	15	$5x - 15$
			Answer	$x^2 + 2x - 15$

$(x - 3)(x + 5)$

×	x	-3	
x	x^2	^-3x	$x^2 + {}^-3x$
5	$5x$	-15	$5x + {}^-15$
		Answer	$x^2 + 2x - 15$

$(x - 3)(x - 5)$

×	x	−	3	
x	x^2	−	$3x$	$x^2 - 3x$
−				−
5	$5x$	−	15	$5x - 15$
			Answer	$x^2 - 8x + 15$

$(x - 3)(x - 5)$

×	x	-3	
x	x^2	^-3x	$x^2 + {}^-3x$
-5	^-5x	15	$^-5x + 15$
		Answer	$x^2 - 8x + 15$

Number and Algebra

Demonstration 2

Using $(x + \alpha)(x + \beta)$ to factorise a quadratic expression

$(x + \alpha)(x + \beta)$

×	x	+	α	
x	x^2	+	αx	$x^2 + \alpha x$
+				+
β	βx	+	$\alpha\beta$	$\beta x + \alpha\beta$
			Answer	$x^2 + (\alpha + \beta)x + (\alpha\beta)$

> To factorise a quadratic expression, $x^2 + bx + c$,
> we need: $\quad x^2 + bx + c = (x + \alpha)(x + \beta)$
> that is: $\quad x^2 + bx + c = x^2 + (\alpha + \beta)x + \alpha\beta$

Factorise $x^2 + 8x + 15$.
Let the factors be $x + \alpha$ and $x + \beta$, then:
$$\alpha + \beta = 8$$
$$\alpha\beta = 15$$

By inspection: $\alpha = 3$, $\beta = 5$.

$$x^2 + 8x + 15 = (x + 3)(x + 5)$$

Factorise $x^2 + 2x - 15$.
Let the factors be $x + \alpha$ and $x + \beta$, then:
$$\alpha + \beta = 2$$
$$\alpha\beta = -15$$

By inspection: $\alpha = -3$, $\beta = 5$.

$$x^2 + 2x - 15 = (x - 3)(x + 5)$$

Factorise $x^2 - 8x + 15$.
Let the factors be $x + \alpha$ and $x + \beta$, then:
$$\alpha + \beta = -8$$
$$\alpha\beta = 15$$

By inspection: $\alpha = -3$, $\beta = -5$.

$$x^2 - 8x + 15 = (x - 3)(x - 5)$$

Key words   binomial factors   factorise   factors   'multiply out the brackets'   product
'product of two binomial factors'   quadratic expression   roots   terms

Worked examples

 Exercise bank

1. Multiply the two binomial factors $(x + \sqrt{2})^2$.

   $$(x + \sqrt{2})^2 = (x + \sqrt{2})(x + \sqrt{2}) = x^2 + \sqrt{2}x + \sqrt{2}x + \sqrt{2}\sqrt{2} = x^2 + 2\sqrt{2}x + 2$$

2. Factorise $x^2 - 5x + 6$.

   Let the factors be $x + \alpha$ and $x + \beta$, then $\alpha + \beta = -5$, and $\alpha\beta = 6$.
   By inspection: $\alpha = -2$, $\beta = -3$
   $x^2 - 5x + 6 = (x - 2)(x - 3)$

Plenary

◉ Discuss the Goals.

Letts I See Maths **Book 3**

Number and Algebra

Number and Algebra

Essential exercises

1 Complete the grids below.

(a) $65 \times 48 = (60 + 5) \times (40 + 8)$

×	60	+	5	
40		+		
+				+
8		+		
			Answer	

(b) $59 \times 37 = (60 - 1) \times (30 + 7)$

×	60	−	1	
30		−		
+				+
7		−		
			Answer	

(c) $(x + 2) \times (x + 5)$

×	x	+	2	
x		+		
+				+
5		+		
			Answer	

(d) $(x - 4) \times (x + 6)$

×	x	−	4	
x		−		
+				+
6		−		
			Answer	

2 Work out the column and row headings in the grids below.

(a)

×		+		
	1000	+	350	1350
+				+
	180	+	63	243
			Answer	1593

(b)

×		−		
	1600	−	40	
+				+
	200	−	5	
			Answer	

(c)

×		+		
	x^2		$3x$	$x^2 + 3x$
+				
	$7x$		21	$7x + 21$
			Answer	$x^2 + 10x + 21$

(d)

×		−		
	x^2	−	$2x$	$x^2 - 2x$
+				+
	$8x$	−	16	$8x - 16$
			Answer	$x^2 + 6x - 16$

Letts I See Maths **Book 3**

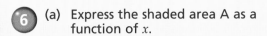

Challenging exercises

3 Multiply out the following brackets.

(a) $(x + 4)(x + 9)$ (b) $(x + 10)(x + 3)$ (c) $(2x + 5)(3x + 4)$
(d) $(x + 6)(x - 11)$ (e) $(x - 3)(x + 10)$ (f) $(4x - 1)(3x + 2)$
(g) $(x + 5)(x + 5)$ (h) $(x + 5)(x - 5)$ (i) $(2x + 4)(2x + 4)$

4 Factorise the following quadratic expressions.

(a) $x^2 + 3x + 2$ (b) $x^2 + 7x + 6$ (c) $x^2 + 6x + 5$
(d) $x^2 + x - 2$ (e) $x^2 + 2x - 15$ (f) $x^2 - 3x - 28$

5
(a) Factorise $x^2 + 5x + 6$.
(b) Work out the value of $x^2 + 5x + 6$ when (i) $x = ^-3$ (ii) $x = ^-2$.
(c) Factorise $x^2 + x - 6$.
(d) Work out the value of $x^2 + x - 6$ when (i) $x = ^-3$ (ii) $x = 2$.
(e) Discuss your answers for parts (a) to (d).

Problem-solving exercise

6
(a) Express the shaded area A as a function of x.

(b) Calculate the area A for the following values of x.

(i) $x = 0$ (ii) $x = 6$ (iii) $x = 8$

(c) For what value of x does A have its maximum value.

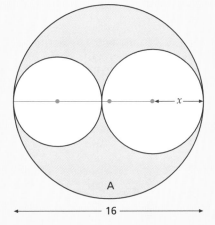

A

16

Homework

Use the grid below to calculate 93×19

×	90	+	3	
10				
+				
9				
			Answer	

Use the vertical algorithm below to calculate 93×19.

$$93$$
$$\times\ 19$$
$$\underline{\hspace{3cm}}$$
$$\underline{\hspace{3cm}}$$
$$\underline{\hspace{3cm}}$$

Goals

By the end of this lesson you will be able to answer questions such as this:

👁 Sketch a graph of $y = x^2 + 2$.

    (a) Describe the shape of the graph.

    (b) State where the graph cuts the y-axis.

    (c) State what transformation this is of $y = x^2$.

Starter

1   Sketch $y = x$.

2   Sketch $y = x + 5$ and answer these questions.
    (a) State where the graph cuts the y-axis (the intercept).
    (b) Describe what transformation this is of $y = x$.

3   Sketch $y = 2x$.

4   Sketch $y = 2x - 4$ and answer these questions.
    (a) State where the graph cuts the y-axis (the intercept).
    (b) Describe what transformation this is of $y = 2x$.

Demonstration 1

x	$^-4$	$^-3$	$^-2$	$^-1$	0	1	2	3	4
$y = x^2$	16	9	4	1	0	1	4	9	16

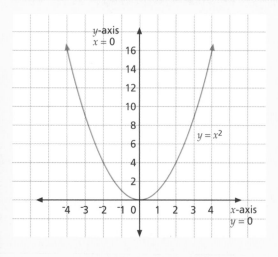

The graph is a curve.

The graph is symmetrical about $x = 0$.

The shape of the graph is a parabola.

The graph touches the x-axis at the origin.

Number and Algebra

Demonstration 2

x	$^-4$	$^-3$	$^-2$	$^-1$	0	1	2	3	4
$y = x^2 - x - 2$	18	10	4	0	$^-2$	$^-2$	0	4	10

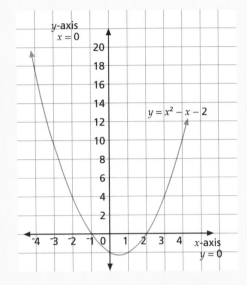

The graph is a curve.

The graph has the same shape as $y = x^2$.

The graph is symmetrical about $x = 0.5$.

The shape of the graph is a parabola.

The graph crosses the x-axis at $x = {}^-1$ and $x = 2$.

The graph is a translation of $y = x^2$ of 0·5 to the right and 2·25 down.

> Note that $y = x^2 - x - 2$
> has the same value as
> $y = (x - 2)(x + 1)$.

Key words   function   parabola   quadratic   translation

Worked example

Exercise bank

1 Sketch the graph of $y = x^2 + 4$.

The graph is a curve. It has the same shape as $y = x^2$. It is symmetrical about $x = 0$. It is a translation of $y = x^2$ of four upwards.

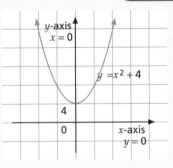

Plenary

Sketch the following graphs and discuss what transformations they are of $y = x^2$.

(a) $y = x^2 + 20$ (b) $y = x^2 + 5x + 10$ (c) $y = x^2 - 6x + 8$ (d) $y = {}^-x^2$

Letts I See Maths **Book 3**

Number and Algebra

Quadratic functions

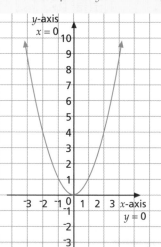

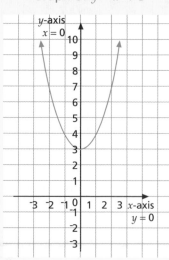

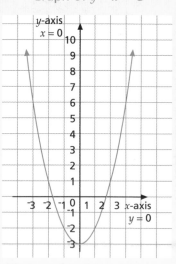

Essential exercises

1 Graph of $y = x^2$ Graph of $y = x^2 + 3$ Graph of $y = x^2 - 3$

Use the following words to complete the sentences below.

> intersects   origin   symmetrical   curve   parabola   translation

(a) The graph of $y = x^2$ is a .... called a ....
(b) The graph of $y = x^2$ passes through the ....
(c) The graph of $y = x^2$ is .... about the y-axis.
(d) The graph of $y = x^2 + 3$ .... the y-axis at (0, 3).
(e) The graph of $y = x^2 + 3$ is a .... of $y = x^2$ with vector $\begin{pmatrix} 0 \\ 3 \end{pmatrix}$.

(f) The graph of $y = x^2 - 3$ is a .... of $y = x^2$ with vector $\begin{pmatrix} 0 \\ -3 \end{pmatrix}$.

2 $y = x^2 + x - 6 = (x + 3)(x - 2)$

(a) Give the coordinates of the two points where the graph cuts the x-axis ($y = 0$).

(b) Use computer software to generate the graph on the right.

(c) On the same axes, generate the graph of $y = x^2 - x - 6 = (x - 3)(x + 2)$.

(d) Discuss the two graphs and comment on the points where the graphs cut the x-axis ($y = 0$).

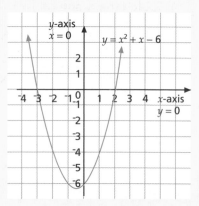

3 Write down the coordinates of the points where the following graphs cut the x-axis ($y = 0$) and use computer software to check your answers.

(a) $y = x^2 + x - 2 = (x + 2)(x - 1)$ (b) $y = x^2 - 2x - 15 = (x - 5)(x + 3)$

Number and Algebra

Quadratic functions

Challenging exercises

4 Complete the following sentences.

(a) If $pq = 0$, then either $p = ...$ or $q = ...$.
(b) If $xy = 0$, then either $x = ...$ or $y = ...$.
(c) If $(x + 1)(x - 4) = 0$, then either $x + 1 = ...$ or $x - 4 = ...$.

5 Find the two values of x satisfying each of the following equations.

(a) $(x - 5)(x + 2) = 0$
(c) $(x + 8)(x - 8) = 0$

(b) $(x - 3)(x - 7) = 0$
(d) $(x + 7)(x + 10) = 0$

6 Write down the equation of a quadratic graph that will cut the x-axis ($y = 0$) at (3, 0) and (⁻4, 0).

Problem-solving exercises

7 Use computer software to generate the following quadratic graphs and then draw sketches of the graphs.

(a) $y = x^2$
(d) $y = x^2 - 4x + 4$
(g) $y = {}^{-}x^2$

(b) $y = x^2 + 4$
(e) $y = x^2 + x + 1$
(h) $y = {}^{-}x^2 + 5$

(c) $y = x^2 - 4$
(f) $y = x^2 - 3x + 10$
(i) $y = {}^{-}x^2 - 3$

8 (a) Draw axes for ⁻4 ≤ x ≤ 4 and 18 ≤ y ≤ 18, and plot the coordinates shown in the grid below. (Use a sharp pencil and draw the curve neatly.)

x	⁻4	⁻3	⁻2	⁻1	0	1	2	3	4
y	18	11	6	3	2	3	6	11	18

(b) Write down the equation of the graph.

Homework

Sketch the graphs of the following quadratic equations and be prepared to explain how you knew what to draw.

(a) $y = x^2 + 6$

(b) $y = x^2 + 0.5$

(c) $y = x^2 - 3$

(d) $y = {}^{-}x^2$

(e) $y = x^2 + 3x - 4$

(f) $y = x^2 + 3x - 10$

Number and Algebra

Quadratic equations

► Goals

By the end of this lesson you will be able to answer questions such as these:

👁 Write down the solutions to these equations.

(a) $(x - 5)(x + 7) = 0$

(b) $(x + \sqrt{2})(x - \sqrt{3}) = 0$

👁 Draw the graph $y = (x - 2)(x + 1)$ and use it to solve the equation
$x^2 - x - 2 = 0$

► Starter

1 Solve the following equations.

(a) $x - 2 = 0$

(b) $x + 1 = 0$

(c) $x - 5 = 0$

(d) $x - 7 = 0$

(e) $x + 5 = 0$

(f) $x + 2 = 0$

2 Explain each of the following results.

(a) $5 \times 0 = 0$

(b) $0 \times 5 = 0$

(c) $0 \times 0 = 0$

3 Explain each of the following results.

(a) $x \times 3 = 0$
$\quad x = 0$

(b) $8 \times x = 0$
$\quad x = 0$

(c) $x \times y = 0$
Either $\ x = 0$
or $\quad\ y = 0$

4 Multiply out the brackets.

(a) $(x - 2)(x + 1)$

(b) $(x - 5)(x - 7)$

(c) $(x + 5)(x + 2)$

► Demonstration 1

(a) Solve: $(x - 2)(x + 1) = 0$
Either $\qquad\quad x - 2 = 0$
$\qquad\qquad\qquad\quad x = 2$
Or $\qquad\qquad x + 1 = 0$
$\qquad\qquad\qquad\quad x = {}^-1$
Solution: $\qquad\quad x = 2$ or $^-1$

(b) Solve: $(x - 5)(x - 7) = 0$
Either $\qquad\quad x - 5 = 0$
$\qquad\qquad\qquad\quad x = 5$
Or $\qquad\qquad x - 7 = 0$
$\qquad\qquad\qquad\quad x = 7$
Solution: $\qquad\quad x = 5$ or 7

When the equation can be factorised, it is easy to identify the two roots.

(c) Solve: $(x + 5)(x + 2) = 0$
Either $\qquad\quad x + 5 = 0$
$\qquad\qquad\qquad\quad x = {}^-5$
Or $\qquad\qquad x + 2 = 0$
$\qquad\qquad\qquad\quad x = {}^-2$
Solution: $\qquad\quad x = {}^-5$ or $^-2$

(d) Solve: $\qquad\qquad (x - 5)^2 = 0$
$(x - 5)^2 = (x - 5)(x - 5) = 0$
Either $\qquad\quad x - 5 = 0$
$\qquad\qquad\qquad\quad x = 5$
or $\qquad\qquad x - 5 = 0$
$\qquad\qquad\qquad\quad x = 5$
Repeated solution: $x = 5$

Demonstration 2

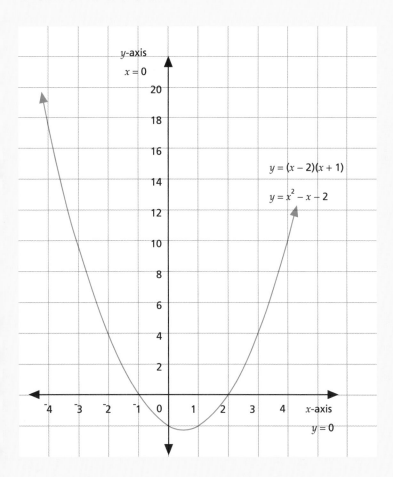

Where does the graph of $y = x^2 - x - 2$ intersect with $y = 0$?

What is the solution of the quadratic equation $x^2 - x - 2 = 0$?

Key words   'Either ... or ...'   solution

Exercise bank

Plenary

👁 Discuss the Goals.

Letts I See Maths **Book 3**

Quadratic equations

Essential exercises

1 Study the graph of $y = x^2 + x - 2$.

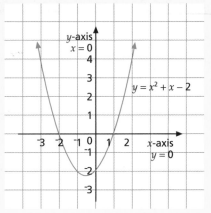

(a) Factorise: $x^2 + x - 2 = ($ $)($ $)$.

(b) Use the graph to write down two solutions of $x^2 + x - 2 = 0$.

(c) What do you notice about your answers to (a) and (b)?

2 Complete the following sentences. The first one has been done for you.

(a) If $(x - 7)(x - 9) = 0$, then either $x = 7$ or $x = 9$.

(b) If $(x - 4)(x - 5) = 0$, then either $x = ...$ or $x = ...$.

(c) If $(x + 6)(x + 7) = 0$, then either $x = ...$ or $x = ...$.

(d) If $(x - 17)(x + 12) = 0$, then either $x = ...$ or $x = ...$.

3 Solve the following quadratic equations.

(a) $x^2 + 5x + 6 = 0$
Factorise: $x^2 + 5x + 6 = ($ $)($ $)$. Then either $x = ...$ or $x = ...$.

(b) $x^2 + 7x + 6 = 0$
Factorise: $x^2 + 7x + 6 = ($ $)($ $)$. Then either $x = ...$ or $x = ...$.

(c) $x^2 - x - 2 = 0$
Factorise: $x^2 - x - 2 = ($ $)($ $)$. Then either $x = ...$ or $x = ...$.

(d) $x^2 - 7x + 10 = 0$
Factorise: $x^2 - 7x + 10 = ($ $)($ $)$. Then either $x = ...$ or $x = ...$.

(e) $x^2 - 10x + 25 = 0$
Factorise: $x^2 - 10x + 25 = ($ $)($ $)$. Then either $x = ...$ or $x = ...$.

(f) $x^2 - 16 = 0$
Factorise: $x^2 - 16 = ($ $)($ $)$. Then either $x = ...$ or $x = ...$.

4 Use computer software to generate appropriate graphs to check your solutions to Exercise 3.

5 (a) Draw the graph of $y = x^2 + x + 4$.

(b) Does the graph cut the x-axis?

(c) Explain why there are no real solutions to $x^2 + x + 4 = 0$.

Number and Algebra

Quadratic equations

Challenging exercises

6 Study the graph of $y = x^2 - x - 2$ on the right.

(a) Use the graph to write down the solution of $x^2 - x - 2 = 0$.

(b) What line would you draw on the diagram to solve $x^2 - x - 4 = 0$?

(c) What line would you draw on the diagram to solve $x^2 - x - 15 = 0$?

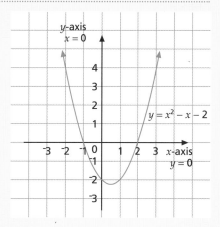

7 General quadratic equation $ax^2 + bx + c = 0$
The general solution of a quadratic equation is given by:

$$x = \frac{^-b \pm \sqrt{b^2 - 4ac}}{2a}$$

Use the formula to solve the following quadratic equations. Give your answers to two decimal places.

(a) $x^2 - 6x + 4 = 0$ (b) $x^2 + 4x - 8 = 0$ (c) $x^2 - 2x - 5 = 0$ (d) $x^2 + 3x - 7 = 0$

Problem-solving exercises

8 The area of rectangle ABCD is 30 cm². Find x.

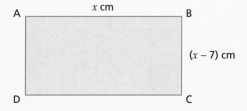

9 The area of trapezium PQRS is 56 cm². Find x.

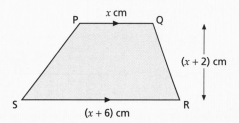

Homework

Calculate the area of the shaded part of the diagram as a function of x and factorise the expression that you get.

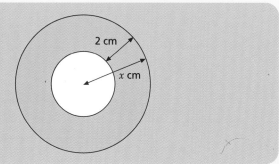

Goals

By the end of this lesson you will be able to answer questions such as these:

👁 Given x is a real number, show $2x + 3 \leq 15$ and $x > 0$ on a number line.

👁 Draw axes to show all points for which $y \leq 5$ and $x < 7$ and $y \leq x$ and $y \geq 0$.

Starter

1 Given n is an integer, look at each of these inequalities. Identify the solutions.

   (a) $5 < n \leq 8$ (b) $5 \leq n < 8$ (c) $5 \leq n \leq 8$ (d) $5 > n > 8$

2 Given x is a real number, look at each of these inequalities. Identify the solutions.

   (a) $5 < x \leq 8$ (b) $5 \leq x < 8$ (c) $5 \leq x \leq 8$ (d) $5 > x > 8$

3 State the two separate inequalities implied in each of these.

   (a) $5 < x \leq 8$ (b) $5 \leq x < 8$ (c) $5 \leq x \leq 8$ (d) $5 > x > 8$

Demonstration 1

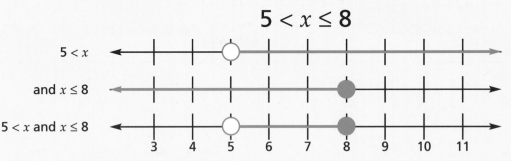

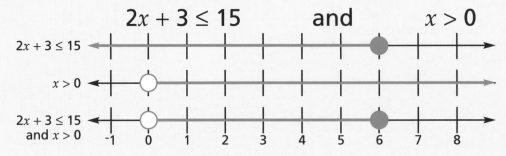

Letts I See Maths **Book 3**

Number and Algebra

Demonstration 2

$$y \leq 5 \text{ and } x < 7 \text{ and } y \leq x \text{ and } y \geq 0$$

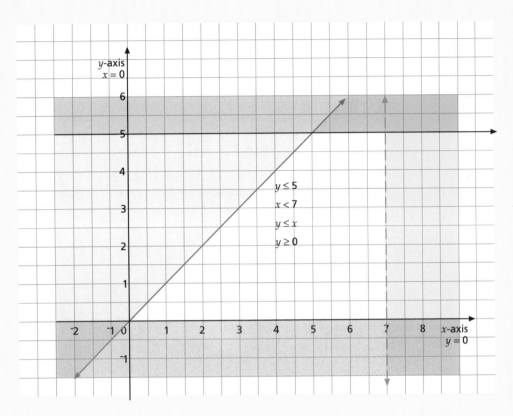

Key words 'and'   greater than   greater than or equal to   less than
less than or equal to   strictly greater than   strictly less than

Exercise bank

Plenary

👁 Discuss the Goals.

Number and Algebra

Inequalities

Essential exercises

1 Use the number line below to help find solutions to the following.

(a) An integer n satisfies $^-9 < 3n \le 15$. List all the possible values of n.

(b) An integer n satisfies $^-1 \le 2n + 3 \le 9$. List all the possible values of n.

(c) An integer n satisfies $^-16 < 5n - 1 < 19$. List all the possible values of n.

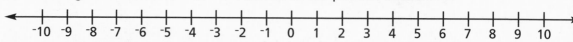

2 In the following questions, the number x can be any real number. Show all the possible solutions of the following inequalities on a number line.

(a) $2 \le 2x \le 10$

(b) $^-2 < x + 3 < 7$

(c) $^-8 \le x - 2 < 2$

(d) $^-1 \le \frac{x}{2} < 3$

(e) $^-3 < 2x + 3 \le 9$

(f) $^-8 < 5x + 2 < 17$

3 In the questions below, the variable x satisfies both of a pair of inequalities. Mark the solution set on a number line.

(a) $2x + 3 < 15$
$x \ge 0$

(b) $3x - 1 > ^-10$
$x < 11$

(c) $x + 5 > 3$
$x \le 14$

(d) $x \ge 0$
$6x + 5 < 11$

4 Draw graphs and shade the region showing the set of points satisfying each group of inequalities below.

(a) $y \le 5$
$x \le 7$
$y \le x$
$y \ge 0$

(b) $y < 2x + 1$
$x \le 3$
$y \ge 1$

(c) $y \ge x + 4$
$y \le 10$
$x \ge 0$

(d) $y \ge 0 \cdot 5x + 1$
$y < 3$
$y \ge 2$

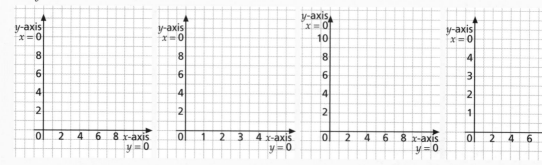

Letts I See Maths **Book 3**

Challenging exercises

5 Draw graphs and shade the region satisfying each group of inequalities below.

(a) $y \geq x^2 + 1$
$y \leq 3$

(b) $y \leq x^2$
$y \geq 0$ and $x \geq 0$
$x \leq 4$

6 For what values of x is the area of the red triangle PQD less than or equal to a quarter of the area of the square ABCD?

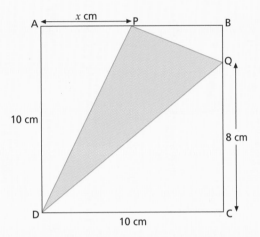

Problem-solving exercise

7 Write inequalities using the variables x and y to represent the following information.

(a) I buy x pens at 69p each and y pencils at 45p each but I must not spend more than £5.

(b) Jane makes x sandwiches that take seven minutes each to make and y baps that take nine minutes each to make. She has to make all the sandwiches and baps in two hours.

(c) A shop sells x cookers, where each cooker makes a profit of £25, and y fridges, where each fridge makes a profit of £32. The manager sets a target of making at least £600 a week.

(d) A boy runs x metres at a speed of 4 m s⁻¹ and walks y metres at a speed of 2·5 m s⁻¹ in less than 10 minutes.

Homework

Write a real-life story for each of the following inequalities.

(a) $x \leq 10$

(b) $3x \geq 5$

(c) $x + y < 70$

Trial and improvement

Goals

By the end of this lesson you will be able to answer questions such as this:

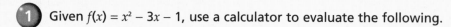 Calculate the positive solution to $x^2 - 3x - 1 = 0$ to one decimal place.

Starter

1 Given $f(x) = x^2 - 3x - 1$, use a calculator to evaluate the following.

(a) $f(-2)$ (b) $f(-1·5)$ (c) $f(·5)$ (d) $f(0)$

2 Given $y = x^2 - 3x - 1$, use a calculator to evaluate y when:

(a) $x = ·5$ (b) $x = 1·5$ (c) $x = 1$ (d) $x = 2$ (e) $x = ·2$

3 Given $y = x^2 - 3x - 1$, use a calculator to evaluate each y value in this table.

x	-2	-1·5	-1	-·5	0	·5	1	1·5	2	2·5	3	3·5	4
y													

4 Use a spreadsheet to calculate the y values in the above table.

Demonstration 1

Simultaneous equations

x	-2	-1	0	1	2	3	4
y	9	3	-1	-3	-3	-1	3

Simultaneous equations

$y = x^2 - 3x - 1$ and $y = 0$

Let the solutions be $x = \alpha$ and $x = \beta$.

Let the positive solution be α. Then: $3 < \alpha < 4$.

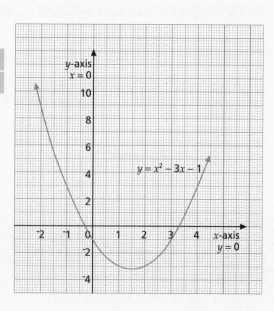

Number and Algebra

Letts I See Maths **Book 3**

Demonstration 2

Calculate the positive solution to $x^2 - 3x - 1 = 0$ to two decimal places.

$y = x^2 - 3x - 1$ and $y = 0$

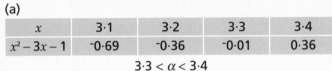

x	-2	-1	0	1	2	3	4
$x^2 - 3x - 1$	9	3	-1	-3	-3	-1	3

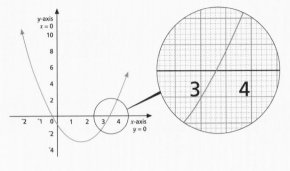

Let solutions be $x = \alpha$ and $x = \beta$.

Let the positive solution be α. Then: $3 < \alpha < 4$.

(a)

x	3·1	3·2	3·3	3·4
$x^2 - 3x - 1$	-0·69	-0·36	-0·01	0·36

$3·3 < \alpha < 3·4$

(b)

x	3·30	3·31
$x^2 - 3x - 1$	-0·01	0·0261

$3·30 < \alpha < 3·31$

(c)

x	3·300	3·301	3·302	3·303
$x^2 - 3x - 1$	-0·01	-0·006 399	-0·002 796	0·000 809

$3·302 < \alpha < 3·303$

(d)

$3·302 < \alpha < 3·303$

$\alpha = 3·30$ (to 2 d.p.)

Worked example

Exercise bank

1 There is a positive solution to $x^3 + x = 160$. Calculate this to one decimal place.

x	$x^3 + x$	How close to 160?
4	68	too small
5	130	too small
6	222	too big
5·3	154·177	too small
5·4	162·864	too big
5·35	158·480375	too small
5·36	159·350656	too small
5·37	160·224153	too big

The value of x lies between 5·36 and 5·37. The solution is 5·4, to 1 d.p.

Plenary

◉ Discuss how you should respond to this instruction (read it carefully because it is not one you have seen before):

Calculate the positive solution to $x^3 - 3x - 1 = 0$ to one decimal place.

Letts I See Maths **Book 3**

Number and Algebra

Trial and improvement

Essential exercises

1 In the following questions we shall consider the positive square root only.

Complete the following inequalities. The first one has been done for you.

(a) $4 < \sqrt{20} < 5$

(b) $... < \sqrt{86} < ...$

(c) $... < \sqrt{3} < ...$

(d) $... < \sqrt{53} < ...$

(e) $... < \sqrt{170} < ...$

(f) $... < \sqrt{232} < ...$

2 Copy the table below and continue the decimal search to eight decimal places.

$x = \sqrt{40} \qquad x^2 = 40$

Estimated value of x	x^2	Too large	Too small
6	36		✔
6·2	38·44		✔
6·3	39·69		✔
6·4	40·96	✔	
6·31	39·8161		✔

3 Use decimal search to work out the following positive square roots to six decimal places.

(a) $\sqrt{96}$

(b) $\sqrt{74}$

(c) $\sqrt{14}$

(d) $\sqrt{140}$

4 Study the graph on the right.

(a) Use the graph to estimate where the graph cuts the x-axis.

(b) The intersection of $y = x^2 - 3x - 5$ with the x-axis gives the solution of $x^2 - 3x - 5 = 0$. Use one of your estimates in (a) to search for a more accurate solution. Put your working in a table.

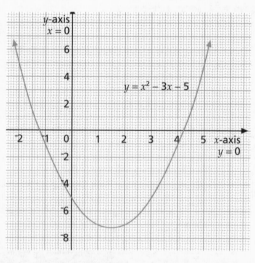

$y = x^2 - 3x - 5$

Estimated value of x	$x^2 - 3x - 5$	Too large	Too small

You want $x^2 - 3x - 4$ to equal zero.

5 Using computer software, draw a graph of $y = x^2 - 2x - 5$ to find a first estimate of the value of x satisfying $x^2 - 2x - 5 = 0$. Use 'trial and improvement' to search for a more accurate solution.

Number and Algebra

6 Study the graph of $y = x^3 - 6x + 2$.

(a) Estimate the values of x where the graph cuts the x-axis.

(b) Explain why these values of x give *three* estimated solutions of $x^3 - 6x + 2 = 0$.

(c) Use 'trial and improvement' to search for more accurate solutions to the equation.

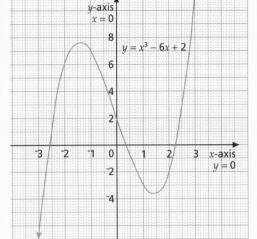

$y = x^3 - 6x + 2$

7 Solve the following equations, giving answers correct to two decimal places.

(a) $x^3 = 35$

(b) $x^3 + x = 70$

(c) $3 \cdot 4x^3 = 19 \cdot 5$

8 (a) A cuboid has a square cross-section (side x cm), height 8 cm and a total surface area of 100 cm². Form and solve an equation in x, giving your answer to one decimal place.

(b) A cuboid has a square cross-section (side x cm), height $(x + 5)$ cm and a total surface area of 80 cm². Form and solve an equation in x, giving your answer to two decimal places.

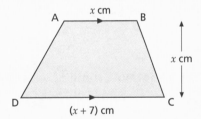

(c) Trapezium ABCD has area 70 cm². Form and solve an equation in x, giving your answer to three significant figures.

(d) A triangle has a perpendicular height x cm and its base is 3 cm more than its height. Its area is 17 cm². Form and solve an equation in x, and give your answer to two decimal places.

Homework

The value of a car depreciates by 5% a month. After how many months will its value have dropped to just below half its original value?

Goals

By the end of this lesson you will be able to answer questions such as these:

 Discuss what is meant by (a) an equation   (b) a formula   (c) an identity.

 'Use this formula ...'

Starter

1 Discuss different ways of evaluating each of these.

(a) $\frac{7}{5} \times 7 \cdot 62 \times 15 \cdot 5$

(b) $\frac{5}{11} \times 7 \cdot 62 \times 15 \cdot 5 - \frac{5}{11} \times 7 \cdot 62 \times 14 \cdot 5$

Demonstration 1

An **equation** contains variables and expresses their relationship.

$z = x + 2y$ is an equation with three variables and expresses the relationship among them.

$y = 3x + 4$ is an equation with two variables and expresses the relationship between them.

$y = 2$ is an equation with one variable and expresses its relationship to a constant.

A **formula** contains variables and expresses their relationship. It is an equation in which the variables are specific measurements.

$z = x + 2y$ (z = final velocity; x = initial velocity; y = time) is a formula with three variables.

$y = 3x + 4$ (y = final velocity; x = initial velocity) is a formula with two variables.

$y = 2$ (y = velocity) is a formula with one variable.

$a + a = 2a$ is an **identity**. It simply expresses the same value in a different appearance. It ought to be written $a + a \equiv 2a$; the symbol is read as 'identically equal'.

A **formula** is a way of remembering how to work things out. The variables are usually chosen to be a reminder of what they stand for. The three formulae in the box above are usually written like this:

$$v = u + at \quad v = at + 4 \quad v = 2$$

Number and Algebra

Letts I See Maths **Book 3**

Demonstration 2

Using a formula carefully

$$v = \frac{d}{t}$$

v = velocity

d = distance travelled

t = time taken

1 A tortoise travels 341 cm in 15 seconds.
Calculate its velocity in centimetres per second.
Let the velocity of the tortoise be v cm s⁻¹.
Then $v = \frac{341}{15}$ = 22·7 cm s⁻¹ (1.d.p.)
v = 22·7 cm s⁻¹ (1 d.p.)

2 A tortoise travels 3·41 metres in a quarter of a minute.
Calculate its velocity in centimetres per second.
Let the velocity of the tortoise be v cm s⁻¹.
Then $v = \frac{341}{15}$ = 22·7 cm s⁻¹ (1.d.p.)
v = 22·7 cm s⁻¹ (1 d.p.)

3 A tortoise travels 3·41 metres in a quarter of a minute.
Calculate its velocity in kilometres per hour.
Let the velocity of the tortoise be v km/h.
Then $v = \frac{.003\,41}{.004\,17}$ = 0·82 km/h (2 sig. figs.)
v = 0·82 km/h (2 sig. figs.)

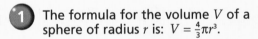

Key words   constant   equation   formula   identity   variable

Worked example

Exercise bank

1 The formula for the volume V of a
sphere of radius r is: $V = \frac{4}{3}\pi r^3$.

Calculate the volume of plastic in a football of
thickness $\frac{1}{2}$ cm and internal radius 15 cm.

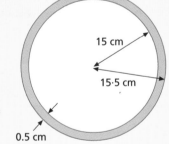

15 cm

15·5 cm

0.5 cm

External volume of football	$= V_e$ = 1·3333 × 3·142 × 15·5³
Internal volume of football	$= V_i$ = 1·3333 × 3·142 × 15³
Volume of plastic	$= V_e - V_i$ = 1·3333 × 3·142 × 15·5³ − 1·3333 × 3·142 × 15³
	= 1462 cm³ (nearest whole number)

Plenary

Given $a = \frac{v-u}{t}$ (a = acceleration; v = final velocity (cm/s); u = initial velocity (cm/s);
t = time taken (s)), discuss the units of acceleration.

Letts I See Maths **Book 3**

Number and Algebra

Formulae 1

Essential exercises

1 Complete the grid below.

x	3	$^-4$	0·1	2·6	$\frac{1}{2}$
x^2					
$3x^2 + 2$					
$2x^3 + 1$					
$7 - 5x^2$					

2 The Greek mathematician, Hero, showed that the area of a triangle with sides a, b and c is given by the formula:

$$A = \sqrt{s(s - a)(s - b)(s - c)}, \text{ where } S = \tfrac{1}{2}(a + b + c).$$

Use Hero's formula to caluculate the areas of the following triangles.

(a) $a = 7$ cm, $b = 6$ cm, $c = 9$ cm   (b) $a = 4.5$ cm, $b = 3.5$ cm, $c = 6$ cm

3 Euler's formula

(i) tetrahedron   (ii) cube   (iii) square-based pyramid   (iv) octahedron

(a) Complete the table below and find a formula showing the relationship between the number of faces, vertices and edges of a polyhedron.

Polyhedron	Number of faces	Number of vertices	Number of edges
(i)			
(ii)			
(iii)			
(iv)			

(b) Use your formula to work out the number of edges for a polyhedron with twenty faces and twelve vertices.

4 Kepler's rule

The capacity of a barrel is given by the formula:

$$V = \tfrac{\pi L}{12} (2D^2 + d^2) \text{ cm}^3$$

Calculate the capacity of a barrel with $L = 80$ cm, $D = 60$ cm and $d = 55$ cm.

Challenging exercise

 5 **(a)** Use the diagram below to prove the identity:

$$(a + b)^2 \equiv a^2 + 2ab + b^2$$

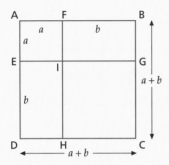

(b) Use the diagram below to prove the identity:

$$a^2 - b^2 = (a - b)(a + b)$$

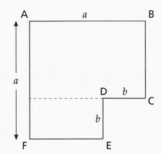

Problem-solving exercise

 6 Pythagoras' theorem

Use Pythagoras' theorem to check which of the following triangles are right-angled.

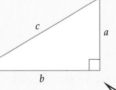

(a) $a = 3$, $b = 4$, $c = 5$ (b) $a = 4$, $b = 5$, $c = 6$

(c) $a = 8$, $b = 3$, $c = 7$ (d) $a = 5$, $b = 12$, $c = 13$

(e) $a = 3$, $b = 5$, $c = 11$ (f) $a = 6$, $b = 8$, $c = 10$

In any right-angled triangle, the square of the hypotenuse is equal to the sum of the squares of the other two sides.

$$c^2 = a^2 + b^2$$

Homework

Learn the following formulae.

(a) The area of a triangle is given by $\frac{1}{2}bh$. (b is the base, h is the perpendicular height)

(b) The area of a parallelogram is given by $\frac{1}{2}bh$. (b is the base, h is the perpendicular height)

(c) The area of a trapezium is given by $\frac{1}{2}(a + b)h$. (a and b are the lengths of the parallel sides, h is the perpendicular height)

(d) The area of a circle is given by πr^2. (r is the radius)

Goals

By the end of this lesson you will be able to answer questions such as these:

- Given $m = \frac{v}{u}$, calculate m when $v = 7$ and $u = 8$.

- Given $m = \frac{v}{u}$, make (a) v the subject of the formula   (b) u the subject of the formula.

Starter

1 Convert each of these formulae into verbal instructions for calculating the area, A, of a triangle (b = base; h = perpendicular height).

(a) $A = \frac{b \times h}{2}$ (b) $A = \frac{1}{2}bh$ (c) $A = \cdot 5bh$

2 Convert this formula into verbal instructions for calculating the area, A, of a trapezium (a and b are the lengths of the two parallel sides; h is the distance between them).

$A = \frac{a + b}{2} \times h$

Demonstration 1

Writing a formula from knowledge of the relationship

'You can find the area of a rectangle by multiplying length by width.'

Let the area of a rectangle be A; let its length be l; let its width be w.

$$A = lw$$

'You can find the perimeter of a rectangle by adding the lengths of all its sides.'

Let the perimeter of a rectangle be P; let its length be l; let its width be w.

$$P = l + w + l + w$$
$$P = 2l + 2w$$
$$P = 2(l + w)$$

$l + w + l + w \equiv 2l + 2w$
$2l + 2w \equiv 2(l + w)$

Letts I See Maths **Book 3**

Demonstration 2

Changing the subject of a formula

$$T = 2\pi\sqrt{\frac{l}{g}}$$

There are three variables (T, g and l).
T is the subject of the formula.
We can make l the subject of the formula.

$l \xrightarrow{\ \div g\ } \dfrac{l}{g} \xrightarrow{\ \text{square root it}\ } \sqrt{\dfrac{l}{g}} \xrightarrow{\ \times 2\pi\ } 2\pi\sqrt{\dfrac{l}{g}}$

$\left(\dfrac{T}{2\pi}\right)^2 g \xleftarrow{\ \times g\ } \left(\dfrac{T}{2\pi}\right)^2 \xleftarrow{\ \text{square it}\ } \dfrac{T}{2\pi} \xleftarrow{\ \div 2\pi\ } T$

$$l = \left(\frac{T}{2\pi}\right)^2 g$$

Key words   'subject of the formula'   'the unknown'   variable

Worked example

Exercise bank

(1) Given $A = \dfrac{a+b}{2} \times h$, make h the subject of the formula.

$h \xrightarrow{\ \times \frac{a+b}{2}\ } \dfrac{a+b}{2} \times h$

$\dfrac{2A}{a+b} \xleftarrow{\ \div \frac{a+b}{2}\ } A$

$$h = \frac{2A}{a+b}$$

Plenary

 Given $m = \dfrac{v}{u}$, where m is the magnification of an object by a lens, u is the distance of the object from the lens and v is the distance of the image from the lens

(a) Calculate the magnification when v cm = 7 cm and u cm = 8 cm
(b) Discuss the units of m.

Letts I See Maths **Book 3**

Formulae 2

Essential exercises

1 (a) The area of a square is 12·96 cm². What is the length of an edge?

(b) The area of a circle is 14·13 cm². What is its radius? (Use $\pi \approx 3{\cdot}14$.)

(c) The volume of a prism is 47·3 cm³ and its height is 8·6 cm. What is the area of its base?

(d) The area of a triangle is 31·5 cm² and its height is 7·5 cm. What is the length of its base?

(e) The volume of a pyramid is 43·4 cm³ and the area of its base is 10·5 cm². What is its perpendicular height?

(f) The volume of a cylinder is 282·6 cm³ and its height is 10 cm. What is the radius of its base? (Use $\pi \approx 3{\cdot}14$.)

2 Trigonometry

Make the letter in the brackets the subject of each formula.

(a) $\cos\theta = \frac{A}{H}$ (A)   (b) $\cos\theta = \frac{A}{H}$ (H)

(c) $\sin\theta = \frac{O}{H}$ (O)   (d) $\sin\theta = \frac{O}{H}$ (H)

(e) $\tan\theta = \frac{O}{A}$ (O)   (f) $\tan\theta = \frac{O}{A}$ (A)

3 Pythagoras' theorem

$$c^2 = a^2 + b^2$$

Make a the subject of the formula.

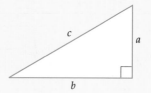

4 Make the letter in brackets the subject of each formula.

(a) $d = st$ (s)   (b) $d = st$ (t)

(c) $V = IR$ (I)   (d) $V = IR$ (R)

(e) $T = \frac{2\pi}{n}$ (n)   (f) $P = \frac{a}{k^2}$ (k)

(g) $T = 2\pi\sqrt{\frac{l}{g}}$ (l)   (h) $T = 2\pi\sqrt{\frac{l}{g}}$ (g)

(i) $t = \sqrt{\frac{s}{a}}$ (a)   (j) $t = \sqrt{\frac{s}{a}}$ (s)

Letts I See Maths **Book 3**

Number and Algebra

Challenging exercises

5 Let x, y be two real numbers such that $x + y = xy$.

(a) Rearrange the equation to make x the subject.

(b) Give three possible solutions to the equation.

6 Make the letter in the brackets the subject of each formula.

(a) $\frac{1}{f} = \frac{1}{u} + \frac{1}{v}$ (f)   (b) $\frac{1}{f} = \frac{1}{u} + \frac{1}{v}$ (u)   (c) $A = \frac{1}{2}(a + b)h$ (b)

(d) $V = I(R_1 + R_2)$ (R_2) (e) $P = \frac{a}{d} + mv$ (a)   (f) $V = \frac{4}{3}\pi r^3$ (r)

Problem-solving exercises

7 (a) Work out a formula for the area A of the shaded sector of the circle (radius r, angle θ).

(b) Work out the value of $\theta°$ when $A = 4\cdot71$ cm² and $r = 4\cdot5$ cm. (Use $\pi \approx 3\cdot14$.)

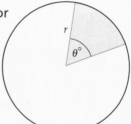

8 (a) Work out a formula for the shaded area A. (The space between concentric circles is called an annulus.) The smaller circle has radius r and the larger circle has radius R.

(b) Work out the length of r when $A = 62\cdot8$ cm² and $R = 6$ cm. (Use $\pi \approx 3\cdot14$.)

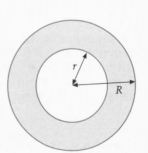

Homework

Make x the subject of each of the following equations.

(a) $y = x + 4$

(b) $x + y = 11$

(c) $y = 3 - x$

(d) $y = 2(x + 5)$

(e) $y = 3 - 7x$

(c) $y = 2 - x^2$

Letts I See Maths **Book 3**

Goals

By the end of this lesson you will be able to answer questions such as these:

👁 Given the formula for the sum of an arithmetic series, $S_n = \frac{n}{2}[2a + (n - 1)d]$,
   (a) identify the meaning of each unknown
   (b) construct an appropriate series
   (c) calculate S_n for your series.

👁 Given the formula for the sum of a geometric series, $S_n = a(1 - r)n$,
   (a) identify the meaning of each unknown
   (b) construct an appropriate series
   (c) calculate S_n for your series.

Starter

1 Look at this sequence: 4, 7, 10, 13, 14, ..., $4 + (n - 1) \times 3$
   (a) What is the value of the 1st term?
   (b) What is the value of the 4th term?
   (c) What is the common difference between successive terms?

2 Look at this sequence: 4, 7, 10, 13, 14, ..., $4 + (n - 1) \times 3$
   The nth term is $4 + (n - 1) \times 3$. It is a formula for the nth term.
   We can write: nth term $= 4 + (n - 1) \times 3$.
   Use the formula to work out:
   (a) the value of the 1st term   (b) the value of the 4th term   (c) the value of the 17th term

3 Look at this sequence: 4, 12, 36, 108, ..., $4 \times 3^{n-1}$
   (a) What is the value of the 1st term?
   (b) What is the value of the 4th term?
   (c) What is the common ratio between successive terms?

4 Look at this sequence: 4, 12, 36, 108, ..., $4 \times 3^{n-1}$
   The nth term is $4 \times 3^{n-1}$. It is a formula for the nth term.
   We can write: nth term $= 4 \times 3^{n-1}$.
   Use the formula to work out:
   (a) the value of the 1st term   (b) the value of the 4th term   (c) the value of the 17th term

Demonstration 1

The general arithmetic sequence

$a, a + d, a + 2d, a + 3d, \ldots a + (n - 1)d$

1st term $= a$

Common difference $= d$

nth term $= a + (n - 1)d$

The general arithmetic series

$a + a + d + a + 2d + a + 3d + \ldots + a + (n - 1)d$

nth term $= a + (n - 1)d$

Common difference $= d$

Sum of n terms: $S_n = \frac{n}{2}[2a + (n - 1)d]$

Demonstration 2

The general geometric sequence

$a, ar, ar^2, ar^3, ar^4, \ldots, ar^{n-1}$

1st term $= a$

Common ratio $= r$

nth term $= ar^{n-1}$

The general geometric series

$a + ar + ar^2 + ar^3 + ar^4 + \ldots + ar^{n-1}$

1st term $= a$

Common ratio $= r$

nth term $= ar^{n-1}$

Sum of n terms: $S_n = \dfrac{a\left(1 - r^n\right)}{1 - r}$

Key words   arithmetic sequence   arithmetic series   common difference
common ratio   geometric sequence   geometric series   sum of n terms

Worked examples

Exercise bank

1   Look at this arithmetic series: $5 + 7 + 9 + \ldots$ to 13 terms

   (a) What is its sum?

$$S_n = \frac{n}{2}\left[2a + (n-1)d\right]$$
$$= \frac{13}{2}(10 + 12 \times 2)$$
$$= \frac{13}{2} \times 34$$
$$= 13 \times 17 = 221$$

   (b) What is the last term?

$$\text{Last term} = a + (n-1)d$$
$$= 5 + (13 - 1) \times 2$$
$$= 29$$

2   The first term of a geometric series is 3 and the common ratio is 2.

   (a) Find the sixth term.

$$\text{6th term} = 3 \times 2^{6-1}$$
$$= 3 \times 2^5$$
$$= 3 \times 32$$
$$= 96$$

   (b) Find the sum of the first five terms.

$$S_5 = \frac{3(1 - 2^5)}{1 - 2}$$
$$= \frac{3 \times (1 - 32)}{^-1}$$
$$= \frac{3 \times {}^-31}{^-1}$$
$$= 93$$

Plenary

👁 Discuss the common ratio in this geometric progression.
8, ⁻4, 2, ⁻1, $\frac{1}{2}$, $\frac{^-1}{4}$

👁 Discuss the Goals.

Letts I See Maths Book 3

Sequences

Essential exercises

1 Generate the next three consecutive terms for each of the following number sequences using the position-to-term rule given.

-	Postion-to-term rule for the nth term	Sequence
(a)	$4n - 3$	⁻3, 1, 5, ...
(b)	$2n^2 + 5$	5, 7, 13, ...
(c)	$\frac{n(n-1)}{2}$	0, 0, 1, ...
(d)	$2^n + 3$	4, 5, 7, ...
(e)	n^3	0, 1, 8, ...

2 An arithmetic sequence is generated by starting with a number a, then adding a constant number d to the previous term.

> Arithmetic sequence: $a, a + d, a + 2d, a + 3d, a + 4d, ...$

Generate the first five terms of the following arithmetic sequences.

(a) $a = 1, d = 3$ (b) $a = 5, d = 7$ (c) $a = \frac{1}{2}, d = \frac{1}{2}$

(d) $a = 20, d = $ ⁻2   (e) $a = 0, d = $ ⁻$\frac{1}{3}$ (f) $a = \frac{1}{4}, d = \frac{1}{2}$

3 The nth term of an arithmetic sequence with 1st term a, and difference d, is $a + (n - 1)d$. Work out the nth terms of the following arithmetic sequences and write your answers in their simplest form.

(a) $a = 2, d = 8$ (b) $a = 7, d = $ ⁻3   (c) $a = \frac{1}{2}, d = 2$

(d) $a = $ ⁻2, $d = 3$ (e) $a = 0.2, d = 0.5$ (f) $a = $ ⁻10, $d = 4$

4 Use difference tables to work out whether the following sequences are linear or quadratic, and find the formula for the nth term.

(a) 7, 9, 11, 13, 15, ...

(b) 4, 7, 12, 19, 28, ...

(c) 1, 4, 7, 10, 13, ...

(d) 8, 18, 32, 50, 72, ...

Letts I See Maths **Book 3**

Challenging exercises

 (a) The 3rd term of an arithmetic sequence is 5 and the 7th term is 13.
Find the first term a, and the common difference d.

(b) The 6th term of an arithmetic sequence is twice the 3rd term and the 1st term a is 3.
Find the common difference d, and the 8th term.

(c) The 7th term of an arithmetic sequence is 6 more than the 5th term and the 1st term a is 5.
Find the common difference d and the 20th term.

 A geometric sequence (or progression) has a first term a and a common ratio r.

> Geometric sequence: a, ar, ar^2, ar^3, ...

(a) Work out the nth term of the geometric sequence above.

(b) Write the first five terms for each of the following geometric sequences.

(i) $a = 2$, $r = 3$ (ii) $a = 1$, $r = \frac{1}{2}$ (iii) $a = 1$, $r = 5$

Problem-solving exercises

(a) Continue the sequence of triangle numbers by writing the next five consecutive terms.
1, 3, 6, ...

(b) Work out the formula for the nth term of the sequence of triangle numbers.

(c) What do you notice when you add any two consecutive terms?
Examples $1 + 3$, $3 + 6$, ...
Explain your result using dot patterns.

8 (a) Copy Pascal's triangle and continue the next three rows.

(b) Add the numbers in each row of Pascal's triangle and explain what you notice.

(c) Work out a formula for the sum of the numbers in the nth row of Pascal's triangle.

Pascal's triangle

```
        1
      1   1
    1   2   1
  1   3   3   1
1   4   6   4   1
```

Homework

$1^3 =$
$1^3 + 2^3 =$
$1^3 + 2^3 + 3^3 =$

What do you notice?
Can you find a formula for $1^3 + 2^3 + 3^3 + ... + n^3 =$

Functions and graphs

Goals

By the end of this lesson you will be able to answer questions such as these:

👁 Given $f(x) = 3x - 2$ calculate   (a) $f(2)$ (b) $f(^-1)$ (c) $f(\frac{1}{2})$.

👁 Given $f: x \longrightarrow 2x + 1$, calculate   (a) $f(2)$ (b) $f(^-1)$ (c) $f(\frac{1}{2})$.

👁 Given $f(x) = 3x - 2$, calculate $f^{-1}(x)$.

👁 Given $f: x \longrightarrow 2x + 1$, calculate the inverse function.

Starter

1 Complete these function diagrams.

(a) $x \longrightarrow 2x \longrightarrow 2x + 3$

(b) $x \longrightarrow x + 3 \longrightarrow 2(x + 3)$

Demonstration 1

Functions and equations

x	y
3	5
4	6
5	7
6	8

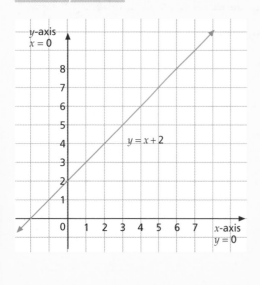

The two variables are related.
y can be obtained from x.
There is a relationship between y and x.
y depends on x.
y is a function of x.
$y = f(x)$
We have: $f: x \longrightarrow x + 2$
We say f such that x maps to $x + 2$
We can write:

$$x \xrightarrow{\;+2\;} x + 2$$

The equation is $y = x + 2$.

$f(3) = 5$

$f(4) = 6$

$f(5) = 7$

$f(2\cdot5) = 4\cdot5$

$f(0) = 2$

A more complicated function

$y = 3x - 2$ $f(x) = 3x - 2$ $f: x \longrightarrow 3x - 2$

$$x \xrightarrow{\;\times 3\;} 3x \xrightarrow{\;-2\;} 3x - 2$$

Letts | See Maths   **Book 3**

Demonstration 2

$$x \xrightarrow{\times 3} 3x \xrightarrow{-2} 3x - 2 \qquad \text{Function diagram} \qquad f(x) = 3x - 2$$

$$x \xleftarrow{\div 3} 3x \xleftarrow{+2} 3x - 2 \qquad \text{Inverse operations} \qquad f(3) = 7$$

$$\frac{x+2}{3} \xleftarrow{\div 3} x + 2 \xleftarrow{+2} x \qquad\qquad\qquad\qquad f(0) = ^-2$$

Inverse function
If we have
$f: x \longrightarrow 3x - 2,$

then we have a related function, the inverse function:

$f^{-1}: x \longrightarrow \dfrac{x+2}{3}$

$f^{-1}(x) = \dfrac{x+2}{3}$

$f^{-1}(7) = 3$

$f^{-1}(^-2) = 0$

Key words   function   inverse function

Worked example

Exercise bank

1 Given $f: x \longrightarrow 7x + 5$, find $f^{-1}(x)$.

$$x \xrightarrow{\times 7} 7x \xrightarrow{+5} 7x + 5$$

$$\frac{x-5}{7} \xleftarrow{\div 7} x - 5 \xleftarrow{-5} x$$

$$f^{-1}(x) = \frac{x-5}{7}$$

Plenary

👁 Given $f(x) = 7x + 5$ and $f^{-1}(x) = \frac{x-5}{7}$, draw the graphs of $y = 7x + 5$ and $y = \frac{x-5}{7}$,

and discuss their positions.

 Letts I See Maths Book 3

Functions and graphs

Essential exercises

1 Sketch the following linear graphs.

(a) $y = 2x + 4$ (b) $y = x - 2$ (c) $y = \frac{1}{2}x + 3$

(d) $y = 3x + 1$ (e) $y = {}^-x$ (f) $y = {}^-x + 2$

2 Write down the gradient and intercept of the following linear graphs.

(a) $y = 4x + 7$ (b) $y = x + 2$ (c) $y = \frac{1}{3}x + 5$

(d) $y = 2(x - 2)$ (e) $y = {}^-x$ (f) $y = {}^-3x - 8$

3 Rearrange the following linear equations in the form $y = ax + b$.

(a) $x + y = 10$ (b) $x + 2y = 5$ (c) $x - y = 14$

(d) $3x + 5y = 27$ (e) $5x = y - 21$ (f) $3y = 2 - 2x$

4 Draw axes for $^-10 \leq x \leq 10$ and $^-10 \leq y \leq 10$, and draw the following linear graphs by working out three coordinates for each.

(a) $y = x + 5$ (b) $y = 2x + 0{\cdot}5$ (c) $2y = 6x + 14$ (d) $3y = 12 - 6x$

5 (a) Complete the table below.

x	-3	-2·5	-2	-1·5	-1	-0·5	0	0·5	1	1·5	2	2·5	3
$2x^2 + 1$													

(b) Use the values in the table to draw accurately the graph of $y = 2x^2 + 1$ for $^-3 \leq x \leq 3$.

(c) Sketch the following graphs.

(i) $y = 2x^2 + 4$ (ii) $y = 2x^2 - 6$ (iii) $y = {}^-2x^2 + 4$

6 Use computer software to generate the following graphs.

(a) (i) $y = x^3$ (ii) $y = x^3 + x^2 - 2x$ (iii) $y = x^3 - 6x^2 + 9x$

(b) (i) $y = x^4$ (ii) $y = x^4 + 3$ (iii) $y = x^4 - 5x^2 + 4$

(c) Comment on any general properties you have noticed for graphs of linear, quadratic, cubic and quartic functions.

Challenging exercises

 7

(a) Draw the graphs of $y = x$, $y = x + 2$, $y = x - 2$, $y = x + 3$ and $y = x - 1$.

(b) Describe the transformation of $y = x$ to $y = x + a$.

(c) Draw the graphs of $y = x^2$, $y = x^2 + 1$, $y = x^2 - 1$, $y = x^2 + 2$, and so on.

(d) Describe the transformation of $y = x^2$ to $y = x^2 + a$.

(e) Make a general statement about the transformation of $y = f(x)$ to $y = f(x) + a$.

 8

(a) Draw the graphs of $y = x$, $y = {}^-x$, $y = x + 2$ and $y = {}^-x - 2$.

(b) Describe the transformation of $y = x + c$ to $y = {}^-x - c$.

(c) Draw the graphs of $y = x^2$, $y = {}^-x^2$, $y = x^2 + 2$ and $y = {}^-x^2 - 2$.

(d) Describe the transformation of $y = x^2 + c$ to $y = {}^-x^2 - c$.

(e) Make a general statement about the transformation of $y = f(x)$ to $y = {}^-f(x)$.

Problem-solving exercises

 9

Find the inverse functions of the following linear functions.

(a) $f: x \longrightarrow 5x$

(b) $f: x \longrightarrow \frac{1}{4}x$

(c) $f: x \longrightarrow x + 2$

(d) $f: x \longrightarrow x - 3$

(e) $f: x \longrightarrow 2x + 1$

(f) $f: x \longrightarrow 3x - 2$

 10

(a) Draw the graph of $y = x$. On the same axes, draw the graphs of the function $y = 2x$ and its inverse $y = \frac{1}{2}x$. Describe what you notice.

(b) Repeat the instructions in part (a) for each of the functions and its inverse in Exercise 9. Make a general statement about the graphs of a function and its inverse function.

Homework

Complete the table below and draw the graph of $y = \frac{12}{x}$.

x	-12	-6	-4	-3	-2	-1	1	2	3	4	6	12
$\frac{12}{x}$	-1			-4				6			2	

Letts I See Maths **Book 3**

Trigonometric functions

Goals

By the end of this lesson you will be able to answer questions such as these:

👁 Use your calculator to evaluate   (a) sin 30°   (b) sin 150°   (c) sin 210°   (d) sin 330°.

👁 Use your calculator to evaluate   (a) cos 30°   (b) cos 150°   (c) cos 210°   (d) cos 330°.

👁 Use a unit circle to explain the calculator answers to the following.

    (a) sin 30°   (b) sin 150°   (c) sin 210°   (d) sin 330°

    (e) cos 30°   (f) cos 150°   (g) cos 210°   (h) cos 330°

Starter

1 Use your calculator to evaluate the following.

    (a) sin 30°   (b) sin 40°   (c) sin 35°

2 Look at $f\colon x \longrightarrow \sin x$ and use your calculator to evaluate the following.

    (a) $f(30°)$ (b) $f(40°)$ (c) $f(35°)$

3 Given $f(x) = \sin x$, use your calculator to evaluate the following.

    (a) $f(30°)$ (b) $f(40°)$ (c) $f(35°)$

4 Evaluate these.

    (a) sin 60°   (b) cos 60°   (c) tan 60°

Demonstration 1

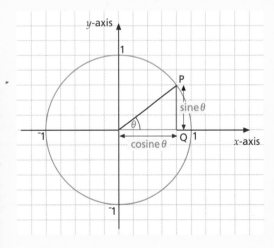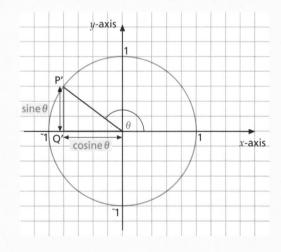

Letts I See Maths Book 3

Number and Algebra

Demonstration 2

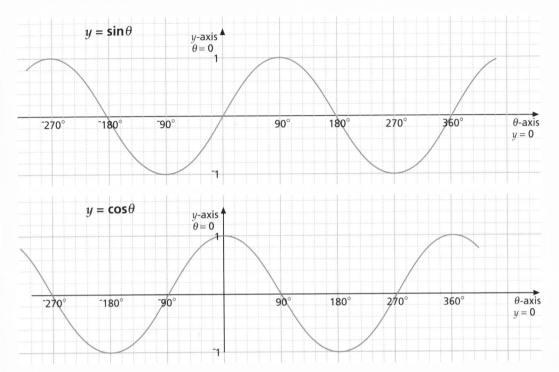

$y = \sin\theta$

$y = \cos\theta$

> **Key words**   'circle with unit radius'   cosine   projection on the x-axis
>   projection on the y-axis   sine   unit circle

Worked example

Exercise bank

1 Given $\sin 60° = \cdot8660$, write down the value of $\cos 30°$.

Angles $60°$ and $30°$ are complementary and

so:

$\sin 60° = \cos 30° = \cdot8660$

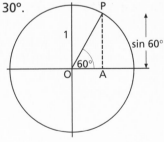

Plenary

◉ Look at the sine curve and discuss $\sin 30°$ and $\sin 390°$.

Look at the sine curve and discuss $\sin {}^-30°$ and $\sin 330°$.

Number and Algebra

Trigonometric functions

Essential exercises

1 Look at the circle in Demonstration 1.

(a) Estimate the values of cos 45° and sin 45°.

(b) Estimate the values of cos 135° and sin 135°.

(c) Use your answers to (a) and (b) to estimate the values of cos 225°, sin 225°, cos 315° and sin 315°.

2 Use the circle in Demonstration 1 to estimate the following values.

(a) cos 25°   (b) cos 65°   (c) cos 125°   (d) cos 245°

(e) sin 15°   (f) sin 95°   (g) sin 205°   (h) sin 355°

3 Look at the graphs in Demonstration 2 and imagine them continuing.

(a) Give six values of θ for which $\cos \theta = 1$.

(b) Give six values of θ for which $\sin \theta = 1$.

4 Use the graphs in Demonstration 2 to estimate the following values.

(a) cos 60°   (b) cos 75°   (c) cos 155°   (d) cos 300°

(e) sin 120°   (f) sin 175°   (g) sin 295°   (h) sin 315°

5 (a) Use the demonstrations to help explain why cos 62° = sin 28° and sin 43° = cos 47°.

(b) Work out the values of x in the following equations.

(i) $\cos 79° = \sin x°$ (ii) $\sin 22° = \cos x°$

(iii) $\cos 52° = \sin x°$ (iv) $\sin 131° = \cos x°$

(v) $\cos 168° = \sin x°$ (vi) $\sin 37° = {}^{-}\cos x°$

6 Use a calculator to write down the values of the following, to two decimal places.

(a) cos 42°   (b) cos 94°   (c) cos 104°   (d) cos 322°

(e) sin 36°   (f) sin 81°   (g) sin 283°   (h) sin 303°

Trigonometric functions

Challenging exercises

 7

(a) Explain why $\cos \theta = \sin (90 - \theta)$.

(b) Explain why $\cos \theta = {}^-\cos (180 - \theta)$.

(c) Explain why $\cos^2 \theta + \sin^2 \theta = 1$.

 8

Using surds: $\cos 60 = \frac{1}{2}$ $\sin 60 = \frac{\sqrt{3}}{2}$

$\cos 30 = \frac{\sqrt{3}}{2}$ $\sin 30 = \frac{1}{2}$

(a) Work out $\cos^2 60 + \sin^2 60$.

(b) Work out $\cos^2 30 + \sin^2 30$.

(c) Show that $\cos (A + B) = \cos A \cos B - \sin A \sin B$ when $A = 60°$ and $B = 30°$.

(d) Show that $\tan A = \frac{\sin A}{\cos A}$ when $A = 60°$ (check with your calculator).

Problem-solving exercise

 9

Use computer software or a graphics calculator to investigate the following transformations of functions.

(a) On the same axes, draw the graphs of $y = \cos x$ and $y = 3 \cos x$ and describe what you notice.

(b) On the same axes, draw the graphs of $y = \cos x$ and $y = \cos 3x$ and describe what you notice.

(c) On the same axes, draw the graphs of $y = \cos x$ and $y = \cos x + 3$ and describe what you notice.

(d) Use the results from parts (a)–(c) to make a conjecture about the transformations of $y = f(x)$ to $y = 3f(x)$, $y = f(3x)$ and $y = f(x) + 3$, and test with the function $f(x) = \sin x$.

Homework

Estimate the values of the following from the graphs in Demonstration 2, then check your answers with a calculator.

(a) $\cos 19°$ (b) $\cos 211°$ (c) $\sin 171°$ (d) $\sin 309°$

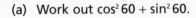

Letts I See Maths Book 3

Coordinate geometry

Goals

By the end of this lesson you will be able to answer questions such as these:

👁 Given the points R($^-$2, $^-$1), S(4, $^-$1) and T(3, 5), calculate the area of $\triangle$RST.

👁 Given the points K(3, 5) and L(13, 9), write down the coordinates of the point S that cuts the line KL in the ratio 5 : 8.

Starter

1 Evaluate the following.

(a) 1^2 (b) 2^2 (c) 3^2 (d) 4^2 (e) $1\cdot7^2$ (f) $3\cdot6^2$ (g) $(^-3\cdot6)^2$ (h) $^-(3\cdot6)^2$

2 Evaluate the following.

(a) $\sqrt{1}$ (b) $\sqrt{1\cdot7}$ (c) $\sqrt{9}$ (d) $\sqrt{25}$ (e) $\sqrt{2\cdot5}$ (f) $\sqrt{(^-3\cdot6^2)}$ (g) $\sqrt{100}$ (h) $\sqrt{10}$

3 Evaluate each of these, giving answers as both decimal fractions and vulgar fractions.

(a) $\dfrac{2 \times 3 + 1 \times 5}{8}$ (b) $\dfrac{2 \times 1 + 1 \times 2}{3}$

Demonstration 1

$AP = 5 - 2 = 3$

$BP = 3 - 1 = 2$

$AB^2 = AP^2 + BP^2$

(Pythagoras' theorem)

$AB^2 = 3^2 + 2^2$

$\quad\ = 9 + 4$

$\quad\ = 13$

$AB\ = \sqrt{13}$

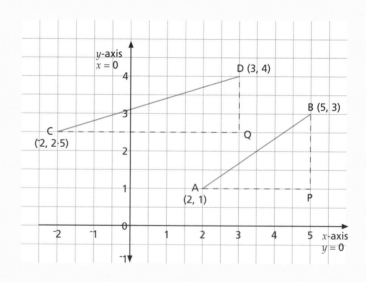

$CQ = 3 - {^-2} = 5$

$DQ = 4 - 2\cdot5 = 1\cdot5$

$CD^2 = CQ^2 + DQ^2$

(Pythagoras' theorem)

$CD^2 = 5^2 + 1\cdot5^2$

$\quad\ = 25 + 2\cdot25$

$\quad\ = 27\cdot25$

$CD = \sqrt{27\cdot25}$

Number and Algebra

Letts I See Maths **Book 3**

Demonstration 2

Midpoint AB $\equiv \left(\dfrac{2+5}{2}, \dfrac{1+3}{2} \right) \equiv (3 \cdot 5, 2)$

Midpoint CD $\equiv \left(\dfrac{^-2+3}{2}, \dfrac{2 \cdot 5+4}{2} \right) \equiv (\cdot 5, 3 \cdot 25)$

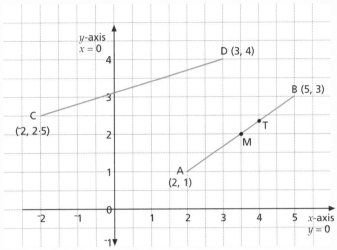

AM : MB = 1 : 1

$M \equiv \left(\dfrac{2 \times 1+5 \times 1}{2}, \dfrac{1 \times 1+3 \times 1}{2} \right) \equiv (3 \cdot 5, 2)$

AT : TB = 2 : 1

$T \equiv \left(\dfrac{2 \times 1+5 \times 2}{3}, \dfrac{1 \times 1+3 \times 2}{3} \right) \equiv (4, 2\tfrac{1}{3})$

Key words   midpoint   Pythagoras' theorem

Exercise bank 👉

....

Plenary

👁 Discuss:

(a) $AB^2 = (x_2 - x_1)^2 + (y_2 - y_1)^2$

(b) AP : PB $= h : k$

$P = \left(\dfrac{hx_2 + kx_1}{h+k}, \dfrac{hy_2 + ky_1}{h+k} \right)$

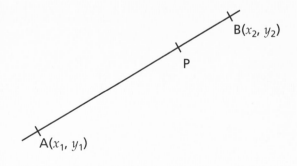

(c) Write down the following ratios.

(i) AP : AB   (ii) PB : AB

Letts I See Maths Book 3

Number and Algebra

Coordinate geometry

 Essential exercises

1 (a) Plot the points A(0, 6), B(6, 8) and C(6, 0). Join ABC to form a triangle.

 (b) Plot the point X(2, 4) and join XB (perpendicular to AC).

 (c) Calculate the lengths of lines AC and XB.

 (d) Calculate the area of triangle ABC.

 (e) Write down the coordinates of the midpoints of AB, BC and CA and mark them as D, E and F on your diagram.

 (f) Draw lines through the midpoints D, E and F, perpendicular to the sides of the triangle, and label the point of intersection of the three lines, Z.

 (g) With centre Z, draw a circle through the vertices A, B and C.

2 Find the length of the line joining each of the following pairs of points. Give your answers to an appropriate degree of accuracy.

 (a) (2, 3) and (5, 7)   (b) (4, 2) and (3, 1)   (c) (3, 1) and (1, 4)

 (d) (⁻1, 5) and (2, 7)   (e) (0, 0) and (⁻2, ⁻3)   (f) (⁻2, ⁻5) and (⁻4, ⁻3)

3 Find the coordinates of the midpoints of the lines joining the pairs of points in Exercise 2.

4 (a) Show that △ABC is isosceles, where the vertices of △ABC are A(1, 2), B(4, 6) and C(8, 3).

 (b) Show, using Pythagoras' theorem, that △DEF is right-angled, where the vertices of △DEF are D(0, 5), E(2, 7) and F(3, 2).

 (c) Show that PQRS is a square with vertices at P(2, 1), Q(4, 3), R(6, 1) and S(4, ⁻1).

 (d) H(4, 7) is the midpoint of line GH, where G is the point (2, 4). Find the coordinates of H.

 (e) The point M(5, 7) is the midpoint of a line AB, where A is the point (1, 4). Find the coordinates of B.

 (f) The point N(2, 6) is a quarter of the way along a line CD. If C is the origin, what are the coordinates of D?

Challenging exercises

5 If R is the point dividing AB internally in the ratio $m : n$, then R has coordinates:

$$\left(\frac{nx_1 + mx_2}{m + n}, \ \frac{ny_1 + mx_2}{n + m} \right)$$

For A(1, 2) and B(8, 5), find the coordinates of R when AB is divided in the following ratios.

(a) $m : n = 1 : 2$ (b) $m : n = 1 : 1$ (c) $m : n = 3 : 4$

6 Two vertices of an equilateral triangle are at A(2, 1) and B(12, 1). Find the third vertex (x, y), where $y > 0$.

7 A circle has centre (0, 0) and radius 4 cm. Write an equation for any point, P, on the circumference of the circle. (Hint: Use Pythagoras' theorem.)

Problem-solving exercise

8
(a) Find the equation of a line with gradient 2 that passes through the point (1, 5).

(b) Find the equation of a line with gradient 4 that passes through the point (2, 6).

(c) Find the equation of a line passing through the points A(1, 4) and B(3, 6).

(d) Find the equation of a line passing through the points C(0, 1) and D(2, ⁻3).

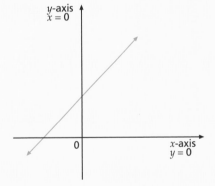

Homework

Give eight different positions for the point B(x, y) such that the line segment AB = 5 cm, where A is the point (2, 3).

1 (a) Find two consecutive whole numbers whose sum is 1575.

(b) Find three consecutive whole numbers whose sum is 378.

(c) Find two numbers whose sum is 15 and whose product is 56.

(d) The mean of four consecutive whole numbers is 28·5. What are the numbers?

2 Complete the grid below.

	(i)	(ii)	(iii)	(iv)	(v)	(vi)	(vii)	(viii)
x	32·3		0·63	2·52			6·06	17·3
y		9·2			23·7	51·8		
$x - y$	19·8	8·4	0·54	0·68	13·9	49·2	1·98	11·7

(b) For each entry in the grid above, write down an equation and solve it. The first one is shown here:

$$(i)\ 32·3 + y = 19·8$$
$$y = 32·3 - 19·8$$
$$= 12·4$$

3 Solve the following equations.

(a) $29 + x = 0$

(b) $x + 101 = 0$

(c) $^-8 + x = 0$

(d) $7 \times x = 1$

(e) $\frac{1}{5} \times x = 1$

(f) $x \times \frac{1}{23} = 0$

(g) $\frac{2}{5} \times x = 1$

(h) $\frac{7}{9} \times x = 1$

(i) $x \times \frac{4}{15} = 1$

4 Use a scientific calculator to work out the following.

(a) $1906 + 29 \times 87$

(b) $2098 + 39 \times \frac{14}{15}$

(c) $^-41·25 \div 5·5$

(d) $48^2 + \frac{14 \times 97}{38 \times 75}$

(e) $\sqrt{(9·2^2 + 4·6^2)}$

(f) $\sqrt[4]{2401}$

5 Simplify the following expressions using index notation.

(a) $2 \times 2 \times 2 \times 2 \times 2 \times 5 \times 5 \times 5$

(b) $2·3 \times 2·3 \times 2·3 \times 2·3 \times 4·5 \times 4·5$

6 Work out the values of the following expressions.

(a) $\sqrt{2} \times \sqrt{2}$

(b) $\sqrt{5} \times \sqrt{5} \times \sqrt{5} \times \sqrt{5}$

(c) $\sqrt{25} + \sqrt{36}$

7 Write the following numbers to (a) two decimal places (2 d.p.) (b) three significant figures (3 sig. figs.).

(i) 0·069 32

(ii) 1·2045

(iii) 2·3998

8 Write the following numbers in standard index form.

(a) 9274

(b) 0·000 35

(c) 1 860 000

Letts I See Maths Book 3

9 In the table below, $y \propto x$ such that $y = kx$. Work out the value of k and complete the table.

x	0	1	2	3	4	5	6	7	8	9	10
y					16·8					37·8	

10 (a) Draw a distance–time graph using the values in the table below.

t (seconds)	0	1	2	3	4	5	6	7	8
d (metres)	0	7·4	14·8	22·2	29·6	37	44·4	51·8	59·2

(b) Write down the equation of the graph.

11 (a) There was a 15% discount in a sale. Jack bought a DVD player for £169·15. What was the original price of the DVD?

(b) An elastic strap measures 2·5 m unstretched. At full stretch, it measures 2·75 m. Find the percentage increase in length.

12 VAT at 17·5% has to be added to the prices of goods in a shop. Work out the prices with VAT, to the nearest pence.

(a) £89·90   (b) £56·30   (c) £148·00   (d) £21

13 Multiply out the following brackets.

(a) $5(2x + 9)$ (b) $7(3x - 4)$ (c) $x(2x + 6y)$

14 Factorise the following expressions.

(a) $24x + 40$ (b) $9x - 12$ (c) $13xy + 11xz$

15 Complete the following equations.

(a) $^-3 + {}^-4 =$ (b) $6 + {}^-7 =$ (c) $^-8 - {}^-6 =$

(d) $^-2 - {}^-10 =$ (e) $3 - {}^-4 =$ (f) $9 - 13 =$

16 Complete the following equations.

(a) $^-2 \times 3 =$ (b) $5 \times {}^-4 =$ (c) $^-3 \times {}^-5 =$

(d) $^-6 \div {}^-2 =$ (e) $^-20 \div 4 =$ (f) $15 \div {}^-3 =$

1 Solve the following linear simultaneous equations.

(a) $\left.\begin{array}{l} 2x + 3y = 13 \\ 3x + 2y = 12 \end{array}\right\}$

(b) $\left.\begin{array}{l} 5x - 2y = 10 \\ 3x + 4y = 32 \end{array}\right\}$

2 Form, and solve, simultaneous equations to answer the following problem.

On 1st January 2009, Sam's dad will be three times Sam's age.
On 1st January 2023, Sam's dad will be twice Sam's age.
How old is Sam on 1st January 2009?

3 Complete the grids below.

(a) $(x + 3)(x + 4)$

×	x	+	3	
x	+			
+				+
4	+			
			Answer	

(b) $(x - 3)(x + 4)$

×	x	−	3	
x		−		
+				+
4		−		
			Answer	

4 Work out the column and row headings in the grids below.

(a)

×		+		
	x^2	+	$2x$	$x^2 + 2x$
+			+	
$3x$	+	6		$3x + 6$
			Answer	$x^2 + 5x + 6$

(b)

×		−		
	x^2	−	$2x$	$x^2 - 2x$
−			−	
$4x$	−	8		$4x - 8$
			Answer	$x^2 + 2x - 8$

5 (a) Draw the graph of $y = x^2 - 2x - 5$.

(b) Estimate the values of x where the graph cuts the x-axis.

(c) Use your answers to part (b) as the first estimates to solve $x^2 - 2x - 5 = 0$ using 'trial and improvement'.

6 The equation $x^2 - 2x - 15 = 0$ has the same value as $(x + 3)(x - 5) = 0$.
When $(x + 3)(x - 5) = 0$, then either $x = \dots$ or $x = \dots$.
What are these values of x?

7 (a) An integer n satisfies $5 \leq 3n + 5 < 35$.
List all the possible value of n.

(b) The number x can be any real number. Show all the possible solutions of the inequality $^-1 < x + 4 \leq 17$ on a number line.

(c) Draw graphs and shade the region showing the set of points satisfying all the inequalities below.
$x \geq 0$ $\qquad$ $y \geq 0$ $\qquad$ $x + y \leq 5$

8 Volume of a sphere: $V = \frac{4}{3}\pi r^3$

Surface area of a sphere: $S = 4\pi r^2$

Calculate the volume and surface area of a sphere with radius 6 cm. (Use $\pi \approx 3 \cdot 14$.)

9 Make the letter in brackets the subject of each formula.

(a) $A = lw$ $\qquad$ (w) $\qquad\qquad$ (b) $A = \frac{1}{2}h(a + b)$ $\qquad$ (h)

(c) $V = \pi r^2 h$ $\qquad$ (h) $\qquad\qquad$ (d) $V = \pi r^2 h$ $\qquad$ (r)

10 Generate the next three consecutive terms of each of the following number sequences using the position-to-term rule given.

	nth term	Sequence
(a)	$\frac{n(n+1)}{2}$	1, 3, 6, ...
(b)	2^n	2, 4, 8, ...

11 Write down the gradient and intercept on the y-axis of each of the following linear graphs.

(a) $y = 3x - 4$ $\qquad\qquad$ (b) $y = 0 \cdot 5x + 9$ $\qquad\qquad$ (c) $y = ^-4x - 2$

12 Rearrange the following equations in the form $y = ax + b$ and write down the gradient of the graph of each equation.

(a) $y - 3x = 6$ $\qquad\qquad\qquad$ (b) $2x + y = 14$

13 (a) Write down the midpoint of the line joining AB, where A is the point (1, 2) and B is the point (6, 10).

(b) Work out the length of the line AB in part (a).

Letts I See Maths **Book 3**

Problem solving

Goals

By the end of this lesson you will be able to answer questions such as these:

- 👁 Identify explicit and implicit information in the diagram.

- 👁 Study the diagram and convince yourself that the sum of the exterior angles of a pentagon is 360°.

- 👁 Given the diagram, prove that the sum of the exterior angles of a pentagon is 360°.

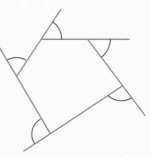

Starter

1 Practise reading these Greek letters.

(a) α (alpha) (b) β (beta) (c) γ (gamma) (d) δ (delta)

(e) ε (epsilon) (f) θ (theta) (g) φ (phi)

2 Discuss the symbols and their relationships in these sketches.

(a)

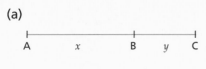

(b)

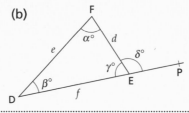

(c)

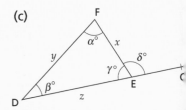

Demonstration 1

Convincing yourself

I can see what α, β, γ and δ are.

- α is 113 because 67 and 113 make 180.

- β is 67 because it is formed by the same movement of the image, RS, as 67°.

- I can see $\hat{BLQ}$ is 67° (in the same position on the // lines as $\hat{LMS}$).

  $\triangle$BLF has two equal base angles – so $\gamma = \delta = 56\frac{1}{2}$.

  (informal contemplation)

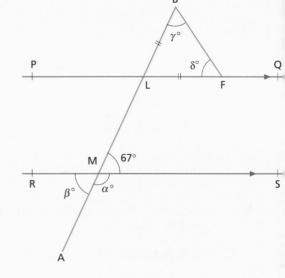

Letts I See Maths Book 3

Demonstration 2

Convincing others

Given: The diagram

Calculate: The values of α, β, γ, δ

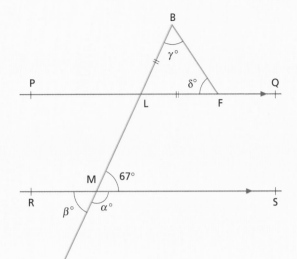

Solution:

$\hat{LMS}$ and $\hat{AMS}$ are supplementary angles.

$$\therefore \alpha + 67 = 180$$
$$\alpha = 113$$

$\hat{LMS}$ and $\hat{RMA}$ are vertically opposite angles.

$$\therefore \beta = 67$$

$\hat{BLF}$ and $\hat{LMS}$ are corresponding angles.

$$\therefore \hat{BLF} = 67°$$

In $\triangle BLF$, $\gamma + \delta + 67 = 180$ (interior angles of $\triangle$).

$$\therefore \gamma + \delta = 113$$

But $\triangle BLF$ is isosceles (LB = LF).

$$\therefore \gamma = \delta$$
$$\therefore \gamma = 56\tfrac{1}{2} \text{ and } \delta = 56\tfrac{1}{2}$$

Answer: $\alpha = 113$, $\beta = 67$, $\gamma = 56\tfrac{1}{2}$, $\delta = 56\tfrac{1}{2}$

> formal exposition
>
> careful regard for conventions

Key words   complementary angles   corresponding angles   exterior angles
'Given...'   interior angles   parallel   proof   supplementary angles
'To prove...'   vertically opposite angles

Exercise bank

Plenary

- 👁 Discuss the conventional form of a proof.
- 👁 Discuss the Goals.
- 👁 Discuss why an answer in Demonstration 2 is $\alpha = 113$ and not $\alpha = 113°$.

Letts I See Maths Book 3

Shape and Space

Exercise Bank Exercise Bank Exercise Bank Exercise Ba

Essential exercises

1 Work out the value of x in each of the diagrams below.

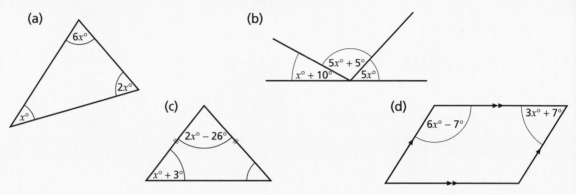

(a)

(b)

(c)

(d)

2 (a) Calculate the sum of the interior angles of a decagon.

(b) Calculate the size of each interior angle of a regular pentagon.

(c) The exterior angle of a regular polygon is one-fifth the size of its interior angle. How many sides has the polygon?

(d) The sum of six of the interior angles of an irregular heptagon is 787°. What is the size of its seventh interior angle?

3

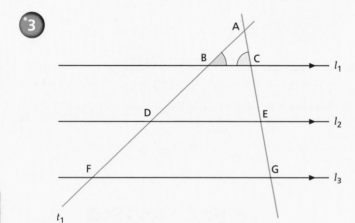

(a) Draw the diagram above and colour all the angles red that are equal to $A\hat{B}C$ and give reasons why they are equal.

(b) Colour all the angles blue that are equal to $A\hat{C}B$ and give reasons why they are equal.

(c) What can be said about triangles ABC, ADE and AFG?

(d) Suppose AF = 3AB and AD = 2AB. If BC = 3 cm, work out the lengths of DE and FG.

Challenging exercise

4 (a) Prove that the sum of the interior angles of a triangle is 180°.

(b) Prove that the exterior angle of a triangle is equal to the sum of the two opposite interior angles.

(c) Show that the sum of the interior angles of an n-sided polygon is $(n - 2) \times 180°$.

(d) Show that the sum of the exterior angles of any convex polygon is 360°.

(e) Prove that the opposite angles of a parallelogram are equal.

(f) Hence prove that adjacent angles of a parallelogram are supplementary.

(g) Prove that the opposite angles of a cyclic quadrilateral are supplementary.

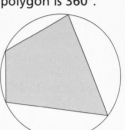

Problem-solving exercise

5 ABCDEF is a regular hexagon.

(a) Prove that FC = 2AB

(b) Prove that ABCF is an isosceles trapezium.

(c) FA and CB are produced to meet at X. Prove that the area of triangle FXC is four times the area of triangle AXB.

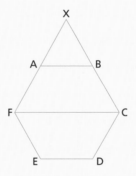

Homework

ABCDEFGH is a regular octagon

(a) Calculate the size of angle OAB.

(b) Prove that AB is parallel to FE.

(c) Prove that ACEG is a square.

(d) If OA = 5 cm, calculate the area of triangle AOC.

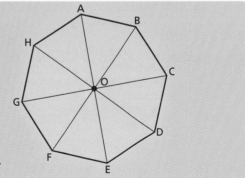

Pythagoras' theorem 1

Goals

By the end of this lesson you will be able to answer questions such as these:

◉ State Pythagoras' theorem.

◉ Given $\triangle PQR$, right-angled at Q, with $p = 3\cdot4$ cm and $r = 7\cdot2$ cm, calculate q.

◉ Given $\triangle LMN$, right-angled at M, with $m = 5\cdot4$ cm and $l = 7\cdot2$ cm, calculate n.

Starter

 1 Look at the explicit information in the sketch.
(a) What is the length of PQ?
(b) It is implicit that PQRS is a square. Why?
(c) What is the length of LM?
(d) It is implicit that LMNO is a square. Why?
(e) Area $\triangle PLO$ =
(f) Area LQM =
(g) Area $\triangle PLO$ + area $\triangle LQM$ =
(h) Area PQRS =
(i) $\frac{1}{2}$ area $\triangle PQRS$ =

2 Discuss and practise: (a) $(a + b)^2 = a^2 + 2ab + b^2$ (b) $a^2 + 2ab + b^2 = (a + b)^2$

Demonstration 1

Area PQRS = $(a + b)^2$
Area LMNO = c^2
Area $\triangle PLO$ + area $\triangle LQM$ + area $\triangle MRN$ + area $\triangle NSO = 4(\frac{1}{2}ab)$

$(a + b)^2 - c^2 = 4(\frac{1}{2}ab)$

$$(a + b)^2 - c^2 = 4(\tfrac{1}{2}ab)$$
$$a^2 + 2ab + b^2 - c^2 = 2ab$$
$$a^2 + b^2 = c^2$$

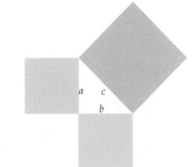

Pythagoras' theorem

In any right-angled triangle the square of the hypotenuse is equal to the sum of the squares of the other two sides.

$$a^2 + b^2 = c^2$$

Pythagoras' theorem

In any right-angled triangle the square on the hypotenuse is equal to the sum of the squares on the other two sides.

$$a^2 + b^2 = c^2$$

Letts I See Maths Book 3

Shape and Space

Demonstration 2

(a)

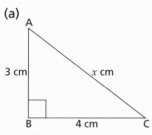

In right-angled $\triangle ABC$:

$AB^2 + BC^2 = AC^2$
$9 + 16 = x^2$
$25 = x^2$
$x = 5$
$AC = 5$ cm

(b)

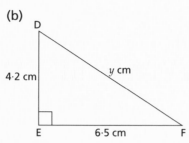

In right-angled $\triangle DEF$:

$DE^2 + EF^2 = DF^2$
$17 \cdot 64 + 42 \cdot 25 = y^2$
$59 \cdot 89 = y^2$
$\sqrt{59 \cdot 89} = y$
$y = 7 \cdot 7$ (to 1 d.p.)
$DE = 7 \cdot 7$ cm (to 1 d.p.)

(c)

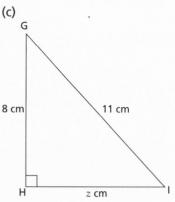

In right-angled $\triangle GHI$:

$GH^2 + HI^2 = GI^2$
$8^2 + z^2 = 11^2$
$z^2 = 11^2 - 8^2$
$= 57$
$z = 7 \cdot 5$ (to 1 d.p.)
$HI = 7 \cdot 5$ cm (to 1 d.p.)

> **Key words**   Pythagoras' theorem

Worked example

Exercise bank 👉

 Given: $\qquad$ A($^-$2, $^-$1), B(3, $^-$1), C(3, 2)

Calculate: $\qquad$ (a) AB $\qquad$ (b) BC
$\qquad\qquad\qquad$ (c) AC $\qquad$ (d) Area $\triangle ABC$

Solution:
Draw diagram.
(a) $AB = 3 - {}^-2 = 5$
(b) $BC = 2 - {}^-1 = 3$
(c) $AC^2 = AB^2 + BC^2$ (Pythagoras' theorem)
$\qquad\quad = 25 + 9$
$\qquad\quad = 34$
$\quad AC = \sqrt{34}$

(d) Area $\triangle ABC = \frac{1}{2}AB \times BC$
$\qquad\qquad\qquad = \frac{1}{2} \times 5 \times 3$
$\qquad\qquad\qquad = 7 \cdot 5$ square units

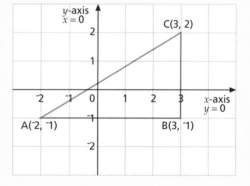

Plenary

👁 $\quad$ Look at the diagram for the Worked example and discuss the length of the altitude BC.

👁 $\quad$ Discuss the Goals.

Letts I See Maths Book 3

Shape and space

Pythagoras' theorem 1

Essential exercises

1 Calculate the lengths of the lines marked with the letter x, to the nearest millimetre.

(a)

x cm   4 cm   3 cm

(b)

x cm   5 cm   12 cm

(c)

x cm   7 cm   6 cm

(d)

x cm   3 cm   11 cm

(e)

8 cm   10 cm x cm

(f)

10 cm   26 cm x cm

(g)

x cm   7 cm   5 cm

(h)

x cm   10 cm   4 cm

(i)

x cm   5·2 cm   3·5 cm

(j)

11·5 cm   15·4 cm x cm

(k)

8·2 cm x cm   12·6 cm

(l)

7·4 cm x cm   2·5 cm

2 Work out whether the following triangles, with sides a cm, b cm and c cm, are right-angled, obtuse-angled or acute-angled.

(a) $a = 3$ $b = 6$ $c = 7$
(b) $a = 6$ $b = 8$ $c = 10$
(c) $a = 9$ $b = 12$ $c = 13$
(d) $a = 5$ $b = 12$ $c = 13$

3 Calculate the lengths of the lines marked with the letter x, to the nearest millimetre.

(a)

12 cm x cm   10 cm

(b)

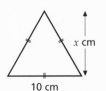

x cm   10 cm

(c)

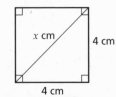

x cm   4 cm   4 cm

(d)

O y cm x cm   A   4 cm   B

(e)

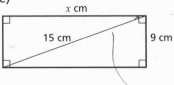

x cm   15 cm   9 cm

(f)

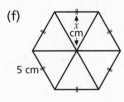

x cm   5 cm

Letts I See Maths Book

Challenging exercises

4 ABCD is a square inscribed in a circle with radius r.

(a) Write an expression, in terms of r, for the length of BC.

(b) Write an expression, in terms of r, for the length of OX.

(c) Write an expression, in terms of r, for the area of the circle with radius OX.

(d) Calculate the ratio below.
area of circle, radius OC : area of circle, radius OX

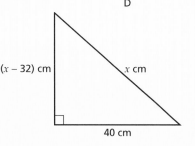

5 Calculate the values of x in the triangles below.

(a)

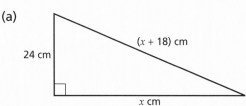

24 cm
$(x + 18)$ cm
x cm

(b)

$(x - 32)$ cm
x cm
40 cm

Problem-solving exercise

6 ABCDEFG is a regular octagon with sides 3 cm. The octagon is cut from a square piece of card as shown.

(a) Calculate the length of x shown in the diagram on the right.

(b) Calculate the area of the octagon ABCDEFG.

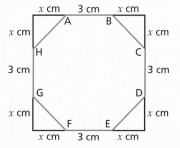

x cm 3 cm x cm
x cm   A   B x cm
H   C
3 cm   3 cm
G   D
x cm   F   E x cm
x cm 3 cm x cm

Homework

Pythagorean triples

The set of numbers (3, 4, 5) is called a Pythagorean triple. It consists of three positive integers satisfying Pythagoras' theorem, i.e. $5^2 = 3^2 + 4^2$.

See how many different Pythagorean triples you can find.

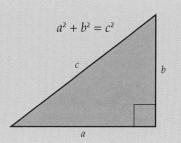

$a^2 + b^2 = c^2$

c b

a

Shape and Space

Goals

By the end of this lesson you will be able to answer questions such as these:

 In a right-angled $\triangle ABC$, a cm = 3 cm and c cm = 4 cm. Calculate b and area $\triangle ABC$.

 Sketch a cuboid 3·4 cm by 5·7 cm by 8·14 cm.

(a) Calculate the length of its longest diagonal.

(b) Discuss the 3-dimensional coordinates of its vertices.

 A ship sails from P on a bearing of 180° for 47·3 km to Q. It then sails on a bearing of 090° for 55·8 km to R. Calculate:

(a) the total distance sailed   (b) the distance PR.

Starter

1 Look at the diagram.

(a) In $\triangle ABC$, a cm = 3 cm, b cm = 4 cm. Calculate c.

(b) In $\triangle ABC$, a cm = 4 cm, b cm = 5 cm. Calculate c.

(c) In $\triangle ABC$, a cm = 3·7 cm, b cm = 4·3 cm. Calculate c.

(d) In $\triangle ABC$, a cm = 12.3 cm, b cm = 17·2 cm. Calculate c.

(e) In $\triangle ABC$, a cm = 3 cm, c cm = 4 cm. Calculate b.

(f) In $\triangle ABC$, b cm = 5·2 cm, c cm = 4 cm. Calculate a.

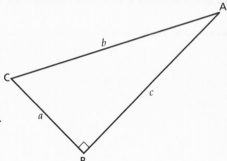

2 Look at the diagram.

(a) In $\triangle ABC$, a = 3 cm, c = 4 cm. Calculate area $\triangle ABC$.

(b) In $\triangle ABC$, b = 5·2 cm, c = 4 cm. Calculate area $\triangle ABC$.

Demonstration 1

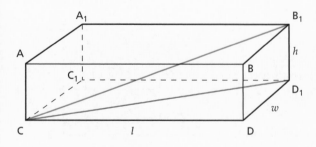

In right-angled triangle CDD_1
$$CD_1{}^2 = CD^2 + DD_1{}^2 = l^2 + w^2$$
$$CD_1 = \sqrt{CD^2 + DD_1{}^2} = \sqrt{l^2 + w^2}$$

In right-angled triangle CD_1B_1
$$CB_1{}^2 = CD_1{}^2 + B_1D_1{}^2 = l^2 + w^2 + h^2$$
$$CB_1 = \sqrt{CD_1{}^2 + B_1D_1{}^2} = \sqrt{l^2 + w^2 + h^2}$$

Shape and Space

Demonstration 2

Look at the diagram. ABCDEFGH is a cuboid drawn on x-, y-, z-axes.

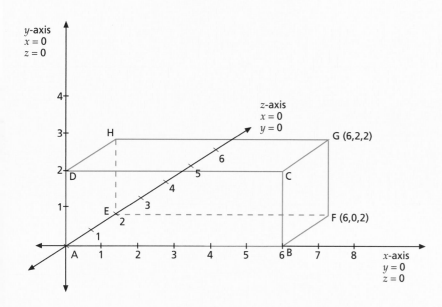

$AF^2 = AB^2 + BF^2$

$\qquad = 6^2 + 2^2 = 40$

$AF = \sqrt{40}$

$AG^2 = AF^2 + FG^2$

$\qquad = \left(\sqrt{40}\right)^2 + 2^2$

$\qquad = 44$

$AG = \sqrt{44}$

> **Key words**   bearing   surd   Pythagoras' theorem   2-dimensional   3-dimensional

....

Worked example

Exercise bank

① A ship sails from P on a bearing of 090° for 27 km to Q.
It then sails on a bearing of 180° for 35 km to R.

(a) Calculate the total distance sailed.
Total distance sailed = 27 km + 35 km = 62 km

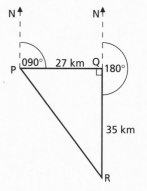

(b) Calculate the distance PR.
In $\triangle PQR$, $P\hat{Q}R = 90°$.
$PR^2 = PQ^2 + QR^2$ (Pythagoras' theorem)
$\therefore PR = 27^2 + 35^2$
$\qquad = 729 + 1225$
$\qquad = 1954$
$\qquad = 44 \cdot 2$ (to 1 d.p.)
The distance PR is 44·2 km (to 1 d.p.).

....

Plenary

👁 Discuss the Goals.

 I See Maths Book 3

Shape and Space

Pythagoras' theorem 2

Essential exercises

1 (a) Calculate the length of the diagonal, AC, of the square ABCD, when AB = 1 cm.

(b) Write down an expression for the length of the diagonal of the square ABCD when AB = x cm.

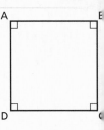

2 ABCDEFGH is a cube with edge lengths 5 cm.

(a) Calculate the length of FH, the diagonal of the base.

(b) Calculate the length FC, the diagonal of the cube.

(c) Write an expression for the length of the diagonal of a cube with edge lengths x cm.

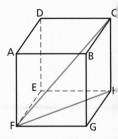

3 IJKLMNOP is a cuboid with length 3 cm, width 4 cm and height 12 cm.

(a) Calculate the length of NP, the diagonal of the base.

(b) Calculate the length of NK, the diagonal of the cuboid.

(c) Write an expression for the length of the diagonal of a cuboid with dimensions: length x cm, width y cm and height z cm.

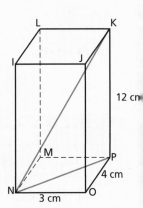

4 VABCD is a square-based pyramid of height 6 cm, and square base with side lengths of 4 cm.

(a) Calculate the length of AO, half the diagonal of the square base.

(b) Calculate the length of VA, the slant edge of the pyramid.

(c) Calculate the length of VM, where M is the midpoint of BC.

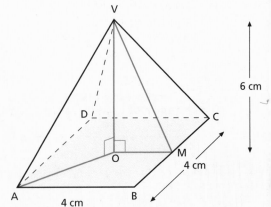

Letts I See Maths Book 3

Challenging exercise

5 In the construction on the right, the lines OA, AB, BC, ... are all of length 1 unit.

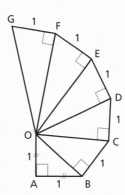

(a) Calculate the length of OG.
(Leave your answer in surd form.)

(b) Write down an expression for the length of the hypotenuse of the nth triangle.

(c) For what value of n will the hypotenuse be exactly 5 units?

(d) Investigate the lengths of the hypotenuse for different constructions. For example, begin with triangle OAB as above. Construct triangles such that BC = 2 units, CD = 3 units, DE = 4 units, etc.

(e) Can you find a construction so that the length of the hypotenuse of the third triangle is $\sqrt{15}$ units?

Problem-solving exercise

6 ABCDEFGH is a cube with edge lengths of 4 cm. A fly walks along the route shown to get from H to X.

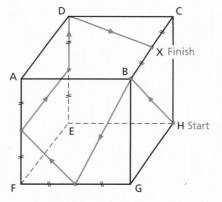

(a) What is the shortest distance from H to X?

(b) How far did the fly walk in going from H to X?
(Give your answer to the nearest millimetre or leave your answer in surd form.)

Homework

(a) Calculate the perpendicular height of an equilateral triangle with sides 3 cm.

(b) Calculate the area of an equilateral triangle with sides 3 cm.

(c) Hence, calculate the area of a regular hexagon with side lengths 3 cm.

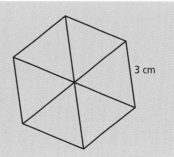

3 cm

Letts I See Maths Book 3

Congruence

Goals

By the end of this lesson you will be able to answer questions such as these:

👁 Interpret this shorthand for the conditions of congruence of triangles: SAS; SSS; ASA; SSR.

👁 Given $\triangle$DEF, where $d = e$, and with altitude FM, prove $\triangle$FDM $\equiv$ $\triangle$FEM.

Starter

1 Practise the descriptions of the blue sides and angles in these triangles.

(a)
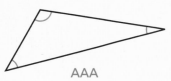

AAA
Three angles

(b)

SAS
Two sides and
the included angle

(c)

SSS
Three sides

(d)
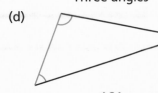

ASA
Two angles and
the included side

(e)

SSA   ASS
Two sides and
a not-included angle

(f)
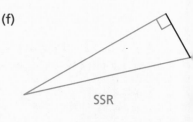

SSR
Two sides and
a right angle

Demonstration 1

Uniqueness of drawing for different given conditions

(a)
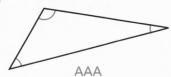

AAA

NOT UNIQUE

(b)

SAS

UNIQUE

(c)

SSS

UNIQUE

(d)
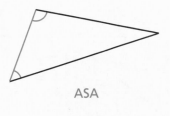

ASA

UNIQUE

(e)
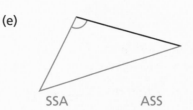

SSA   ASS

NOT UNIQUE

(f)

SSR

UNIQUE

Shape and Space

Letts I See Maths Book 3

Demonstration 2

Necessary and sufficient conditions for congruence

(a)
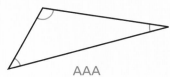

AAA

> The condition is not sufficient for all triangles to be congruent.

(b)

SAS

> The condition is sufficient for all triangles to be congruent.

(c)
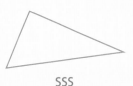

SSS

> The condition is sufficient for all triangles to be congruent.

(d)
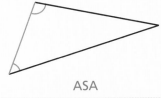

ASA

> The condition is sufficient for all triangles to be congruent.

(e)
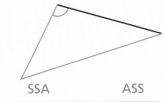

SSA   ASS

> The condition is not sufficient for all triangles to be congruent.

(f)

SSR

> The condition is sufficient for all triangles to be congruent.

Key words   condition   congruent   'is congruent to'   necessary
not unique   unique   sufficient

Worked examples

Exercise bank

1 An object is enlarged with scale factor m. Are the object and image congruent?

If $m = 1$, the object and image are congruent. If $m \neq 1$, they are not congruent.

2 An object is rotated $\theta°$ with (a, b) as the centre of rotation. Are the object and image congruent?

Rotation does not alter the size or shape of the object. The object and image are congruent.

Plenary

👁 Discuss the Goals.

👁 Sketch the Worked examples for specific values of m, θ, a and b.

👁 Are all pentagons with sides of 1 cm, 2 cm, 3 cm, 4 cm and 5 cm congruent?

 I See Maths Book 3

Shape and space

Essential exercises

1 ABCD is a quadrilateral.

Given that BA = BC and AD = CD,

prove that $B\hat{A}D = B\hat{C}D$.

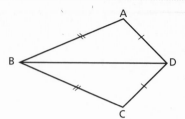

2 Triangle ABC is an isosceles triangle. Given that AB = AC and X is the midpoint of BC:

(a) prove that $A\hat{B}C = A\hat{C}B$

(b) prove that AX bisects $B\hat{A}C$.

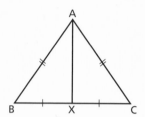

3 ABCD is a parallelogram.

(a) Prove that the opposite angles of a parallelogram are equal.

(b) Prove that the diagonals of a parallelogram bisect each other.

4 ABCD is a rhombus.

Prove that the diagonals of a rhombus bisect each other at right angles.

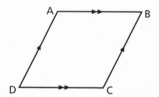

5 O is the centre of the circle. AB and CD are diameters of the circle.

(a) Prove that AC = DB and AD = CB.

(b) If you join ACBD with straight lines, what is the name of the resulting shape?

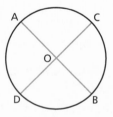

6 O is the centre of a circle. AB is a chord of the circle with midpoint M.

Prove that $O\hat{M}A = O\hat{M}B = 90°$

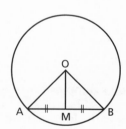

7 O is the centre of a circle.
TA and TB are tangents to the
circle, touching at A and B respectively.

Prove that TA = TB.

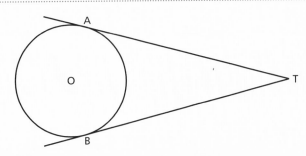

8 An object A is transformed into an image A′.
For which of the transformations below is the image A′ congruent to the object A?

(a) translation   (b) reflection   (c) rotation   (d) shear   (e) enlargement

Problem-solving exercise

9 The shape on the right is an ancient Chinese
puzzle called a tangram.

ABCD is a square. E is the midpoint of DC; G is
the midpoint of BC; H is the midpoint of IB
and J is the midpoint of DI.

(a) Name all the pairs of congruent triangles.

(b) Make a tangram and cut out each shape.
See if you can fit it back together again.

(c) There are many different shapes you can
make with the parts of a tangram. See
what you can make.

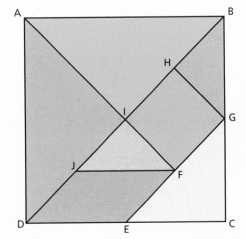

Homework

In each of the shapes below identify any congruent triangles.

(a)

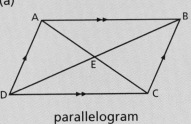

parallelogram

(b)

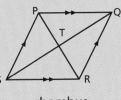

rhombus

(c)

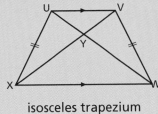

isosceles trapezium

Goals

By the end of this lesson you will be able to answer questions such as these:

👁 Interpret the shorthand AAA as a test for similar triangles.

👁 An object and an image are similar pentagons. The length of one side in the object is 3·4 cm and the corresponding side in the image is 4·7 cm.

(a) What is the scale factor of the enlargement?
(b) What is the scale factor for the enlargement of the perimeter?
(c) What is the scale factor for the enlargement of the area?

Starter

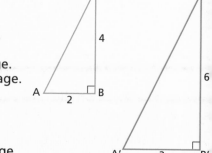

1 Look at the object ABC and the image A'B'C' in the diagram.

(a) Name all corresponding the sides in the object and image.
(b) Name all the corresponding angles in the object and image.

2 In the diagram, the scale factor of the enlargement is $\frac{3}{2}$.

(a) Discuss the lengths of the sides in the image.
(b) Calculate the area of the object and the area of the image.

Demonstration 1

'These two shapes are similar' means that all corresponding angles are equal and all corresponding sides are in the same ratio.	'These two shapes have all corresponding angles equal and all corresponding sides in the same ratio' means they are similar.

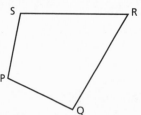
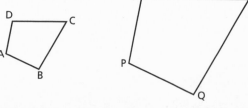

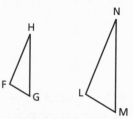

Explicit information:
ABCD and PQRS are similar.

Implicit information:
$D\hat{A}B = S\hat{P}Q$, $A\hat{B}C = P\hat{Q}R$,
$B\hat{C}D = Q\hat{R}S$, $C\hat{D}A = R\hat{S}P$
$\frac{AB}{PQ} = \frac{BC}{QR} = \frac{CD}{RS} = \frac{DA}{SP}$

Explicit information:
$H\hat{F}G = N\hat{L}M$, $F\hat{G}H = L\hat{M}N$, $G\hat{H}F = M\hat{N}L$
$\frac{FG}{LM} = \frac{GH}{MN} = \frac{HF}{NL}$

Implicit information:
HFG and NLM are similar.

Letts I See Maths Book 3

Shape and Space

Demonstration 2

Given an enlargement, the object and image are similar.

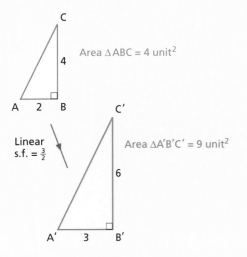

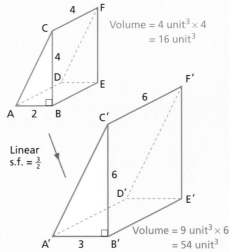

$$\frac{A'B'}{AB} = \frac{B'C'}{BC} = \frac{C'A'}{CA} = \frac{3}{2}$$

$$\frac{\text{Area } \triangle A'B'C'}{\text{Area } \triangle ABC} = \left(\frac{3}{2}\right)^2 = \frac{9}{4}$$

$$\text{Area s.f.} = \left(\frac{3}{2}\right)^2$$

$$\frac{\text{Volume } A'B'C'D'E'F'}{\text{Volume } ABCDEF} = \left(\frac{3}{2}\right)^3 = \frac{27}{8}$$

$$\text{Volume s.f.} = \left(\frac{3}{2}\right)^3$$

Key words	enlargement	image	object	scale factor	similar

Worked example

Exercise bank

1. An object and an image are similar hexagons. The length of one side in the object is 3 cm and the corresponding side in the image is 5 cm.

   (a) What is the scale factor of the enlargement? $\frac{5}{3}$

   (b) What is the scale factor for the enlargement of the perimeter? $\frac{5}{3}$

   (c) What is the scale factor for the enlargement of the area? $\left(\frac{5}{3}\right)^2 = \frac{25}{9}$

Plenary

- The scale factor for the enlargement of an area is $\frac{7}{3}$.
  Discuss the scale factor for the enlargement of (a) length (b) volume.

- Discuss the Goals.

Essential exercises

1

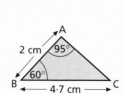 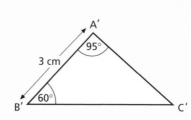 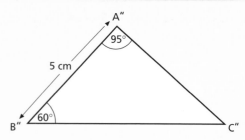

(a) Explain why triangles ABC, A'B'C' and A''B''C'' are similar.

(b) Calculate the ratios $\frac{A'B'}{AB}$ and $\frac{A''B''}{AB}$.

(c) Calculate the lengths of B'C' and B''C''.

2 (a) Explain why △ABC is similar to △AXY.

(b) Calculate the length of BC.

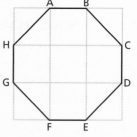

3 ABCDEFGH is the cross-section of an octagonal-based prism. AB = 1 cm.

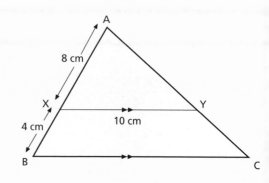

(a) Calculate P, the perimeter of the octagon. (Leave your answer in surd form.)

(b) Calculate A, the area of the octagon.

(c) Calculate V, the volume of the prism if its height is 6 cm.

(d) The prism is enlarged with a linear scale factor $\frac{3}{2}$. Calculate the following.
   (i) P^1, the perimeter of the enlarged prism
   (ii) A^1, the area of the enlarged prism
   (iii) V^1, the volume of the enlarged prism

(e) The prism is enlarged with a linear scale factor n. Write down expressions for the following.
   (i) P^n, the new perimeter
   (ii) A^n, the new area
   (iii) V^n, the new volume

Challenging exercises

4 ABC is a right-angled triangle with $A\hat{B}C = 90°$.
BX is the perpendicular from B to AC.

(a) Prove that triangle AXB is similar to triangle BXC.
(b) Show that AX.XC = BX²
(Note: AX.XC means AX × XC.)

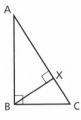

5 ABCD is a parallelogram.
X is the point on DC such that DX : XC = 2 : 1.

(a) Show that triangle AYB is similar to triangle CYX.

(b) Show that BY : YX = 3 : 1.

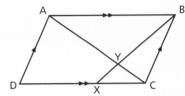

Problem-solving exercise

6 A tower, height x metres, has to be demolished. Emma has to order a machine for this and needs to know the height of the tower. To calculate the height, Emma places a pole in line with the top of the tower as shown in the diagram. Emma looks at the tower from a height of 1·65 metres above the ground. Calculate the height of the tower.

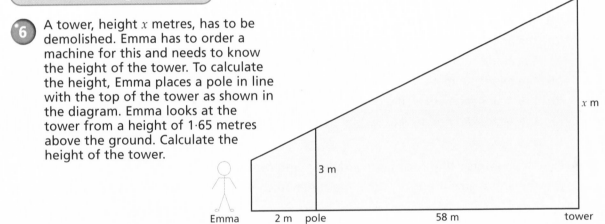

Homework

A 1 cm cube A is enlarged by the linear scale factor 3. Calculate the following.

(a) the total distance along all the edges of A
(b) the total surface area of A
(c) the volume of A
(d) the total distance along all the edges of B
(e) the total surface area of B
(f) the volume of B

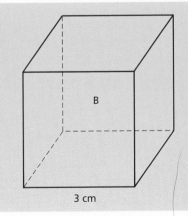

Letts I See Maths Book 3

Goals

By the end of this lesson you will be able to answer questions such as these:

👁 Two spheres have radii of 3 cm (object) and 7 cm (image). For the object to image enlargement, state:

    (a) the linear scale factor   (b) the area scale factor   (c) the volume scale factor.

👁 A circle, centre C and radius 5·2 cm, has chord AB of length 3·7 cm. Calculate the area of the minor sector defined by chord AB.

Starter

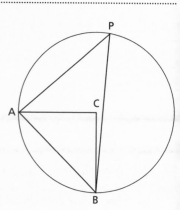

1 Look at the sketch of a circle and identify:

    (a) the centre

    (b) the chord AB

    (c) the minor arc AB

    (d) the major arc AB

    (e) the angle subtended at the centre by the chord AB

    (f) the angle subtended at the circumference by the chord AB

    (g) the minor segment defined by chord AB and minor arc AB

    (h) the major segment defined by chord AB and major arc AB

    (i) the sector defined by AC, BC and minor arc AB.

2 Draw two intersecting circles (same radius) with centres P_1 and P_2. Identify:

    (a) the line segment P_1P_2 (b) the common chord MN   (c) two isosceles triangles.

Demonstration 1

All circles are similar

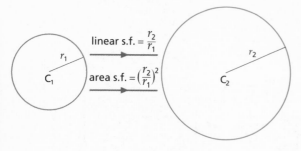

Circumference of circle: $C = \pi d$

Area of circle: $A = \pi r^2$

All spheres are similar

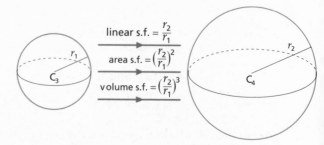

Surface area of sphere: $A = 4\pi r^2$

Volume of sphere: $V = \frac{4}{3}\pi r^3$

Demonstration 2

Figure 1

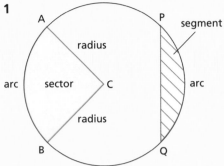

Figure 2

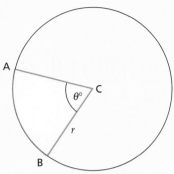

$$\frac{\text{Area of sector}}{\text{Area of circle}} = \frac{\theta}{360}$$

Figure 3

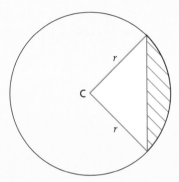

Area of segment = area of sector − area of triangle

Key words   arc   chord   major arc   major sector   minor arc
minor sector   sector   segment   similar   subtended

Worked example

Exercise bank

① Calculate the area of the minor sector of a circle of radius 3·8 cm defined by an arc subtending an angle of 42° at the centre.

Area of circle = $\pi(3\cdot8)^2$
∴ Area of required sector = $\pi(3\cdot8)^2 \times \frac{42}{360}$
= 5·3 cm (to 1 d.p.)

Plenary

👁 Discuss the Goals.

 I See Maths Book 3

Shape and space

Essential exercises

1 This motif is used to make a frieze pattern.

(a) Reproduce the motif and extend it to make a frieze pattern.

(b) Calculate the area of the blue motif.

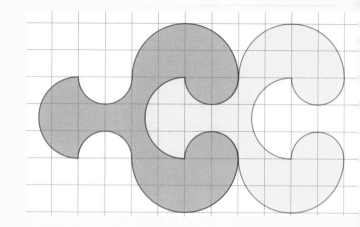

2 (a) Reproduce this spiral.

(b) Calculate the area of the coloured part.

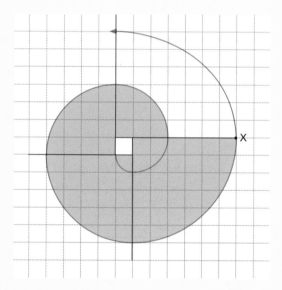

3 O is the centre of both the circles shown in the diagram. The large circle has radius R and the small circle has radius r.

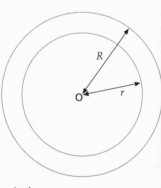

Work out the following when $r = 3$ and $R = 5$.

(a) the circumference of each circle as a multiple of π

(b) the area of each circle as a multiple of π

(c) the ratio $r : R$

(d) the ratio of circumference of small circle : circumference of large circle

(e) the ratio of area of small circle : area of large circle

Challenging exercises

4 (a) Calculate the area of the circle with radius 4 cm. (Leave your answer as a multiple of π.)

(b) Calculate the area of the shaded sector of the circle when AÔB = 36°.

(c) Calculate the area of triangle AOB when AB = 2·4 cm.

(d) Calculate the area of the shaded segment of the circle.

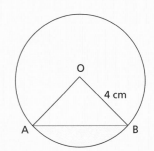
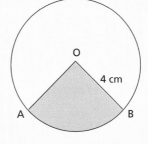

5 A cone is made from the sector of the circle on the right. Calculate the radius of the circular base of the cone.

6 cm

Problem-solving exercise

6 Drawing regular polygons using angles at the centre of a circle

(a) **Regular pentagon:** Angle at the centre of the circle is 360° ÷ 5 = 72°.

Draw a circle, radius 5 cm. Draw any radius. Measure an angle of 72° at the centre and draw a second radius. Continue to draw angles of 72° at the centre of the circle until you have completed the pentagon.

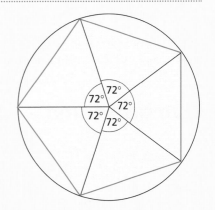

(b) Use a circle to draw the following regular shapes.
   (i) square   (ii) regular hexagon   (iii) regular heptagon   (iv) regular octagon

Homework

The shaded shape is cut from a square of side 8 cm. The area of the shape is A cm² and its perimeter is P cm. Which of the following statements is true?

(i) $A < 64$ (ii) $A > 32$ (iii) $P < 32$ (iv) $P > A$ (v) $P = 8\pi$

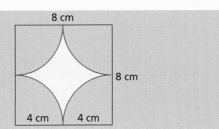

Goals

By the end of this lesson you will be able to answer questions such as these:

- 👁 State the theorem about 'Angles at the centre and circumference'.
- 👁 State the theorem about 'Angles at the circumference'.
- 👁 State the Alternate segment theorem.
- 👁 Illustrate the three theorems (above) with a sketch.
- 👁 Define a 'cyclic quadrilateral'.

Starter

1 Look at the sketch of a circle and identify:
 (a) the centre
 (b) the chord AB
 (c) the minor arc AB
 (d) the major arc AB
 (e) the angle subtended at the centre by the chord AB
 (f) the angle subtended at the circumference by the chord AB
 (g) the minor segment defined by chord AB and minor arc AB
 (h) the major segment defined by chord AB and major arc AB
 (i) the sector defined by AC, BC and minor arc AB.

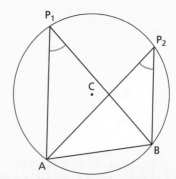

2 Draw a circle and draw a cyclic quadrilateral.

3 Draw a circle and mark three points, A, B and C, on its circumference. Mark another point D so that ABCD is a quadrilateral that is not cyclic.

Demonstration 1

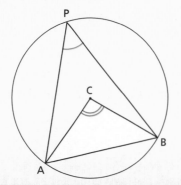

Circle theorem 1:
Angles at the centre and circumference
The angle subtended at the centre is twice the angle subtended at the circumference by the same chord (in the same segment).

Circle theorem 2:
Angles at the circumference
Angles subtended at the circumference by the same chord (in the same segment) are equal.

Shape and Space

Demonstration 2

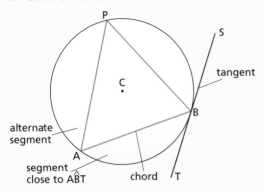

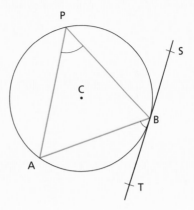

$A\hat{B}T$: the angle between the chord and the tangent

$A\hat{P}B$: the angle subtended by the chord AB

> **Circle theorem 3:**
> Alternate segment theorem
> The angle between a chord and a tangent is equal to the angle subtended by the chord in the alternate segment.

Key words   alternate segment   Alternate segment theorem   arc   chord
cyclic quadrilateral   major arc   major sector   minor arc
minor sector   sector   segment   similar   subtended   theorem

---

Worked example

Exercise bank 👉

1 Study the sketch. Calculate angle ALT and angle ACT.

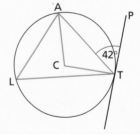

Angle ALT = angle ATP (Alternate segment theorem)
    = 42°

Angle ACT = 2 × angle ALT (angles at centre and circumference
                subtended by chord AT)

    = 84°

Plenary

◉ Draw a circle. Draw a chord GH. Sketch a tangent at H. Sketch an angle subtended at the circumference by GH in the alternate segment. Mark the two angles that are known to be equal from the Alternate segment theorem. Repeat this exercise with different circles and with GH marked at a variety of positions.

◉ 'Cyclic quadrilaterals have opposite angles supplementary.' Sketch and discuss.

◉ Discuss the Goals.

Letts | See Maths Book 3

Shape and space

Circle theorems

Essential exercises

1 Calculate the angles marked by letters in the circles below where O is always the centre of the circle. Give reasons for your answers.

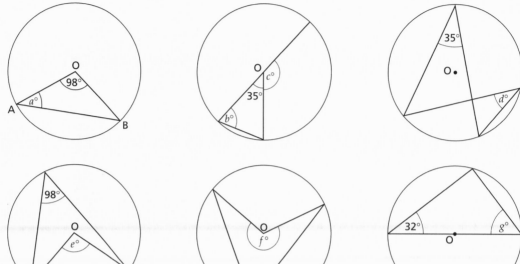

2 (a) ABCD is a quadrilateral. $\hat{ABC} = 73°$ and $\hat{ADC} = 107°$.
Explain why ABCD is a cyclic quadrilateral.

(b) PQRS is a cyclic quadrilateral. PQRS is also a parallelogram. Explain why PQRS must be a rectangle.

(c) EFGH is a cyclic quadrilateral. $\hat{EFG} = 84°$.
Calculate $\hat{EHG}$.

3 Calculate the angles marked by letters in the circles below where O is always the centre of the circle. Give reasons for your answers.

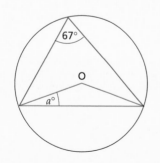
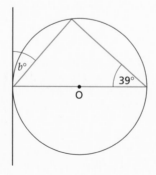
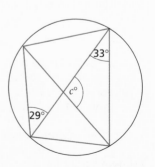

Letts I See Maths Book 3

Challenging exercises

4 The Alternate segment theorem

PAQ is a tangent to the circle at A.

Prove that $\hat{BAQ} = \hat{ACB}$.

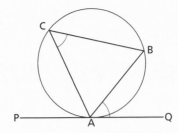

5 TAX is a tangent to the circle at A.

(a) Prove that triangles TAC and TBA are similar.

(b) Hence show that $TC.TB = TA^2$.

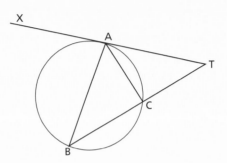

Problem-solving exercises

6 ABCDE is a pentagon with ABCD a cyclic quadrilateral. Angle ABC = 105°.

(a) Make a sketch of ABCDE.

(b) Calculate $\hat{ADC}$.

(c) If $\hat{AEC} = 75°$, what can you conclude about point E?

7 XAT is a tangent to the circle at A and YBT is a tangent to the circle at B.

Calculate $\hat{ACB}$.

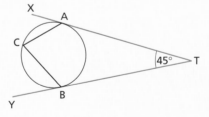

Homework

Reproduce the proof that angles in the same segment are equal, i.e. $\hat{APB} = \hat{AQB}$.

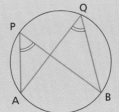

Goals

By the end of this lesson you will be able to answer questions such as these:

👁 Visualise a triangular prism and sketch its plan, front elevation and side elevation.

👁 Visualise and sketch the 3-dimensional shape generated by a semi-circle rotated through 360°, with the straight edge as the axis of rotation.

Starter

1 Look at these 2–dimensional sketches of 3-dimensional shapes. For each sketch, name the solid.

(a) 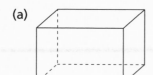　(b) 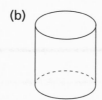　(c) 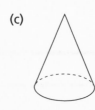　(d)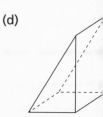

2 Look at the sketches above. For each one, sketch the plan, front elevation and side elevation.

Demonstration 1

Visualising shapes generated by rotation

Figure 1

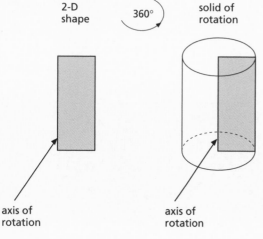

Figure 2

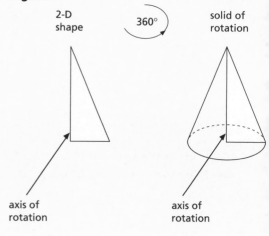

Letts I See Maths Book 3

Demonstration 2

Volume of a cone $V = \frac{1}{3}\pi \,(\text{radius})^2\,(\text{height})$

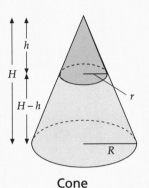

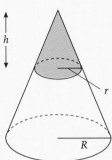

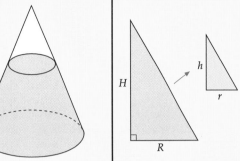

Cone (volume V)	Small cone (volume V_1)	Truncated cone (volume V_2)	

s.f. $= \dfrac{h}{H}$

$r = \dfrac{h}{H} \times R$

$$V = \tfrac{1}{3}\pi\, R^2 H$$

$$V_1 = \tfrac{1}{3}\pi \left(\tfrac{hR}{H}\right)^2 h$$

$$V_2 = \tfrac{1}{3}\pi\, R^2 H - \tfrac{1}{3}\pi \left(\tfrac{hR}{H}\right)^2 h$$

Key words   axis of rotation   solid of rotation

Worked example

Exercise bank

1. (a) Sketch the plan of a truncated cone.

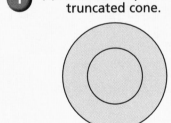

(b) Sketch a 2-dimensional shape that could be used to generate a truncated cone. (Show the axis of rotation.)

axis of rotation

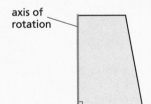

Plenary

👁 Discuss the solid of rotation formed by rotating this plane shape through 360°, with:
   (a) the red line segment as the axis of rotation
   (b) the green line segment as the axis of rotation.

👁 Discuss the Goals.

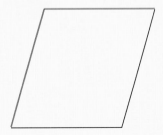

Visualisation

Shape and Space

Essential exercises

1 (a) Visualise a cube. Put a dot in the centre of each face of the cube. Join the dots on adjacent faces with straight lines. What shape is generated by these lines?

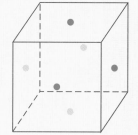

(b) Visualise the shape generated in part (a). Put a dot in the centre of each face of the shape. Join the dots on adjacent faces with straight lines. What shape is generated by these lines?

(c) What do you notice?
What happens if you keep repeating the process?

2 (a) 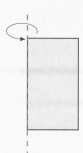 (b) (c)  (d)

Each of the shapes above is rotated through 360° about the axis shown. Describe the 3-dimensional shape traced out in each case.

3 Identify and sketch the solids below from their descriptions.

	Front elevation	Side elevation	Plan
(a)	circle	circle	circle
(b)	rectangle	rectangle	circle
(c)	rectangle	triangle	rectangle
(d)	triangle	triangle	square
(e)	rectangle	rectangle	rectangle

4 (a) Imagine slicing a square-based pyramid parallel to its base. Describe the two shapes you get and compare the results for slices at different heights above the base.

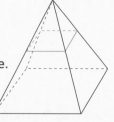

(b) Imagine slicing a square-based pyramid perpendicular to its base. Describe the two shapes you get and compare the results for slices in different positions.

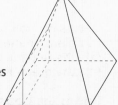

Letts I See Maths **Book 3**

Visualisation

Challenging exercises

5 Imagine a hollow cone. Describe how you would cut the cone to make:

(a) a circle (b) an ellipse (c) a parabola.

6 A tetrahedron is cut from a cube a shown.

(a) Explain why each face is an equilateral triangle.

(b) If the cube has edge length 4 cm, calculate the edge length of the tetrahedron.

(c) What is the following ratio?
volume of the tetrahedron : volume of the cube

Problem-solving exercise

7 Joanne is in Class 1 (Mr Patel's class). Joanne likes building animals with small plastic cubes that click together. Each cube has a volume of ·93 cm³ and density of 1·13 g/cm³. Look at the orthogonal projection of the 'dog' that Joanne made.

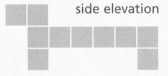

side elevation

front elevation

plan

(a) Sketch Joanne's dog.

(b) (i) What is the volume of the dog? (ii) What is its mass? (iii) What is its density?

(c) Joanne decided to make 'double-dog'. Mr Patel was impressed that she made every dimension twice the original.
(i) What is the volume of 'double-dog'? (ii) What is its mass?

(d) There was a great deal of excitement in Class 1 when they decided to make '100-dog'. They wanted to get started straight away and asked Mr Patel to buy the cubes at lunchtime. How should he respond?

(e) Joanne's older brother looked at 'dog' standing on the table and wondered about the ratio of the surface area exposed to the air compared to the total surface area of the dog. And then he wondered about 'double-dog', 'treble-dog' and '100-dog'. Help him.

(f) Joanne's sister was also studying the **I See Maths** course. She looked at the front elevation in the diagram, visualised the line along the top of the body as an axis of rotation and mentally rotated the front elevation through 360°.
(i) Describe the solid of revolution.
(ii) What would be the volume of revolution?

Homework

Sketch nets for the following solids.
(a) cuboid (b) tetrahedron (c) square-based pyramid
(d) hollow cone (e) open cylinder

Transformations

Goals

By the end of this lesson you will be able to answer questions such as this:

👁 If $y = f(x)$, discuss: (a) $y = f(x) + k$ (b) $y = f(x + k)$ (c) $y = kf(x)$

Starter

1 Sketch: (a) $y = x^2$ for $^-3 \le x \le 3$ (b) $y = (x + 2)^2$ for $^-3 \le x \le 3$

Demonstration 1

Graph 1

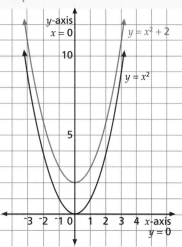

$y = f(x) \longrightarrow y = f(x) + 2$

Graph 2

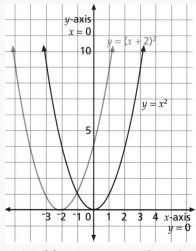

$y = f(x) \longrightarrow y = f(x + 2)$

Graph 3

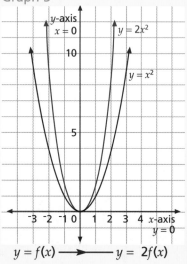

$y = f(x) \longrightarrow y = 2f(x)$

Table:

x	$^-3$	$^-2$	$^-1$	0	1	2	3
$y = x^2$	9	4	1	0	1	4	9
$y = x^2 + 2$	11	6	3	0	3	6	11
$y = (x + 2)^2$	1	0	1	4	9	16	25
$y = 2x^2$	18	8	2	0	2	8	18

Letts I See Maths **Book 3**

Demonstration 2

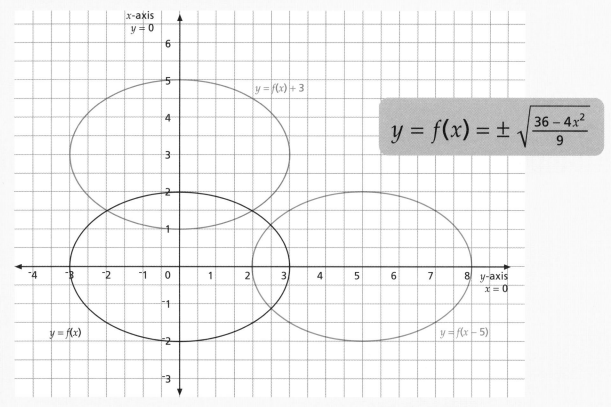

$$y = f(x) = \pm \sqrt{\frac{36 - 4x^2}{9}}$$

y = f(x) + 3

y = f(x)

y = f(x − 5)

Worked example

Exercise bank

1 Show that $\frac{x^2}{9} + \frac{y^2}{4} = 1$ has the same value (different appearance) as $y = \pm\sqrt{\frac{36 - 4x^2}{9}}$.

$$\frac{x^2}{9} + \frac{y^2}{4} = 1$$

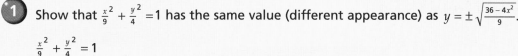

$y \xrightarrow{\text{square it}} y^2 \xrightarrow{\div 4} \frac{y^2}{4} \xrightarrow{+ \frac{x^2}{9}} \frac{y^2}{4} + \frac{x^2}{9}$

$\pm\sqrt{\frac{36 - 4x^2}{9}} \xleftarrow{\text{square root it}} 4\left(\frac{9 - x^2}{9}\right) \xleftarrow{\times 4} 1 - \frac{x^2}{9} \xleftarrow{- \frac{x^2}{9}} 1$

$$y = \pm\sqrt{\frac{36 - 4x^2}{9}}$$

Plenary

👁 If $y = x^3$, discuss: (a) $y = x^3 + 1 + k$ (b) $y = (x + 1 + k)^3$ (c) $y = k(x^3 + 1)$

👁 Discuss the Goals.

Letts I See Maths **Book 3**

Shape and Space

Transformations

Essential exercises

1
(a) Draw axes ⁻4 ≤ x ≤ 10, ⁻1 ≤ y ≤ 10.

(b) Draw object ABCD with vertices A(2, 1), B(2, 3), C(2, 4) and D(3, $3\frac{1}{2}$).

(c) Reflect ABCD in the lines given below and complete the table.

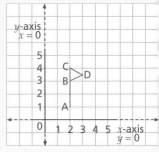

Axis of reflection	Coordinates of image ABCD
$x = 0$	
$x = 1$	
$x = 2$	
$x = 3$	
$x = 4$	

(d) Look for patterns in the table and write down the coordinates of the image ABCD when reflected in the line $x = n$.

2
(a) Draw axes and object ABCD as in Exercise 1.

(b) Translate object ABCD with vector $\begin{pmatrix} 3 \\ 1 \end{pmatrix}$ and draw its image A′B′C′D′.

(c) Translate A′B′C′D′ with vector $\begin{pmatrix} 2 \\ 3 \end{pmatrix}$ and draw its image A″B″C″D″.

(d) Translate A″B″C″D″ with vector $\begin{pmatrix} ⁻1 \\ ⁻1 \end{pmatrix}$ and draw its image A‴B‴C‴D‴.

(e) What single transformation will map ABCD onto A‴B‴C‴D‴?

(f) What single transformation will map A‴B‴C‴D‴ onto ABCD?

(g) What single transformation is equivalent to a translation $\begin{pmatrix} 4 \\ 2 \end{pmatrix}$, followed by a translation $\begin{pmatrix} 3 \\ 7 \end{pmatrix}$, followed by a translation $\begin{pmatrix} 6 \\ 1 \end{pmatrix}$?

3
(a) Draw axes and object ABCD as in Exercise 1.

(b) Rotate ABCD 90° anticlockwise about (0, 0) and draw its image A′B′C′D′.

(c) Rotate A′B′C′D′ 90° anticlockwise about (0, 0) and draw its image A″B″C″D″.

(d) Rotate A″B″C″D″ 90° anticlockwise about (0, 0) and draw its image A‴B‴C‴D‴.

(e) What single transformation will map ABCD onto A‴B‴C‴D‴?

(f) What single transformation will map A‴B‴C‴D‴ onto ABCD?

(g) What single transformation is equivalent to a 30° rotation anticlockwise about (0, 0), followed by a 70° rotation anticlockwise about (0, 0), followed by a 20° rotation anticlockwise about (0, 0)?

Shape and Space

Challenging exercises

4 (a) Draw axes $^-5 \le x \le 18$, $0 \le y \le 25$.

(b) Complete the table below and use the values to draw the graph of $y = x^2$.

x	$^-5$	$^-4$	$^-3$	$^-2$	$^-1$	0	1	2	3	4	5
$y = x^2$	25					0					25

(c) Reflect the graph in the line $x = 1$ and draw the image of $y = x^2$ in this line.

(d) Work out the equation of the image.

(e) Use your results to work out the equation of the image of $y = x^2$ when it is reflected in the line $x = n$.

5 (a) Draw the graph of $y = x^2$ as in Exercise 5.

(b) Translate $y = x^2$ with vector $\begin{pmatrix} 0 \\ 3 \end{pmatrix}$ and draw its image.

(c) Write down the equation of the image.

(d) What would be the equation of the image of $y = x^2$ when it is translated by the vector $\begin{pmatrix} 0 \\ n \end{pmatrix}$?

Problem-solving exercises

6 ABC is an isosceles triangle with AB = BC.
What type of quadrilateral is produced when ABC is reflected in

(a) AC   (b) BC?

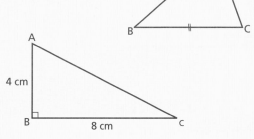

7 ABC is a right-angled triangle.
AB = 4 cm, BC = 8 cm and $A\hat{B}C = 90°$.
Draw ABC and its image when reflected in:

(a) AC   (b) AB

(c) the perpendicular bisector of BC

(d) the bisector of $A\hat{B}C$.

Homework

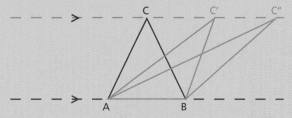

The diagram shows △ABC being transformed by two shears. Explain why △ABC has the same area as △ABC' and has the same area as △ABC".

Constructions and loci

Goals

By the end of this lesson you will be able to answer questions such as these:

- 👁 Draw a line segment AB and use a straight edge, compasses and a set square to strike it into seven equal segments. Identify the point P such that AP : AB = 2 : 7, and state the ratio AP : PB.

- 👁 A circle, centre C, has a chord AB. Construct the altitude, CM, of △ABC.

- 👁 Describe the locus of a point that moves so its distance from a straight line is 3 cm.

- 👁 Describe the locus of a point that moves so its distance from a straight-line segment is 3 cm.

- 👁 Describe the relationship of the centroid, orthocentre, circumcentre and incentre of an equilateral triangle.

Starter

1 Follow these instructions to strike any line segment into five equal segments using a straight edge, a set square and a pair of compasses.

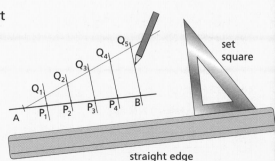

set square

straight edge

(a) Draw any line segment AB.
(b) Draw a line through A at an angle (approximately 30°) to AB.
(c) Using compasses, strike five equal divisions along this line.
(d) Label these from A as Q_1, Q_2, Q_3, Q_4 and Q_5.
(e) Draw the line Q_5B.
(f) Draw lines parallel to Q_5B through Q_4, Q_3, Q_2 and Q_1 to cut AB.
(g) Label AB as A, P_1, P_2, P_3, P_4 and B.
(h) These points strike AB into five equal parts.

Demonstration 1

Study these constructions

Identifying the centroid of a triangle

(i) Draw any triangle ABC.
(ii) Construct the perpendicular bisector of BC and mark the midpoint D.
(iii) Draw the line AD.
(iv) Similarly, draw lines BE and CF, where E and F are the midpoints of AC and AB respectively.
(v) The unique point of intersection of the three lines, AD, BE and CF, is the centroid of △ABC.

Identifying the orthoentre of a triangle

(i) Draw any triangle ABC.
(ii) With centre A, and appropriate radius, draw an arc to strike BC at P_1 and P_2.
(iii) With centres P_1 and P_2, and appropriate radius, draw two arcs to intersect outside the triangle at L.
(iv) Draw line AL. This is an altitude to BC.
(v) Similarly, draw altitudes BM and CN.
(vi) The unique point of intersection of the three altitudes is the orthocentre of △ABC.

Discuss these constructions using the idea of 'locus' and 'loci'.

Shape and Space Lesson

Demonstration 2

Drawing any regular polygon

Example: drawing a regular pentagon

(i)   Draw any circle, centre C.
(ii) Draw a diameter AB.
(iii) Use an auxiliary construction to strike AB into five equal parts.
(iv) Label AB as A, P_1, P_2, P_3, P_4 and B.
(v)   Identify P, where AB = AP = PB.
(vi) Draw line PP_2 to strike the circle beyond P_2 at X_1.
(vii) AX_1 is the length of the sides of the pentagon.
(viii) Use compasses to strike lengths equal to AX_1 round the circle.
(ix) Label the strikes A, X_1, X_2, X_3 and X_4.
(x) $AX_1X_2X_3X_4$ is a regular pentagon.

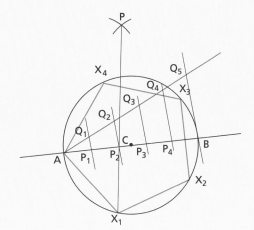

Key words   altitude   auxiliary construction   centroid   line   line segment   loci   locus   orthocentre   'with centre C and radius ..., strike an arc'

Worked examples

Exercise bank

1 Describe the locus of a point that moves so it is equidistant from two fixed points A and B.

The locus is a straight line bisecting the line segment AB at right angles (i.e. the perpendicular bisector of AB).

2 Describe the locus of a point that moves so its distances from two fixed parallel lines, LM and PQ, remain in the ratio 5 : 3.

The locus is a straight line, parallel to LM and PQ. It is closer to PQ than to LM. A line segment perpendicular to LM and PQ is cut at $\frac{5}{8}$ of its length (from L) by the locus.

Plenary

👁 Sketch the loci in the Worked examples.

👁 Discuss the Goals.

Shape and Space

Constructions and loci

Essential exercises

1 (a) Use a ruler and a pair of compasses to construct △ABC with AB = 6 cm, CB = 5 cm and AC = 4 cm.

(b) Use a pair of compasses to construct the perpendicular bisectors of two sides of △ABC.

(c) Use the point of intersection of the two perpendicular bisectors to construct the circle that passes through vertices A, B and C. (The circle circumscribes the triangle.)

2 (a) Construct △ABC as in Exercise 1(a).

(b) Use a pair of compasses to construct the angle bisectors of two of the interior angles of △ABC.

(c) Use the point of intersection of the angle bisectors to construct the circle that just touches the sides of the triangle. (The circle inscribes the triangle.)

3 (a) Construct an equilateral triangle PQR with sides 6 cm.

(b) Construct the circle that circumscribes the triangle PQR and construct the circle that inscribes triangle PQR. What do you notice?

4 (a) How many different triangles can you construct using line segments that are 2 cm, 3 cm, 4 cm and 6 cm in length?

(b) Which combinations will not work, and why?

5 (a) Draw two intersecting circles with the same radii, and with centres A and B. Join C and D, the points of intersection of the circles.

(i) Explain how the diagram relates to the construction of the perpendicular bisector of the line segment AB?

(ii) What type of quadrilateral is ACBD?

(iii) Describe the line CD when the two circles just touch.

(iv) Describe the line CD when the radii of the circles are not equal.

(b) Draw a line segment AB = 7 cm. Mark a point P anywhere above the line. Construct the line from P to AB that is perpendicular to AB.

6 Using compasses and ruler only, construct △ABC, where AC = 7 cm, AB = 11 cm and AĈB = 90°.

Letts I See Maths **Book 3**

Shape and Space

Constructions and loci

 7 Point P moves such that it is always the same distance from the origin.

(a) Describe the locus of P.

(b) Use Pythagoras' theorem to write down the equation of the locus of P.

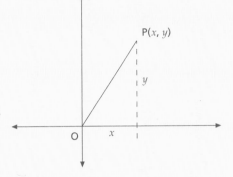

8 Point Q moves such that it is always 6 cm from the point (2, 1).

(a) Describe the locus of Q.

(b) Use Pythagoras' theorem to write down the equation of the locus of Q.

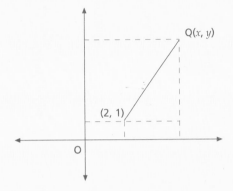

Problem-solving exercise

 9 Forbidden space

(a) A glowing organism, A, is suspended in space. It is forbidden to get closer than 5 m to the organism. Describe the locus of the boundary of the forbidden space.

(b) It is impossible to get within 120 cm of a hot piece of metal, PQ. Describe the locus of the boundary of the limited region.

(c) A robot has to be placed so that it is always the same distance from two production lines in a factory. Describe the locus of the points satisfying this condition.

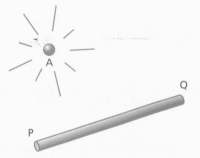

Homework

Use a straight edge and a pair of compasses to construct the following angles. (Do not use a protractor.)

(a) 45°   (b) 60°   (c) 120°   (d) 30°

Measures and scales

Goals

By the end of this lesson you will be able to answer questions such as these:

👁 Given 1 hectare = 10 000 m², convert 7·6 hectares to square metres.

👁 Given 8 km = 5 m,
(a) convert 8² km² to square miles   (b) express 1 square mile in square kilometres.

👁 Discuss basic units and their relationship with derived units using examples selected by yourself.

Starter

1   Express the following in index form.   (a) 10 000   (b) 1 000 000   (c) ·0001   (d) ·01

2   Recite these from memory:
milli-   centi-   deci-   [basic unit]   deca-   hecta-   kilo-

and use these prefixes for:
(a) length   (b) mass   (c) a made-up unit of your own.

Demonstration 1

Conversion of units of area and volume

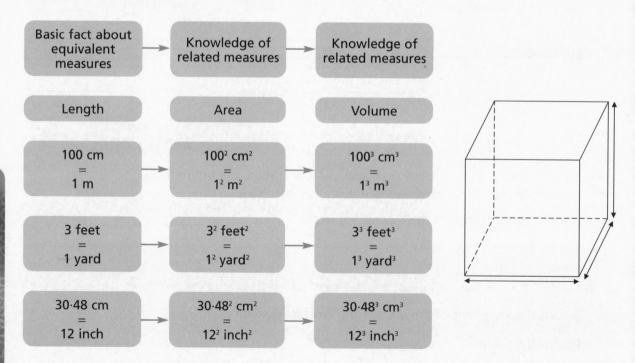

Letts I See Maths **Book 3**

Demonstration 2

Basic measure and derived measure

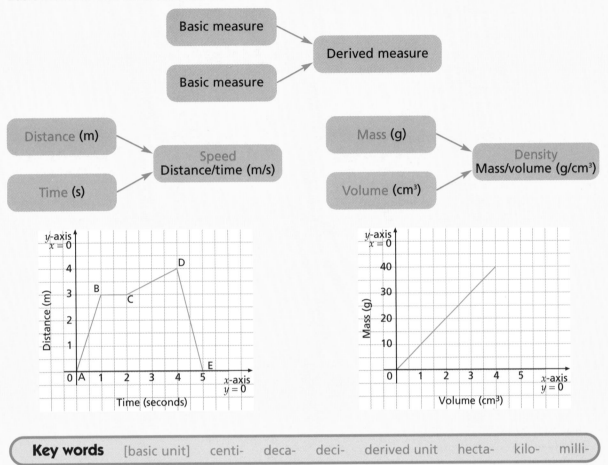

Key words   [basic unit]   centi-   deca-   deci-   derived unit   hecta-   kilo-   milli-

Worked example

Exercise bank

1 Given t = time (s), v = velocity (m/s) and a = acceleration, use the formula $a = \frac{v}{t}$ to deduce the units of acceleration.

Units of acceleration are m/s/s or m/s^2 or m s^{-2}.

Plenary

◉ Discuss the variations of the units in the Worked example.

◉ Discuss the Goals.

 Letts I See Maths **Book 3**

Shape and Space

Measures and scales

Essential exercises

1 1 hectare (ha) = 10 000 m²

Convert the following areas from square metres to hectares.

(a) 7000 m²　　　(b) 425 000 m²　　　(c) 6970 m²　　　(d) 1 263 000 m²

2 Convert the following areas from square metres into square centimetres.

(a) 3 m²　　　(b) 6·25 m²　　　(c) 972 m²　　　(d) 0·25 m²

3 Convert the following volumes from cubic centimetres into litres.

(a) 6250 cm³　　　(b) 750 cm³　　　(c) 29 400 cm³　　　(d) 25 cm³

4 A ship travels on a bearing of 70° for 215 nautical miles, and then on a bearing of 82° for a further 175 nautical miles.

(a) Draw a sketch of the ship's journey.

(b) Construct an accurate scale drawing of the ship's journey.
(Scale: 50 nautical miles to 1 cm.)

(c) What is the ship's final distance and bearing from the starting point?

(d) Give instructions for the ship to return to its starting point in one journey.

5 The graph on the right shows the distance–time graph for Yosef's journey on a hill walk.

(a) If Yosef started walking at 1025, at what time would he reach B?

(b) How far is it from A to B?

(c) What was Yosef's average speed on the journey from A to B?

(d) What was Yosef's average speed on the journey from C to D?

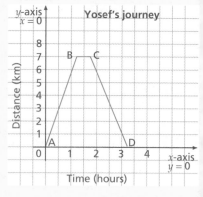

6 A rectangular plot of land is measured as 35 m by 27 m, to the nearest metre. Give the maximum and minimum area for the plot.

7 The density of air under normal conditions is about 1·2 kg/m³. Work out the mass of air in a room that measures 6 m by 4 m by 2·5 m.

Shape and Space

Challenging exercises

Radian measure: 2π radians = 360°; 1 radian (ᶜ) ≈ 57°

8 Use a calculator to convert the following angles from degrees to radians.

(a) 30°   (b) 45°   (c) 60°   (d) 90°   (e) 120°   (f) 180°   (g) 270°

9 Use a calculator to convert the following angles from radians to degrees.

(a) 1.5^c (b) 0.5^c (c) 2^c (d) 0.3^c (e) 5^c (f) 3.5^c (g) 4.5^c

10 Arc length is given by $s = r\theta$ and area of the sector by $\frac{1}{2}r^2\theta$, where θ is in radians.

Calculate the arc length and the area of the sector where r and θ are given as follows.

(a) $r = 4$ cm, $\theta = 0.8^c$ (b) $r = 6$ cm, $\theta = 1.5^c$

Problem-solving exercises

11 Use the conversion graph below to estimate the cost of food on the menu in euros.

Menu

Soup	£2·75
Salad	£4·50
Garlic Bread	£0·95
Fish & Chips	£6·25
Steak, Peas and Chips	£9·50
Grilled Pork Chop	£8·30
Vegetable Lasagne	£5·60
Pizza of the day	£3·40

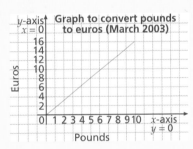

12 A car is advertised as accelerating from 0 to 60 m.p.h. in 30 seconds. Work out its acceleration.

Homework

Draw a distance–time graph to show one of the following journeys that you have completed recently.

(a) travel to and from school   (b) a walk in the country
(c) a car journey to visit someone   (d) a holiday journey.

Goals

By the end of this lesson you will be able to answer questions such as these:

- Describe how to calculate the volume of (a) a cylinder (b) a prism (c) a pyramid.

- Sketch the following, insert symbols for appropriate dimensions and write a formula for finding the volume of (a) a cylinder (b) a prism (c) a pyramid.

- Sketch the following, insert symbols for appropriate dimensions and write a formula for finding the surface area of (a) a cylinder (b) a prism (c) a pyramid.

Starter

1 Sketch the net for (a) a cylinder (b) a prism (c) a pyramid.

Demonstration 1

Volume of a pyramid

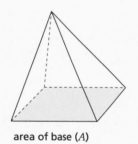

area of base (A)

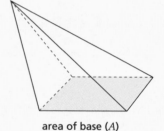

perpendicular height (h)

area of base (A)

$$\text{Volume} = \tfrac{1}{3} \times A \times h$$

Volume of a cone

area of base (A)

perpendicular height (h)

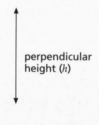

area of base (A)

$$\text{Volume} = \tfrac{1}{3} \times A \times h$$

 I See Maths **Book 3**

Demonstration 2

Cylinder

linear scale factor = m
area scale factor = m^2
volume scale factor = m^3

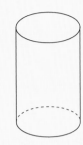

Pyramid

linear scale factor = m
area scale factor = m^2
volume scale factor = m^3

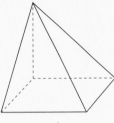

Cone

linear scale factor = m
area scale factor = m^2
volume scale factor = m^3

Key words   area scale factor   cone   cylinder   linear scale factor   pyramid
right cone   right cylinder   right pyramid   volume scale factor

Worked example

Exercise bank

1 A closed cylinder has radius of its cross-section 5·3 cm and height 7·2 cm.
Calculate its surface area.

Surface area = area of end × 2 + area of curved surface
Area of end = $\pi \times 5\cdot3^2 \times 2$ cm²
Area of curved surface = $2 \times \pi \times 5\cdot3 \times 7\cdot2$ cm²
Surface area = $\pi \times 5\cdot3^2 \times 2 + 2 \times \pi \times 5\cdot3 \times 7\cdot2$ cm²
= $\pi \times 2(5\cdot3^2 + 5\cdot3 \times 7\cdot2)$ cm²
= $132\cdot5\pi$ cm² (to 1 d.p.)

Plenary

   Discuss the Goals.

Shape and Space

Area and volume

Essential exercises

1 The prism on the right has a cross-section that is a trapezium. Its measurements are shown on the diagram.

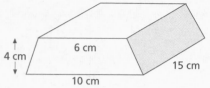

6 cm

4 cm

10 cm

15 cm

(a) Calculate the total surface area of the prism.

(b) Calculate the volume of the prism.

2 The circular cross-section of the cylinder on the right has a radius of 5 cm.

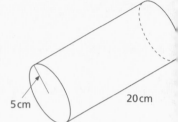

5 cm

20 cm

(a) Calculate the total surface area of the cylinder. (Use $\pi \approx 3\cdot14$.) Give your answer to three significant figures.

(b) Calculate the volume of the cylinder. (Use $\pi \approx 3\cdot14$.) Give your answer to three significant figures.

3

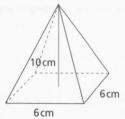

10 cm

6 cm

6 cm

The square-based pyramid on the left has a square base of side 6 cm and a perpendicular height of 10 cm.

Calculate the volume of the pyramid.

4

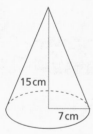

15 cm

7 cm

The cone on the left has a circular base of radius 7 cm and a perpendicular height of 15 cm.

Calculate the volume of the cone. (Use $\pi \approx 3\cdot14$.) Give your answer to three significant figures.

5

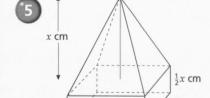

x cm

$\frac{1}{2}x$ cm

x cm

x cm

The shape on the left consists of a cuboid with length x cm, width x cm and height $\frac{1}{2}x$ cm, and a square-based pyramid with perpendicular height x cm.

Write an expression in x for the volume of this shape.

Challenging exercises

6

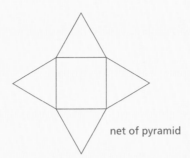

net of pyramid

The square-based pyramid above has a square base with sides 4 cm and a perpendicular height 6 cm.

(a) Calculate the volume of the pyramid.

(b) Calculate the area of the net of the pyramid.

7 A pyramid has as its base an equilateral triangle of sides 10 cm and a perpendicular height of 12 cm. Calculate the volume of the pyramid.

Problem-solving exercises

8 A litre of orange juice is sold in a cylindrical bottle with base diameter 7 cm. What is its height, to the nearest millimetre? (Use $\pi \approx 3 \cdot 14$.)

9 Chocolates are made in the shape of square-based pyramids with each edge of the square base 1·5 cm. Each chocolate has a volume of 1·5 cm³. What is the height of the chocolate pyramid?

10 What volume of steel is required to make a girder with cross-sectional area 190 cm² and length 10 m.

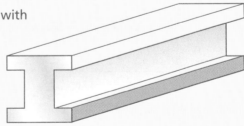

Homework

Design a container to hold 100 cm³ of speciality tea. Draw the net of the container to scale, giving its dimensions.

Letts I See Maths Book 3

Goals

By the end of this lesson you will be able to answer questions such as this:

👁 Discuss the relationship between sine and cosine, their calculator values, their graphs and their applications.

Starter

1 Check the coordinates on the graphs in Demonstration 1 by using a calculator.

Demonstration 1

$y = \sin \theta$

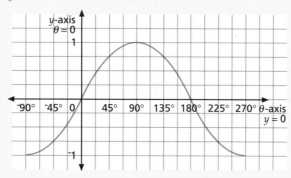

$y = \cos \theta$

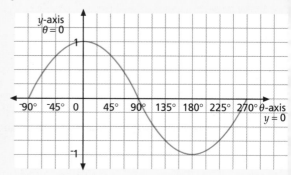

Unit circle

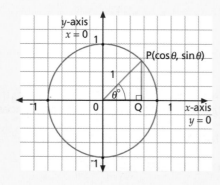

$\triangle OQP$ is similar
to $\triangle ABC$

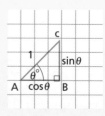

Letts I See Maths **Book 3**

Shape and Space

Demonstration 2

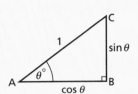

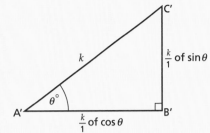

linear scale factor $\frac{k}{1}$

$\triangle ABC$ is similar to $\triangle A'B'C'$.

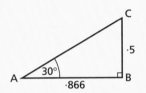

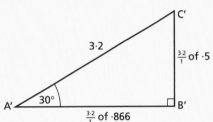

linear scale factor $\frac{3 \cdot 2}{1}$

$\triangle ABC$ is similar to $\triangle A'B'C'$.

> **Key words** $\cos \theta$ cosine $\sin \theta$ sine   unit circle

Worked example

Exercise bank

 Given $\triangle ABC$ in the diagram, show that:

(a) $\sin \theta = \frac{a}{b}$

(b) $\cos \theta = \frac{c}{b}$.

Draw $\triangle A'B'C'$ similar to $\triangle ABC$ so that $A'C' = 1$.

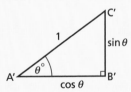

linear scale factor $\frac{b}{1}$

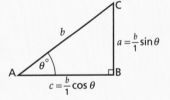

(a) $a = \frac{b}{1} \sin \theta$

$\sin \theta = \frac{a}{b}$

(b) $c = \frac{b}{1} \cos \theta$

$\cos \theta = \frac{c}{b}$

Plenary

◉ Examine the graphs of $y = \sin \theta$ and $y = \cos \theta$ and discuss the similarities and differences.

◉ Discuss the values of the sine and cosine functions for 0°, 180°, 270°, 360° and 450°.

◉ Discuss the (x, y) values on the unit circle for 0°, 180°, 270°, 360° and 450°.

Shape and Space

Trigonometry 1

Essential exercises

1 Calculate the lengths of the sides of the right-angled triangles marked with letters, to the nearest millimetre.

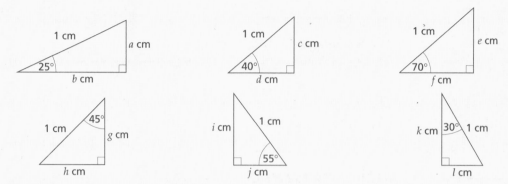

2 Calculate the lengths of the sides marked with letters, to the nearest millimetre.

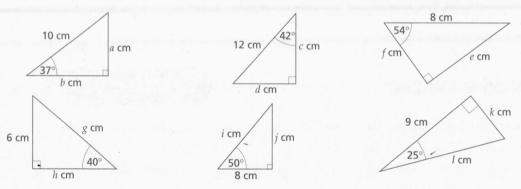

3 Calculate the angles marked with letters, to the nearest tenth of a degree.

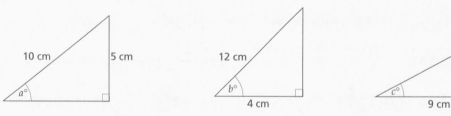

4 Calculate the lengths marked with letters, to the nearest millimetre.

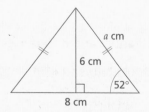

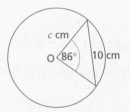

Letts I See Maths **Book 3**

Challenging exercise

5 ABCDEFGH is a regular octagon with sides of 2 cm. O is the intersection of the diagonals.

(a) Calculate the angle $x°$.

(b) Calculate the perpendicular height of △BOC. (Give the full calculator display.)

(c) Calculate the area of △BOC. (Give the full calculator display.)

(d) Hence, calculate the area of the octagon, to two significant figures.

(e) Write an expression for the area of an n-sided regular polygon.

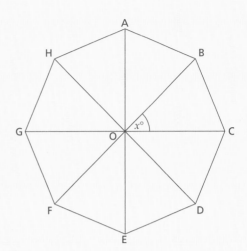

Problem-solving exercise

6 A wooden skateboarding ramp is being made. The ramp will be 1·5 m above the ground at its highest point and the slope of the ramp must be 35°.

What length (l m) of wood is needed, to the nearest 0·01 m?

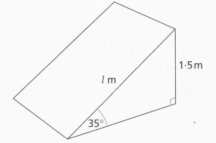

7 A 10 m ladder is placed against a wall. The greatest angle of inclination it can reach before slipping is 75°. What is the highest point it can be placed at on the wall, to the nearest 0·1 m?

Homework

Triangle ABC is enlarged, with scale factor 2·75, to A'B'C'.

Calculate the lengths of A'C', A'B' and C'B', to the nearest millimetre.

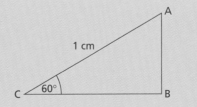

Shape and Space

Goals

By the end of this lesson you will be able to answer questions such as these:

- Use a calculator to evaluate the following.
  (a) sin 35·2°   (b) cos 35·2°   (c) sin⁻¹ ·5764   (d) cos⁻¹ ·8171

- Given △ABC, with angle BAC = 90°, a = 4·8 cm and angle ABC = 46°, calculate c.

- Given △ABC, with angle BAC = 90°, a = 4·8 cm and b = 3·5 cm, calculate angle ABC.

- Sketch a cuboid that is 4·8 cm by 6·3 cm by 17·2 cm and calculate the length of its longest diagonal.

Starter

1 Use a calculator to evaluate the following.
   (a) sin 35·2°   (b) cos 35·2°   (c) sin 123·7°   (d) cos 123·7°

2 Use a calculator to evaluate the following.
   (a) sin⁻¹ ·5764   (b) cos⁻¹ ·8171   (c) sin⁻¹ ·8319   (d) cos⁻¹ ⁻·5548

Demonstration 1

Given △ABC, calculate θ.

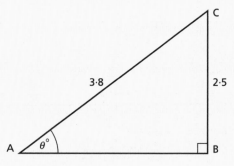

Draw △A′B′C′ similar to △ABC with unit hypotenuse.

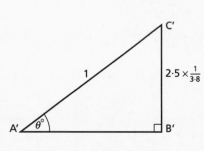

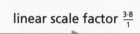
linear scale factor $\frac{3·8}{1}$

△A′B′C′ is similar to △ABC.

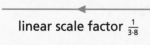
linear scale factor $\frac{1}{3·8}$

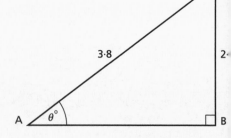

$\sin θ = 2·5 \times \frac{1}{3·8} = ·6579$
$θ = 41·1°$ (to 1 d.p.)

Letts I See Maths **Book 3**

Shape and Space

Demonstration 2

The sine rule

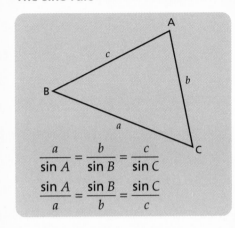

$$\frac{a}{\sin A} = \frac{b}{\sin B} = \frac{c}{\sin C}$$

$$\frac{\sin A}{a} = \frac{\sin B}{b} = \frac{\sin C}{c}$$

Calculate θ.

$$\frac{\sin A}{a} = \frac{\sin B}{b}$$

$$\frac{\sin \theta}{3 \cdot 8} = \frac{\sin 34°}{4 \cdot 2}$$

$$\sin \theta = \frac{\cdot 559}{4 \cdot 2} \times 3 \cdot 8$$

$$\sin \theta = \cdot 5059$$

$$\theta = 30 \cdot 4° \text{ (to 1 d.p.)}$$

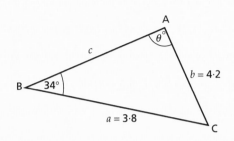

Key words $\sin \theta$ $\sin^{-1} \theta$ sine $\cos \theta$ $\cos^{-1} \theta$ cosine   inverse cosine   inverse sine

Worked example

Exercise bank 👉

① Look at the cuboid. Calculate $B\hat{A}C$.

$$AC^2 = 8^2 + 4^2 = 64 + 16 = 80$$

$$AC = \sqrt{80}$$

$$AB^2 = \left(\sqrt{80}\right)^2 + 4^2 = 80 + 16 = 96$$

$$AB = \sqrt{96}$$

Draw $\triangle A'B'C'$ similar to $\triangle ABC$ with unit hypotenuse.

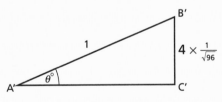

linear s.f. $= \frac{\sqrt{96}}{1}$

linear s.f. $= \frac{1}{\sqrt{96}}$

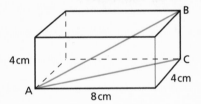

$$\sin \theta = 4 \times \frac{1}{\sqrt{96}} = \cdot 4082$$

$$\theta = 24 \cdot 1° \text{ (to 1 d.p.)}$$

Plenary

  Discuss the Goals.

Shape and Space

Essential exercises

1

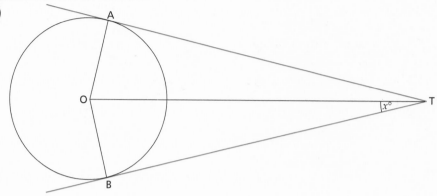

If TO = 4 m and AO = 25 cm, calculate B$\hat{\text{T}}$O.

2 ABCDEFGH is a cube of side 1 cm.

(a) Calculate the length of AC.

(b) Calculate the length of AG.

(c) Calculate the angle between AG and the edge GC.

(d) Calculate the angle between AG and the base EFGH.

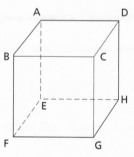

3 VABCD is a square-based pyramid. The edge of the square base is 4 cm. The height, VX, of the pyramid is 6 cm, and M is the midpoint of AB.

(a) Calculate the angle between the edge VB and the base ABCD, to the nearest 0·1°

(b) Calculate the angle between the face VAB and the base ABCD, to the nearest 0·1°.

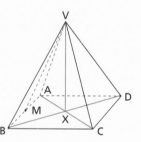

4 A is a place on the earth lying on the line of latitude 62°N. The radius of the earth is approximately 6400 km.

Calculate the radius, XA, of the line of latitude 62°N.

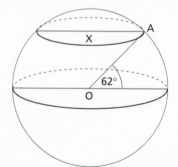

Letts I See Maths Book 3

Shape and Space

Challenging exercise

5 ΔABC is not a right-angled triangle. Let the perpendicular height of the triangle be h.

(a) Write down an expression for sin A in terms of h and c.

(b) Write down an expression for sin C in terms of h and a.

(c) Use your two expressions to show that $\frac{a}{\sin A} = \frac{c}{\sin C}$.

(d) Draw the perpendicular from A to BC and follow a similar argument to that above to show that $\frac{b}{\sin B} = \frac{c}{\sin C}$ and hence that $\frac{a}{\sin A} = \frac{b}{\sin B} = \frac{c}{\sin C}$ for any triangle ABC.

This is called the 'Sine rule'.

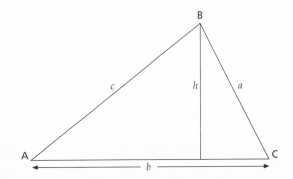

Problem-solving exercises

6 A road is built on four pillars, each 25 m apart. Calculate the height of each pillar.

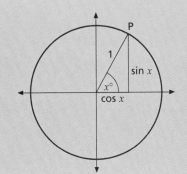

25 m 25 m 25 m 25 m

7 In the Louvre in Paris there is a square-based pyramid with height 21 m. The angle between the slant edge and the square base is 41°. Work out the length of the side of the square base.

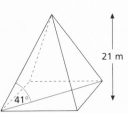

21 m

41°

Homework

$\cos^2 x + \sin^2 x = 1$

Use this formula to calculate the following to three significant figures.

(a) If sin x = 0·7986, find cos x.

(b) If cos x = 0·2756, find sin x.

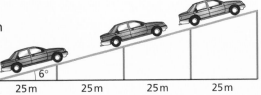

1 Calculate the angles marked by letters in the circles below. In all cases, O is the centre of the circle.

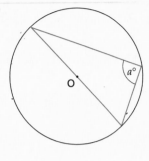
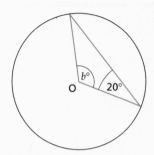
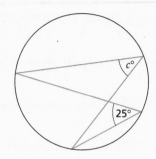

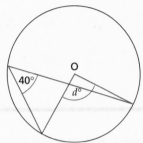
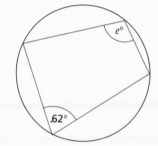
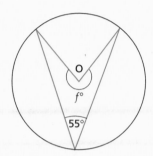

2 Draw the front elevation, side elevation and plan for each of the following shapes

(a) cuboid
(b) tetrahedron
(c) square-based pyramid

3 (a) Draw axes for ⁻10 ≤ x ≤ 10 and ⁻10 ≤ y ≤ 10.

(b) Draw the object ABC with vertices A(1, 1), B(4, 1) and C(4, 3).

(c) Translate △ABC with vector $\binom{2}{3}$ and label the image A′B′C′.

(d) Reflect △ABC in the line $x = {}^-2$ and label the image A″B″C″.

(e) Rotate △ABC 270° anticlockwise about the origin and label the image A‴B‴C‴.

(f) Enlarge △ABC with scale factor 2 and centre of enlargement (0, 0), and label the image A‴B‴C‴.

(g) In which of the transformations is the image congruent to the object?

4 Use a ruler and pair of compasses to construct the circle that circumscribes the triangle ABC which has sides AB = 3 cm, CB = 4 cm and AC = 5 cm.

Letts I See Maths Book 3

5 A ship travels on a bearing of 055° for 175 nautical miles, and then on a bearing of 075° for a further 200 nautical miles.

(a) Draw a sketch of the ship's journey.

(b) Draw an accurate scale drawing of the ship's journey. (Use a scale of 50 nautical miles to 1 cm.)

(c) What is the ship's final distance and bearing from the starting point?

(d) Give instructions for the ship to return to the starting point in one journey.

6 (a) Calculate the volume of a prism with cross-sectional area 124 cm² and height 23 cm.

(b) Calculate the volume of a cylinder with circular base of diameter 10 cm. (Use π ≈ 3·14.)

(c) Calculate the volume of a square-based pyramid with edges of the square base 5 cm and perpendicular height 8 cm.

(d) Calculate the volume of a cone with circular base of radius 9 cm and perpendicular height 22 cm.

7 Draw an accurate net of a tetrahedron with edge lengths 3 cm.

8 Calculate the lengths of the sides of the right-angled triangles below that are marked with letters, to the nearest millimetre.

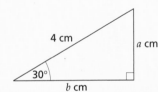

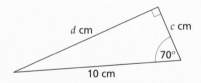

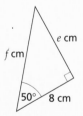

9 Calculate the angles marked with letters, to the nearest tenth of a degree.

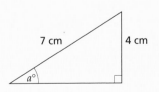

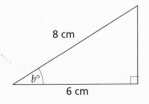

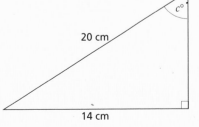

Shape and Space

1 Work out the value of x in each of the diagrams below.

(a)

(b)

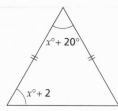

(c)

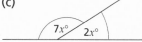

(d)

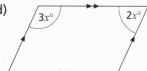

2 (a) Write down the sum of the interior angles of any octagon.

(b) Write down the sum of the exterior angles of any polygon.

3 Calculate the length of each of the lines marked with the letter x.
Give your answer to the nearest millimetre.

(a)

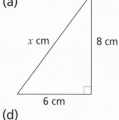

(b)

(c)

(d)

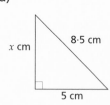

(e)

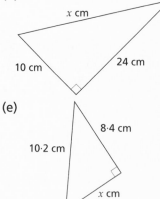

(f)

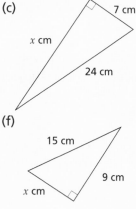

4 (a) Calculate the length of the diagonal of a square of side 5 cm.

(b) Calculate the height of an equilateral triangle of side 6 cm.

(c) Calculate the length of BC in $\triangle$ABC, shown on the right, where AB = 20 cm and AX = 15 cm.

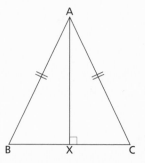

Letts I See Maths Book 3

5 Calculate the length of the diagonal FC if the cube ABCDEFGH has edge length of 4 cm.

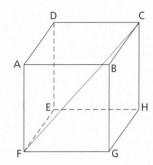

6 △ABC is an isosceles triangle. Given that AB = AC and X is the midpoint of BC, prove that:

(a) $A\hat{B}C = A\hat{C}B$

(b) AX bisects $B\hat{A}C$.

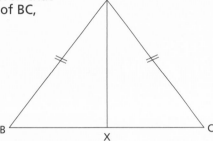

7 (a) Explain why △ABC is similar to △AXY.

(b) Calculate the length of BC.

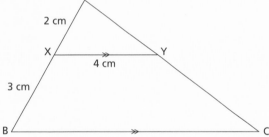

8 A cube has edge length of 4·2 cm.

(a) Calculate the total surface area of the cube.

(b) Calculate the volume of the cube.

(c) The cube is enlarged with a scale factor 2·5. Calculate:
(i)   the edge-length of the enlarged cube
(ii) the total surface area of the enlarged cube
(iii) the volume of the enlarged cube.

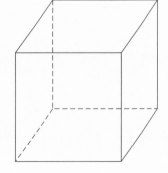

9 A map is drawn to the scale 1 : 50000. What area on the map represents an area of 1 hectare of land?

10 Calculate the circumference and area of a circle with radius 2·5 cm. (Use $\pi \approx 3·14$.)

Goals

By the end of this lesson you will be able to answer questions such as these:

- 👁 Discuss the main features of frequency diagrams and box-and-whisker diagrams.

- 👁 Draw and interpret cumulative frequency diagrams.

Starter

1 Study the data and calculate the median and the mean.

Raw data for a sample: variable x

15·47	15·65	15·78	15·86	16·00	16·14	16·19	16·24	16·28	16·30	16·35	16·40	16·45	16·46	16·48
16·48	16·48	16·50	16·52	16·54	16·60	16·80	17·00	17·25	17·32	17·42	17·44	17·44	17·48	17·50

2 Study the data and estimate the median and the mean.

(a) Grouped data for a sample – equal class intervals

x	$f(x)$
$15·45 \leq x < 16·45$	12
$16·45 \leq x < 17·45$	16
$17·45 \leq x < 18·45$	2

(b) Grouped data for a sample – equal class intervals

x	$f(x)$
$15·45 \leq x < 15·75$	2
$15·75 \leq x < 16·05$	3
$16·05 \leq x < 16·35$	5
$16·35 \leq x < 16·65$	11
$16·65 \leq x < 16·95$	1
$16·95 \leq x < 17·25$	1
$17·25 \leq x < 17·55$	7

Demonstration 1

Grouped frequency diagram

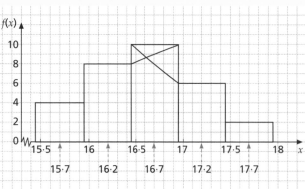

Box-and-whisker diagram for raw data

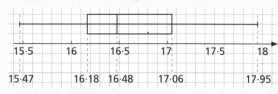

x	$f(x)$
$15·45 \leq x < 15·95$	4
$15·95 \leq x < 16·45$	8
$16·45 \leq x < 16·95$	10
$16·95 \leq x < 17·45$	6
$17·45 \leq x < 17·95$	2

Estimated mean = 16·6 (to 1 d.p.)
Estimated median = 16·6

Letts I See Maths Book 3

Handling Data

Demonstration 2

x	Cumulative frequency
$15{\cdot}45 \leq x < 15{\cdot}95$	4
$15{\cdot}45 \leq x < 16{\cdot}45$	12
$15{\cdot}45 \leq x < 16{\cdot}95$	22
$15{\cdot}45 \leq x < 17{\cdot}45$	28
$15{\cdot}45 \leq x < 17{\cdot}95$	30

Cumulative frequency diagram

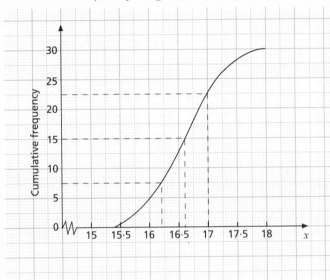

$Q_1 = 16{\cdot}22$
$Q_2 = 16{\cdot}58$
$Q_3 = 17{\cdot}00$

Key words   box-and-whisker diagram   class boundaries   class intervals   class widths
cumulative frequency diagram   cumulative percentage frequency table
frequency diagram   lower quartile   median   upper quartile

Exercise bank 👉

Plenary

👁 Discuss the Goals.

👁 Discuss how to draw a cumulative percentage frequency table for the data in Demonstration 2.

Essential exercises

1 All the pupils in Y9 of Camelbrook School took part in a charity cross-country race.
The results are shown in the table on the right.

(a) Copy the table and complete the cumulative frequency column.

(b) How many students took less than 42 minutes to complete the race?

(c) What percentage of students took less than 54 minutes to complete the race?

Time taken x minutes	Frequency $f(x)$	Cumulative frequency
$30 \leq x < 34$	4	
$34 \leq x < 38$	25	
$38 \leq x < 42$	32	
$42 \leq x < 46$	45	
$46 \leq x < 50$	50	
$50 \leq x < 54$	42	
$54 \leq x < 58$	36	
$58 \leq x < 62$	6	
Total	240	

(d) Draw a frequency diagram to represent the data.

(e) Draw a cumulative frequency diagram to represent the data.

(f) Use the cumulative frequency diagram to estimate Q_1 (the lower quartile), Q_2 (the median) and Q_3 (the upper quartile).

(g) Draw a box-and-whisker diagram to represent the data.

(h) Estimate the mean average time taken to complete the race.

(i) Estimate the mode from the frequency diagram.

(j) Compare the values of the mode, median and mean, and discuss which value best represents the data.

(k) Discuss the merits of each of the different ways of representing the data.

2 The cumulative frequency diagram on the right shows the heights of a sample of school students.

(a) Use the diagram to estimate:
Q_1 (the lower quartile),
Q_2 (the median) and
Q_3 (the upper quartile).

(b) Draw a box-and-whisker diagram to represent this data.

(c) Use the information to describe the heights of the students.

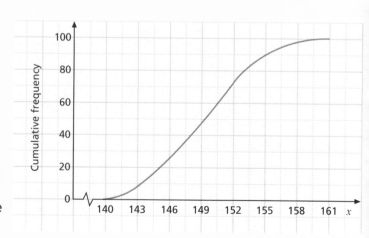

Handling Data

Letts I See Maths **Book 3**

Cumulative frequency

Challenging exercise

3 The grouped frequency table on the right shows the science test results for two classes, Class M and Class N.

(a) Draw the cumulative frequency diagram for each population.

(b) Use the diagrams to estimate Q_1, Q_2 and Q_3 for each population.

(c) The pass mark was set at 55%. How many students in each class passed the test?

(d) Estimate the 60th percentile for each population.

(e) Compare the test results for the two classes.

Mark x%	Frequency for Class M $f(x)$	Frequency for Class N $g(x)$
$0 \leq x < 10$	0	1
$10 \leq x < 20$	0	1
$20 \leq x < 30$	2	3
$30 \leq x < 40$	4	4
$40 \leq x < 50$	5	5
$50 \leq x < 60$	7	5
$60 \leq x < 70$	6	4
$70 \leq x < 80$	4	3
$80 \leq x < 90$	2	2
$90 \leq x < 100$	0	2
Total	30	30

Problem-solving exercise

4 The grouped frequency table on the right provides details of the annual salaries of one hundred employees randomly selected from a company.

(a) Draw a frequency diagram to represent this data.

(b) Complete the cumulative frequency column in the table and draw a cumulative frequency diagram.

(c) Use the cumulative frequency diagram to estimate Q_1 (the lower quartile), Q_2 (the median) and Q_3 (the upper quartile).

(d) Estimate the percentage of employees earning between £25 000 and £40 000.

(e) Discuss using the median and the mean for describing the average salary of the employees in this data set.

(f) Write a short report describing the salaries of the employees in this company.

Salary x in thousands of pounds	Frequency $f(x)$	Cumulative frequency
$17 \leq x < 20$	18	
$20 \leq x < 23$	20	
$23 \leq x < 26$	16	
$26 \leq x < 29$	18	
$29 \leq x < 32$	16	
$32 \leq x < 35$	6	
$35 \leq x < 38$	3	
$38 \leq x < 41$	0	
$41 \leq x < 44$	2	
$44 \leq x < 47$	0	
$47 \leq x < 50$	0	
$50 \leq x < 53$	1	
Total	100	

Homework

Use the glossary to help you know how to define and calculate the mode, median and mean of a set of data.

Flexibility in using statistics

Goals

By the end of this lesson you will be able to answer questions such as these:

- Describe how to calculate the mean, median and mode.

- Discuss the important features of each of the mean, median and mode.

- Discuss the symbols in the formulae for calculating the mean of a sample and a population.

Starter

1 Invent a data set with ten values of x (variable x, $n = 10$).

(a) Calculate the sum of the values of $x (\Sigma x)$.

(b) Calculate the mean of the data set $(\bar{x} = \frac{\Sigma x}{n})$.

(c) Calculate the deviation from the mean $(x - \bar{x})$ for each value of the variable x.

(d) Calculate the sum of the deviations from the mean $(\Sigma(x - \bar{x}))$.

(e) Identify the median (M_e).

(f) Discuss the mode (M_o).

Demonstration 1

Measures of central tendency

The median

M_e is found by identifying the middle score when the values of the variable x are listed in order of magnitude.

The median responds to the number of values of the variable that lie below or above it, but not to how far away the values may be.

$$5 \quad 5 \quad 6 \quad 7 \quad 8 \quad 9 \quad 10 \qquad M_e = 7$$
$$4 \quad 5 \quad 6 \quad 7 \quad 8 \quad 24 \quad 26 \qquad M_e = 7$$

The median is less responsive to extreme values than the mean.

The main use is for description.

$$x \longrightarrow x + a \Rightarrow M_e \longrightarrow M_e + a$$

$$x \longrightarrow x + a \Rightarrow M_o \longrightarrow M_o + a$$

The mode

M_o is found by identifying the value of the variable x that appears the most frequently. M_o is such that $f(x)$ is a maximum.

M_o is the only measure of central tendency that can be used for data using a nominal scale (e.g. eye colour).

Distributions can be uni-modal, bi-modal or multi-modal.

When data is grouped you describe the modal class.

The main use is for description.

$$x \longrightarrow kx \Rightarrow M_e \longrightarrow kM_e$$

$$x \longrightarrow kx \Rightarrow M_o \longrightarrow kM_o$$

Letts I See Maths **Book 3**

Demonstration 2

The mean

x is the variable, $f(x)$ is the frequency

Sample: $\overline{x} = \dfrac{\sum x}{n}$

Population: $\mu = \dfrac{\sum x}{N}$

Sample: $\overline{x} = \dfrac{\sum xf(x)}{\sum f(x)}$

Population: $\mu = \dfrac{\sum xf(x)}{\sum f(x)}$

For grouped data, use the midpoint of each interval.

Transforming the variable x

Adding the constant a to each value of the variable:

Sample: $x \longrightarrow x + a \Rightarrow \overline{x} \longrightarrow \overline{x} + a$

Population: $x \longrightarrow x + a \Rightarrow \mu \longrightarrow \mu + a$

Multiplying each value of the variable by a constant k:

Sample: $x \longrightarrow kx \Rightarrow \overline{x} \longrightarrow k\overline{x}$

Population: $x \longrightarrow kx \Rightarrow \mu \longrightarrow k\mu$

The mean is:

- responsive to the exact position of each score in the distribution

- more sensitive to extreme scores than the median or the mode

- the measure that gives an idea of **all** values of the variable

- very useful for analysis.

Key words central tendency   mean   median   modal class   mode
nominal scale   'responsive to …'

Exercise bank

Plenary

◉ Invent a grouped data set and discuss the mean, median and mode of its variable.

Flexibility in using statistics

Essential exercises

1 The heights, in centimetres, of a sample of thirty children are recorded in the table below.

140	142	142	145	146	146	147	148	149	150
150	150	151	151	152	152	152	153	153	154
154	154	156	156	156	157	157	157	163	165

(a) Calculate the mode, the median and the mean for the heights of the sample.

(b) Three students grouped the data into equal class intervals in the following ways:

Height x (in cm)	Frequency $f(x)$
$140 \leq x < 150$	9
$150 \leq x < 160$	19
$160 \leq x < 170$	2
Total	30

Height x (in cm)	Frequency $f(x)$
$140 \leq x < 145$	3
$145 \leq x < 150$	6
$150 \leq x < 155$	13
$155 \leq x < 160$	6
$160 \leq x < 165$	1
$165 \leq x < 170$	1
Total	30

Height x (in cm)	Frequency $f(x)$
$140 \leq x < 143$	3
$143 \leq x < 146$	1
$146 \leq x < 149$	4
$149 \leq x < 152$	6
$152 \leq x < 155$	8
$155 \leq x < 158$	6
$158 \leq x < 161$	0
$161 \leq x < 164$	1
$164 \leq x < 167$	1
Total	30

(i) Draw frequency diagrams and cumulative frequency diagrams for each set of grouped data and compare the information from each grouping.

(ii) Estimate the mode, the median and the mean for each set of grouped data.

(iii) Compare your estimated results in part (ii) with your calculations using the raw data in part (a).

(c) Think about using each of the mode, median and mean to describe this data. Discuss the quality of the information.

(d) Heights of 1000 children are recorded with a range from 138 cm to 172 cm. Discuss how you would group the data. Describe what diagrams you could draw. Discuss using measures of central tendency to represent the data.

2 Which measures of central tendency (mode, median, mean) would you find to help you answer the following questions? Give your reasons.

(a) What is the most popular colour of car?

(b) What is the average height of 4-year-old children?

(c) What is the average salary of teachers?

(d) What is the average length of words in a certain book or paper?

(e) What is the best-selling CD in a particular week?

(f) What is the average mark in a science test?

Letts I See Maths Book 3

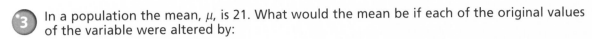
Challenging exercises

3 In a population the mean, μ, is 21. What would the mean be if each of the original values of the variable were altered by:

(a) adding 20?   (b) subtracting 13?   (c) multiplying by 2?   (d) dividing by 3?

4 Three groups of applicants for a job were given an aptitude test. Look at the data.

Group 1 $\bar{x}_1 = 52$, $n_1 = 10$ Group 2 $\bar{x}_2 = 54$, $n_2 = 20$ Group 3 $\bar{x}_3 = 60$, $n_3 = 25$

(a) What is the mean score for all fifty-five applicants?

(b) Write down a set of numbers with the characteristics of Group 1.

(c) The test scores were each out of a total of 75. What would be the mean for each group if the scores were changed into percentages?

Problem-solving exercises

5 A newspaper reported that more than half of all American families earned a below-average income. Could this be true?

6 The National Association of Manufacturers of Widgets has stated that the average wage for their workers is higher than the Widget Makers Union says it is. They have both been careful to do the correct calculations. Could both be right?

7 A teacher is interested in knowing whether Y10 or Y11, as a group, spend more hours per day studying. What measures of central tendency (mode, median, mean) should the teacher use, and why?

8 The Widget Company has to check the accuracy of its machines. A sample of ten widgets is measured and recorded. The Quality Manager calculates the percentage error for each widget. What measure of central tendency might the QM use, and why?

Homework

(a) Calculate the mean of this set of numbers.

3   7   8   10   11   15

(b) Use this set of numbers to write down a set of six numbers whose mean is each of the following.

(i) 12   (ii) 18   (iii) 0

Goals

> By the end of this lesson you will be able to answer questions such as these:

- 👁 Discuss the formula for standard deviation.
- 👁 Discuss the relationship between standard deviation and variance.

Starter

(a) Calculate the mean, median and range of the data set 2, 5, 6, 7,10.
(b) Calculate the mean, median and range of the data set 2, 2, 6, 10,10.
(c) Are these statistics sufficient to describe the data sets?

Demonstration 1

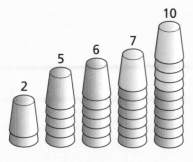

Sample A

$n = 5$ $\Sigma x = 30$ $\bar{x} = 6$

range = 8

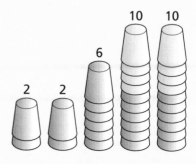

Sample B

$n = 5$ $\Sigma x = 30$ $\bar{x} = 6$

range = 8

	Sample A					Sample B				
Variable x	2	5	6	7	10	2	2	6	10	10
Mean	$\bar{x} = 6$					$\bar{x} = 6$				
Deviation from mean $(x - \bar{x})$	$(2-6)$ $= ^-4$	$(5-6)$ $= ^-1$	$(6-6)$ $= 0$	$(7-6)$ $= 1$	$(10-6)$ $= 4$	$(2-6)$ $= ^-4$	$(2-6)$ $= ^-4$	$(6-6)$ $= 0$	$(10-6)$ $= 4$	$(10-6)$ $= 4$
Square of deviation from mean $(x - \bar{x})^2$	$(^-4)^2 = 16$	$(^-1)^2 = 1$	$(0)^2 = 0$	$(1)^2 = 1$	$(4)^2 = 16$	$(^-4)^2 = 16$	$(^-4)^2 = 16$	$(0)^2 = 0$	$(4)^2 = 16$	$(4)^2 = 16$
$\Sigma(x - \bar{x})^2$	34					64				
Mean of squares of deviations from mean $\dfrac{\Sigma(x - \bar{x})^2}{n}$	$S^2 = 34 \div 5 = 6 \cdot 8$			variance		$S^2 = 64 \div 5 = 12 \cdot 8$			variance	
Square root of mean of squares of deviations from mean $\sqrt{\dfrac{\Sigma(x - \bar{x})^2}{n}}$	$S = \sqrt{6 \cdot 8} = 2 \cdot 6$		standard deviation			$S = \sqrt{12 \cdot 8} = 3 \cdot 6$		standard deviation		

S provides implicit information about the spread of the sample.
S gives a rough idea of the sample's 'spread-out-i-ness'.

Demonstration 2

Standard deviation for a sample

$$S = \sqrt{\frac{\Sigma(x - \bar{x})^2}{n}}$$

> S provides implicit information about the spread of the sample.
> S gives a rough idea of the sample's 'spread-out-i-ness'.

Standard deviation for a population

$$\sigma = \sqrt{\frac{\Sigma(x - \mu)^2}{N}}$$

> σ provides implicit information about the spread of the population.
> σ gives a rough idea of the population's 'spread-out-i-ness'.

Data set for a population

x	$f(x)$	$xf(x)$	$x - \mu$	$(x - \mu)^2$	$(x - \mu)^2 f(x)$
155	2	310	‾9·17	84·16	168·32
156	0	0	‾8·17	66·81	0·00
157	0	0	‾7·17	51·47	0·00
158	1	158	‾6·17	38·12	38·12
159	0	0	‾5·17	26·77	0·00
160	1	160	‾4·17	17·42	17·42
161	1	161	‾3·17	10·07	10·07
162	1	162	‾2·17	4·73	4·73
163	3	489	‾1·17	1·38	4·13
164	2	328	‾0·17	0·03	0·06
165	3	495	0·83	0·68	2·05
166	2	332	1·83	3·33	6·67
167	2	334	2·83	7·99	15·97
168	1	168	3·83	14·64	14·64
169	2	338	4·83	23·29	46·58
170	1	170	5·83	33·94	33·94
171	1	171	6·83	46·60	46·60
Total	23	3776			409·30
Mean		$\mu = 164.2$			Variance $\sigma^2 = 17\cdot80$ S.d. $\quad\quad\quad \sigma = 4\cdot22$

> **Key words**   For a population: standard deviation (σ)   variance (σ^2)
> For a sample: standard deviation (S)   variance (S^2)

Exercise bank ☞

Plenary

◉   Invent a data set and calculate the standard deviation of the variable.

◉   Add a constant to each value of your data set and discuss its standard deviation.

◉   Multiply each value of your data set by a constant and discuss its standard deviation.

Handling Data

Essential exercises

1 (a) Copy and complete the table below.

Variable	6	9	14	15	16	18	20	22	x
Mean									$\bar{x}$
Deviation from mean									$x - \bar{x}$
Square of deviation from mean									$(x - \bar{x})^2$
Sum of squares of deviations from mean									$\Sigma(x - \bar{x})^2$
Mean of squares of deviations from the mean (variance, S^2)									$\dfrac{\Sigma(x - \bar{x})^2}{n}$
Square root of mean of squares of deviations from the mean (standard deviation, S)									$\sqrt{\dfrac{\Sigma(x - \bar{x})^2}{n}}$

(b) Each value of the variable x is increased by 10 to give the following data set.

16   19   24   25   26   28   30   32

Calculate the mean and standard deviation for this data set.

(c) Each value of the variable x is increased by a multiple of 10 to give the following data set.

60   90   140   150   160   180   200   220

Calculate the mean and standard deviation for this data set.

(d) Write down a set of eight values of x with a standard deviation five times that of the original set in part (a).

2 The frequency table on the right gives the results of a spelling test, with marks out of ten.

(a) How many students took the test?

(b) Work out the mode, the median and the mean scores. (These are the measures of central tendency.)

(c) Calculate the standard deviation S for these marks. Give your answer to two decimal places.

(d) Draw a bar chart to represent the test results.

(e) Use the statistics you have calculated to help you describe the test results.

(f) Fifty students in a different school took the same test with the following results.

Spelling test marks

Mark x	Frequency $f(x)$
0	0
1	3
2	4
3	7
4	15
5	14
6	15
7	13
8	12
9	9
10	8

Mark x	0	1	2	3	4	5	6	7	8	9	10
Frequency $f(x)$	2	1	1	2	3	3	7	11	7	7	6

Compare the two sets of results using appropriate statistics.

Challenging exercises

 3 The heights of a sample of 300 children are recorded in the grouped frequency table on the right.

(a) Calculate the mid-class values.

(b) Calculate the frequency for each class interval.

(c) Calculate the mean of the sample.

(d) Calculate the standard deviation, S, of the sample.

(e) Use the statistics you have calculated to describe the sample.

Heights

Height x (in cm)	Cumulative frequency
$140 \leq x < 145$	7
$145 \leq x < 150$	23
$150 \leq x < 155$	139
$155 \leq x < 160$	253
$160 \leq x < 165$	284
$165 \leq x < 170$	292
$170 \leq x < 175$	300

4 (a) Calculate the mean, $\bar{x}$, and standard deviation, S_x, of the following data set, X.

| 4 | 5 | 5 | 6 | 6 | 6 | 7 | 8 | 9 |

(b) Each member of the data set is transformed using $y = 2x + 3$. Write down the new data set, Y, its mean, $\bar{y}$, and standard deviation, S_y.

Problem-solving exercise

5 Study the two sets of test results for a group of thirty students.

English test results

56	56	57	57	57	58	58	59	60	60
60	62	62	62	62	62	62	63	63	64
64	64	65	66	66	66	66	66	67	68

Maths test results

12	15	18	20	22	34	44	50	54	58
62	62	64	66	68	68	70	70	72	75
80	84	86	87	88	90	92	96	98	98

(a) Calculate the mode, median, mean and standard deviation for each test.

(b) Use an appropriate diagram to represent the two tests.

(c) Compare the two sets of test results.

(d) Angela had marks of 66 for English and 70 for maths. Comment on her results.

Homework

Describe two situations where you would expect the standard deviation of a data set to be small.

Goals

By the end of this lesson you will be able to answer questions such as these:

👁 Invent a data set and calculate:
   (a) its mean
   (b) its standard deviation
   (c) the z score for each value of the variable.

👁 Discuss the importance of z scores.

Starter

1 Standard deviation measures the amount of 'spread-out-i-ness' of the variable in a distribution. Discuss.

2 Discuss and compare these distributions.
   (a) $\bar{x} = 67$, $S = 15$ (b) $\bar{x} = 67$, $S = 23$ (c) $\bar{x} = 32$, $S = 3$

3 Discuss and compare these distributions.
   (a) $\mu = 67$, $\sigma = 15$ (b) $\mu = 67$, $\sigma = 23$ (c) $\mu = 32$, $\sigma = 3$

Demonstration 1

Sample A: 2   5   6   7   10

$n = 5$ $\Sigma x = 30$ $\bar{x} = 6$
range $= 8$ $S = \sqrt{6 \cdot 8}$

Sample	2	5	6	7	10
Mean			$\bar{x} = 6$		
$(x - \bar{x})$	$(2 - 6) = {}^-4$	$(5 - 6) = {}^-1$	$(6 - 6) = 0$	$(2 - 6) = 1$	$(10 - 6) = 4$
Standard deviation, S			$\sqrt{6 \cdot 8}$		
$\Sigma(x - \bar{x})$			0		
$z = \dfrac{(x - \bar{x})}{S}$	$\dfrac{{}^-4}{\sqrt{6 \cdot 8}}$	$\dfrac{{}^-1}{\sqrt{6 \cdot 8}}$	$\dfrac{0}{\sqrt{6 \cdot 8}}$	$\dfrac{1}{\sqrt{6 \cdot 8}}$	$\dfrac{4}{\sqrt{6 \cdot 8}}$
Σz			0		
$\bar{z} = \dfrac{\Sigma z}{n}$			$\bar{z} = 0$		

Standardising the scores

Compare each deviation to the standard deviation.

$(x - \bar{x})$ compared to S.

↓

$\dfrac{(x - \bar{x})}{S}$

$z = \dfrac{(x - \bar{x})}{S}$ is called the

standardised score.

Letts I See Maths **Book**

Demonstration 2

Data set for a population

$$\mu = 164 \cdot 2 \qquad \sigma = 4 \cdot 22$$

x	$x - \mu$	z
155	‾9·2	‾2·1
155	‾9·2	‾2·1
158	‾6·2	‾1·4
160	‾4·2	‾1·0
161	‾3·2	‾0·7
162	‾2·2	‾0·5
163	‾1·2	‾0·3
163	‾1·2	‾0·3
163	‾1·2	‾0·3
164	‾0·2	0·0
164	‾0·2	0·0
165	0·8	0·2
165	0·8	0·2
165	0·8	0·2
166	1·8	0·4
166	1·8	0·4
167	2·8	0·7
167	2·8	0·7
168	3·8	0·9
169	4·8	1·1
169	4·8	1·1
170	5·8	1·4
171	6·8	1·6
$\Sigma x = 3776$	$\Sigma(x - \mu) = 0$	$\Sigma z = 0$
$\sigma = 4 \cdot 22$		$z = 0$

Standardising the scores

Compare each deviation $(x - \mu)$ to the standard deviation, σ.

The standardised score is: $z = \dfrac{(x - \mu)}{\sigma}$

If the value of x is 165, then its standardised score is 0·2, to 1 d.p.

Key words   standard deviation   standardised score z score

 **Exercise bank**

Plenary

👁 A group of students had an English test and a maths test. For the group, $\mu_{\text{maths}} = 55$, $\sigma_{\text{maths}} = 10$, $\mu_{\text{english}} = 50$ and $\sigma_{\text{english}} = 5$. Alicia was in the group and she achieved a mark of 60 in maths and a mark of 50 in English. Discuss her performance in the tests.

 I See Maths Book 3

Handling Data

Essential exercises

1 Compare:

(a) 10 to 2   (b) 8 to ⁻2   (c) 3 to 21   (d) ⁻5 to ⁻30.

2 Work out the value of z in the following equations.

(a) $z = \frac{16 - 7}{3}$ (b) $z = \frac{4 - 9}{2 \cdot 5}$ (c) $z = \frac{24 - 48}{6 \cdot 4}$

3 Copy and complete the table below.

Sample	12	15	16	17	20
Mean					
$(x - \bar{x})$					
Standard deviation, S					
$\Sigma(x - \bar{x})$					
$z = \dfrac{(x - \bar{x})}{S}$					
Σz					
$\bar{z} = \dfrac{\Sigma z}{n}$					

4 Here are the results of eight students' geography and history tests.

Geography results Mean mark $\bar{x} = 18$ for the year group Standard deviation $S_x = 6\cdot2$								**History results** Mean mark $\bar{y} = 15$ for the year group Standard deviation $S_y = 8\cdot5$							
A	B	C	D	E	F	G	H	A	B	C	D	E	F	G	H
16	20	10	22	9	14	15	18	14	25	20	22	5	12	18	24
Deviation from the mean $(x - \bar{x})$								Deviation from the mean $(y - \bar{y})$							

(a) Copy the table and calculate the deviation from the mean for each mark.

(b) Use the formula $z = \frac{(x - \bar{x})}{S}$ to standardise each student's score.
Give your answers to two decimal places (2 d.p.).

(c) Student D had a mark of 22 in each subject. Does this mean that she performed equally well in both subjects?

(d) Student A had a mark of 16 in geography and a mark of 14 in history. In which test did he perform the best?

(e) A student decided to use her test scores to help her decide which subjects to study in Y10. Explain why this might not be the best information to use.

Challenging exercise

5 (a) Copy and complete the table below.

x	0	1	2	3	4	5	6	7	8	9	10
$f(x)$	1	2	3	5	9	10	8	6	4	1	1
$\overline{x}$											
$(\overline{x} - x)$											
S											
z											
$f(z)$	1	2	3	5	9	10	8	6	4	1	1

(b) Draw a bar chart to represent the distribution of x.
(c) Draw a frequency polygon to represent the distribution of x.
(d) Draw a frequency diagram to represent the distribution of z.
(e) Draw a frequency polygon to represent the distribution of z.
(f) Discuss the four diagrams you have drawn.
(g) Discuss the advantages of standardising the values of x.

Problem-solving exercise

6 Mrs Webb's tutor group compared their test results for maths and English.

English test results

56	56	57	57	57	58	58	59	60	60
60	62	62	62	62	62	62	63	63	64
64	64	65	66	66	66	66	66	67	68

Maths test results

12	15	18	20	22	34	44	50	54	58
62	62	64	66	68	68	70	70	72	75
80	84	86	87	88	90	92	96	98	98

(a) Calculate the mean mark for each test.
(b) Calculate the standard deviation for each test.
(c) Work out the standardised scores for each test.
(d) Discuss the results for the following students.

Student	English	Maths
Angela	66	70
David	56	22
George	62	50
Mary	68	72

Homework

Work out the standardised scores for the following students' test results where the mean score is 19 and the standard deviation 5·8.
Andrew 15   Sally 23   Emma 9   Frank 26

Letts I See Maths Book 3

Representing data

Goals

By the end of this lesson you will be able to answer questions such as these:

👁 Explain what type of data you are dealing with.

👁 Explain and justify your choice of representation.

Starter

 Discuss:

(a) $\frac{2}{4} = \frac{4}{8} = \frac{5}{10} = \frac{3}{6}$

(b) $2 : 4 = 4 : 8 = 5 : 10 = 3 : 6$

(c) $\frac{2}{4} = \frac{4}{8} = \frac{5}{10} \neq \frac{1 \cdot 5}{6}$

(d) $2 : 4 = 4 : 8 = 5 : 10 \neq 1 \cdot 5 : 6$

Demonstration 1

Raw data for a sample: variable x

15·47	15·65	15·78	15·86	16·00	16·14	16·19	16·24	16·28	16·30	16·35	16·40	16·45	16·46
16·48	16·48	16·48	16·50	16·52	16·54	16·60	16·80	16·98	17·00	17·02	17·04	17·16	17·18

Figure 1

$15·45 \leq x < 15·95$	4
$15·95 \leq x < 16·45$	8
$16·45 \leq x < 16·95$	10
$16·95 \leq x < 17·45$	6

Continuous data

Equal class intervals – use a frequency diagram.

Figure 2 Frequency diagram

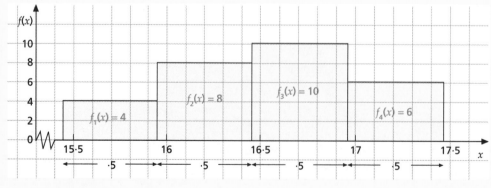

Letts I See Maths **Book 3**

Demonstration 2

Unequal class intervals
Use a histogram and frequency density.
Area equals frequency.
Total area equals total frequency.

Figure 3

$15\cdot45 \leq x < 15\cdot95$	4
$15\cdot95 \leq x < 16\cdot45$	8
$16\cdot45 \leq x < 16\cdot95$	10
$16\cdot95 \leq x < 17\cdot20$	6

Figure 4 Histogram

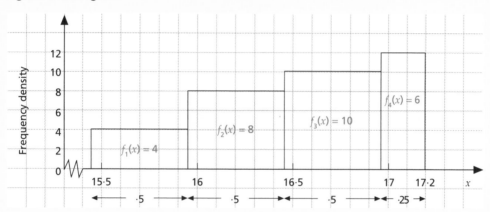

A	$A_1 = \cdot5 \times 4$	$A_2 = \cdot5 \times 8$	$A_3 = \cdot5 \times 10$	$A_4 = \cdot25 \times 12$
	$= 2$	$= 4$	$= 5$	$= 3$
$f(x)$	$f_1(x) = 4$	$f_2(x) = 8$	$f_3(x) = 10$	$f_4(x) = 6$
$A : f(x)$	$2 : 4 \quad =$	$4 : 8 \quad =$	$5 : 10 \quad =$	$3 : 6$

In a histogram: area under curve $\propto$ frequency

Key words   class width   frequency   grouped data   proportional

Exercise bank 👉

Plenary

👁 Discuss which of the following sets of data are discrete and which are continuous, and explain how you might represent them.

(a) estimated lengths of lines

(b) numbers of letters in words

(c) heights of fifteen-year-old boys

(d) preferred modes of travel

(e) test scores

Letts I See Maths Book 3

Handling Data

Representing data

Essential exercises

1 Ninety students took an examination in which the maximum mark possible was 100. The following results were obtained and recorded in a grouped frequency table.

Marks	10–19	20–29	30–39	40–49	50–59	60–69	70–79	80–89
Frequency	1	10	14	22	20	12	7	4

(a) What is each class width?
(b) What is the modal class?
(c) Draw a frequency diagram to represent this data.
(d) Use the mid values of the class intervals to draw a frequency polygon to represent this data.
(e) Draw a cumulative frequency diagram to represent this data and use it to estimate the median mark.
(f) Discuss the merits of each diagram.

2 In a garden centre, the whole stock of wooden stakes is sorted according to their lengths. Jack measured each stake, to the nearest centimetre, and recorded the results in a table.

Length x (in cm)	$15 \leq x < 20$	$20 \leq x < 30$	$30 \leq x < 45$	$45 \leq x < 55$	$55 \leq x < 60$
Frequency $f(x)$	5	24	87	80	25

(a) Work out the class width for each class interval.
(b) Draw a histogram to represent this data.
(c) What is the modal class for this set of data?
(d) Estimate the median and mean for this set of data.
(e) Draw a frequency polygon for this data.
(f) Discuss the merits of the diagrams and calculations you have made.

3 Study the histogram below.

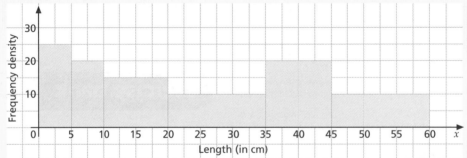

(a) Use the histogram above to complete the frequency table on the right.
(b) What is the modal class for this set of data?
(c) Estimate the median and mean value of x.

Variable x	Frequency
$0 \leq x < 5$	
$5 \leq x < 10$	
$10 \leq x < 20$	
$20 \leq x \leq 35$	
$35 \leq x < 45$	
$45 \leq x < 60$	

Challenging exercises

4 A frequency polygon is drawn below.

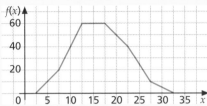

Use the diagram above to draw the corresponding histogram.

5 Sketch a histogram for a frequency distribution in which the mode is larger than the mean.

6 Sketch the outline of a histogram with a positive skew.

Problem-solving exercise

7 A market gardener sorts tomatoes according to their mass. The table below shows the numbers of tomatoes picked from two greenhouses on one day.

Greenhouse A		Greenhouse B	
Mass x (in grams)	Frequency $f(x)$	Mass x (in grams)	Frequency $f(x)$
$10 \leq x < 20$	220	$10 \leq x < 20$	30
$20 \leq x < 25$	180	$20 \leq x < 25$	140
$25 \leq x < 30$	150	$25 \leq x < 30$	370
$30 \leq x < 40$	360	$30 \leq x < 40$	580
$40 \leq x < 50$	450	$40 \leq x < 50$	310
$50 \leq x < 60$	230	$50 \leq x < 60$	90
$60 \leq x < 65$	110	$60 \leq x < 65$	25

Write a report to compare the day's pickings from the two greenhouses and use appropriate diagrams to illustrate your report.

Use a selection of the following diagrams and statistics.

> mode   median   mean   standard deviation   histogram
> cumulative frequency diagram   frequency polygon

Homework

(a) Explain the difference between a frequency diagram and a histogram.

(b) Use the glossary to help you explain the following terms.

   frequency table   frequency diagram   frequency polygon

Probability

Goals

By the end of this lesson you will be able to answer questions such as these:

- 👁 Give an example of two mutually exclusive events.

- 👁 Give an example of two independent events.

- 👁 Describe the addition rule of probability and when to use it.

- 👁 Describe the multiplication rule of probability and when to use it.

Starter

1 Describe a calculation of theoretical probability.

2 Describe an estimation of experimental probability.

3 Discuss:
(a) Rolling a die is an incident.
(b) Rolling a die and recording whether or not the score is a 'four' is a trial.
(c) I rolled a die and was interested when the score was a 'four'. Getting a score of 'four' is an event.

4 A die is rolled. John was interested in trials with the outcome 'four' and Jane was interested in trials with the outcome 'prime'. Which trial was favourable to both 'four' and 'prime'?

Demonstration 1

Figure 1	Figure 2
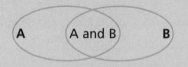	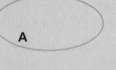
$P(A)$ is the probability of event A. $P(B)$ is the probability of event B. $P(A$ and $B)$ is the probability of event A **and** event B occurring together. <div align="center">$0 < P(A$ and $B) \leq 1$</div>	$P(A)$ is the probability of event A. $P(B)$ is the probability of event B. $P(A$ and $B)$ is the probability of event A **and** event B occurring together. <div align="center">$P(A$ and $B) = 0$</div> <div align="center">Event A and event B are MUTUALLY EXCLUSIVE</div>
<div align="center">Event A and event B are NOT MUTUALLY EXCLUSIVE</div> <div align="center">$P(A$ or $B) = P(A) + P(B) - P(A$ and $B)$</div>	<div align="center">**Addition Rule:** When events A and B are mutually exclusive, $P(A$ or $B) = P(A) + P(B)$</div>

Demonstration 2

Events A and B are independent if the occurrence of event A does not alter the probability of event B occurring and the occurrence of event B does not alter the probability of event A occurring.

Multiplication Rule: If event A and event B are independent,

$$P(A \text{ and } B) = P(A)P(B)$$

Rolling two dice

1st die   2nd die

$P(6) = \frac{1}{6}$

$P(6) = \frac{1}{6}$ $P(6) = \frac{1}{6}$ $P(6 \text{ and } 6) \quad = \frac{1}{6} \times \frac{1}{6}$

$P(6') = \frac{5}{6}$

$P(6 \text{ and } 6') \quad = \frac{1}{6} \times \frac{5}{6}$

$P(6' \text{ and } 6) \quad = \frac{5}{6} \times \frac{1}{6}$

$P(6') = \frac{5}{6}$ $P(6) = \frac{1}{6}$

$P(6') = \frac{5}{6}$ $P(6' \text{ and } 6') = \frac{5}{6} \times \frac{5}{6}$

Multiplication Rule for two independent events

four mutually exclusive events

$P[(6 \text{ and } 6) \text{ or } (6' \text{ and } 6')] = P(6 \text{ and } 6) + P(6' \text{ and } 6')$ ← Addition Rule for mutually exclusive events

$$= \frac{1}{6} \times \frac{1}{6} + \frac{5}{6} \times \frac{5}{6}$$

Key words and   dependent events   event   incident   independent events
mutually exclusive events   not mutually exclusive events   or   trial

Exercise bank

Plenary

◉   Discuss the Goals

◉   Discuss how to avoid confusing mutually exclusive events and independent events.

Letts I See Maths Book 3

Probability

Essential exercises

1 The numbers 1 to 8 are written on each face of a regular octahedral die. When the die is thrown, each number is equally likely to occur. The outcome of throwing the die is a number, n.

Work out the following theoretical probabilities.

(a) $P(n = 5)$ (b) $P(n = 0)$ (c) $P(n$ is even$)$ (d) $P(n$ is a square number$)$

(e) $P(n$ is prime$)$ (f) $P(n < 6)$ (g) $P(n > 0)$ (h) $P(n$ is a cubic number$)$

2 Copy and complete the possibility space diagram on the right which shows the total of the two numbers scored when throwing two regular octahedral dice.

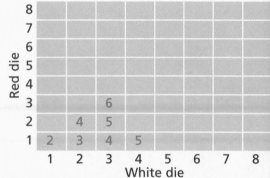

(a) Is the number on the red die dependent on the number on the white die?

(b) What is the total number of outcomes?

(c) What is the theoretical probability of getting a total of 5 when throwing the two die?

(d) What is the most frequent total? Explain your answer.

(e) What is the highest possible total?

(f) Work out the probabilities of getting the following totals, t.

     (i) $P(t = 10)$ (ii) $P(t = 1)$ (iii) $P(t > 8)$ (iv) $P(t < 14)$

3 A company makes microchips for computer games. Samples of ten microchips are tested throughout each day to check whether any are defective. Here are the results of tests on one particular day.

	Sample A	Sample B	Sample C	Sample D	Sample E	Sample F	Sample G	Sample H
Number defective	1	0	2	1	0	1	2	1
Relative frequency as a vulgar fraction								
Relative frequency as a decimal fraction								

(a) Complete the table above by writing the relative frequency as a vulgar fraction and then as a decimal fraction.

(b) From the experimental data, after testing eighty microchips, what is the probability of getting one that is defective?

(c) Use this probability to estimate the number of faulty microchips in a batch of 50 000.

Letts I See Maths **Book 3**

Challenging exercises

4 Which of the following events are mutually exclusive and which are dependent?

(a) Selecting a student at random from a class list followed by selecting another student at random from the same class list.
(b) Selecting two different students at random to represent a class.
(c) Selecting a ball from a bag, replacing it and selecting another ball from the same bag.
(d) Selecting a ball from a bag, keeping it and selecting another ball from a bag.

5 The probability that a train arrives on time in Paddington is $\frac{3}{5}$ and the probability of a train arriving on time in Euston is $\frac{3}{4}$. For two trains selected at random from each station, find:

(a) the probability that they both arrive on time
(b) the probability that only one of them arrives on time
(c) the probability that neither arrives on time.

6 The probability of a golfer sinking a put is $\frac{2}{5}$. Find the probability that, for three successive puts, the golfer sinks:

(a) all three   (b) less than three   (c) at least two.

Problem-solving exercise

7 A game for two players is played with an ordinary pack of cards with aces and picture cards (jack, queen or king) valued as ten. The game consists of selecting two cards, adding their values and then replacing them. The first player selects a heart and a spade.

(a) Produce a table showing all the possible totals with the two cards.
(b) What is the highest possible score? What is the lowest possible score?
(c) What score has the highest probability?
(d) What is the probability of the player selecting two picture cards?
(e) To stay in the game a player has to score a total greater than 10. What is the probability of this player staying in the game?
(f) A second player selects two clubs. Produce a table showing all the possible totals with these two cards.
(g) Which player has the higher chance of staying in the game?

Homework

(a) You throw an ordinary unbiased die and get a six. You throw the die again. Are the chances of getting another six (i) higher (ii) lower (iii) the same as the first time?

(b) You select a red ball from a bag containing six red, four blue and five green balls. You keep the ball and select another ball from the bag. Is the probability of getting another red ball (i) greater (ii) less than (iii) the same as your first selection?

Interpreting diagrams

Goals

By the end of this lesson you will be able to answer questions such as these:

- Invent data sets to illustrate that you know what is meant by:
  - (a) discrete data
  - (b) continuous data
  - (c) grouped data
  - (d) class width in grouped data
  - (e) mid value of a class in grouped data.

- Describe the important feature of a histogram.

- Discuss the area under the graph of a probability density function plotted against x.

Starter

1 Calculate the unknown for each of these (A = area, h = height, w = width).

(a)
$A = 2$ $h = 1$
w

(b)
$A = \cdot 1$ h
$w = 1$

(c)
$A = \frac{1}{10}$ h
$w = 1$

(d)
$A = \frac{1}{20}$ h
$w = 1$

(e)
$A = \frac{1}{20}$ h
$w = \cdot 5$

(f)
$A = \frac{1}{6}$ h
$w = 1$

(g)
$A = \frac{1}{6}$ h
$w = \frac{1}{3}$

(h)
A $h = 1$
$w = \frac{1}{3}$

(i)
$A = \cdot 2$ h
$w = \cdot 01$

(j)
$A = \cdot 3$ h
$w = \cdot 2$

Demonstration 1

Experiment
Random selection of one number from 0, 1, 2, 3, 4, 5, 6, 7, 8, 9
Large number of trials = N
$\frac{f(x)}{N} \approx P(x)$

> discrete data

Figure 1 Probability distribution

> height represents probability

Experiment
Random selection of any number from $0 \leq x < 10$
Large number of trials = N

> continuous data

> area represents probability

Figure 2 Histogram

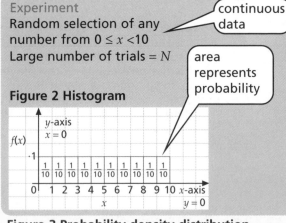

Figure 3 Probability density distribution

> probability density

Class width = 1
Area $A_1 = \cdot 1$
Height = $\cdot 1$

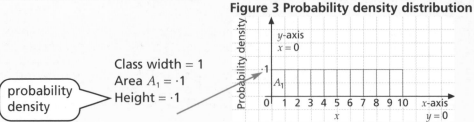

Letts I See Maths Book 3

Demonstration 2

Figure 1 Probability density function

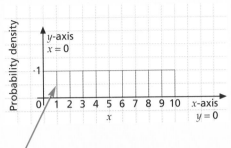

Area = ·1 $\quad\Big)\Rightarrow$ Height = ·1
Class width = 1 $\quad/\Rightarrow$ Probability density = ·1

Figure 2 Probability density function

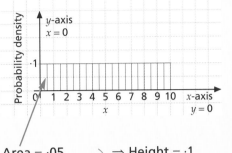

Area = ·05 $\quad\Big)\Rightarrow$ Height = ·1
Class width = ·5 $\quad/\Rightarrow$ Probability density = ·1

Figure 3 Probability density function

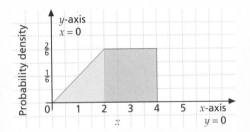

We can see that $P(2 \leq x < 4) > P(0 \leq x < 2)$.

Figure 4 Probability density function

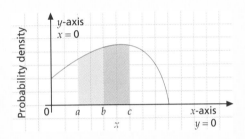

We can see that $P(a < x < b) < P(b < x < c)$.

Key words   class width in grouped data   continuous data   discrete data
grouped data   histogram   mid value of a class in grouped data
probability density function

Exercise bank 👉

Plenary

👁 Discuss the Goals..

👁 Discuss the idea of 'Probability density function', trying to be clear about how
the word 'density' is being used.

Letts I See Maths Book 3

Exercise Bank Exercise Bank Exercise Bank

Essential exercises

1 The diagrams below have all lost their titles. Match each diagram to the correct title from this list.

(a) bar chart
(b) pie chart
(c) frequency table
(d) frequency diagram
(e) frequency polygon
(f) histogram
(g) cumulative frequency diagram
(h) box-and-whisker diagram
(i) stem-and-leaf diagram
(j) scatter diagram
(k) probability density function

(i)

$0 \leq x < 5$	2
$5 \leq x < 10$	9
$10 \leq x < 20$	15
$20 \leq x < 35$	4
$35 \leq x < 45$	26
$45 \leq x < 60$	3

(ii)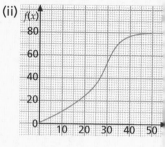

(iii)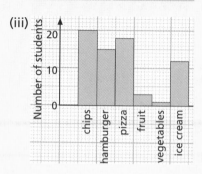

(iv)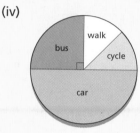

(v)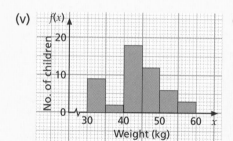

(vi)

```
Stem   Leaf
 1   7 7 8 9
 2   0 0 0 0 1 1 1 1 1 1 1 2 2 2
 3   0 0 0 1
 4   0 1
```

(vii)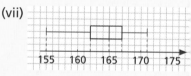

(viii)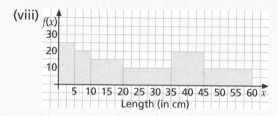

(ix)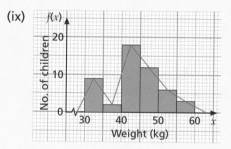

(x)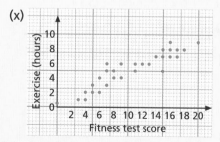

(xi)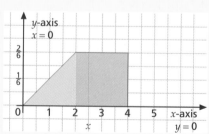

2 Which of the diagrams in Exercise 1 would you use to represent (a) discrete data (b) continuous data?

Letts I See Maths **Book 3**

Handling Data

Challenging exercises

(a) Describe the frequency distribution that is represented by the cumulative frequency diagram on the right.

(b) Sketch a frequency diagram to represent this data.

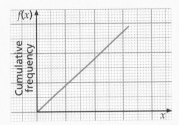

(a) Describe the frequency distribution that is represented by the frequency diagram on the right.

(b) Sketch the cumulative frequency diagram to represent this distribution.

(c) Describe the shape of the cumulative frequency diagram.

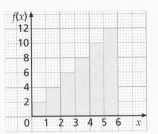

5

(a) Describe the frequency distribution that is represented by the cumulative frequency diagram on the right.

(b) Sketch the frequency diagram to represent this distribution.

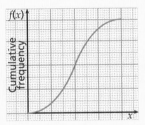

Problem-solving exercise

6 Darren counted the number of letters in each word of a sample section in a book and drew the diagram on the right. Write a report explaining his findings.

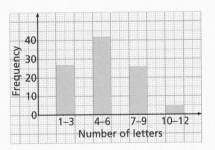

Homework

Use the glossary to help you learn the meanings of the following terms:

discrete data; continuous data; bar chart; frequency diagram; histogram

Letts | See Maths **Book 3**

Handling Data

Goals

By the end of this lesson you will be able to answer questions such as these:

👁 Describe the probability density function of the normal curve.

👁 Discuss the area under the curve of a probability density function.

👁 Specify the area $\Phi(z)$ in the standardised normal curve of a probability density function.

Starter

1 Identify the variable in these distributions:
(a) 200 people estimate the length of a stick
(b) 350 people pour out roughly half a litre of water and measure the actual quantity poured
(c) 327 people throw a dart at a point marked on the wall and measure the height at which their darts hit the wall.

2 Check in the three activities in question 1 that:
(a) all the variables are continuous
(b) the distributions are likely to be symmetric about the mean
(c) the probability of getting a result in a certain interval will decrease with the distance of the interval from the mean.

Demonstration 1

Normal distribution: probability density functions

Figure 1

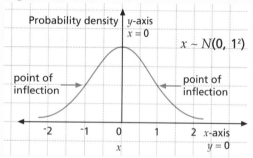

$x \sim N(0, 1^2)$

Figure 2

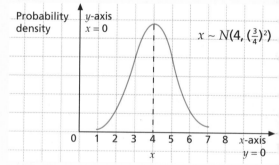

$x \sim N(4, (\frac{3}{4})^2)$

Figure 3

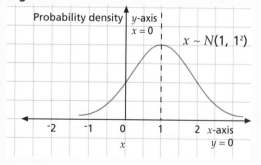

$x \sim N(1, 1^2)$

Figure 4

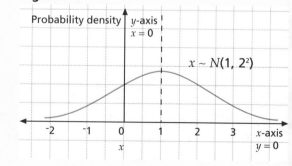

$x \sim N(1, 2^2)$

Letts I See Maths **Book 3**

Handling Data

Demonstration 2

Standardised normal curve: probability density function

Figure 1

	Probability
z	$\Phi(z)$
0·00	0·5000
0·20	0·4207
0·40	0·3446
0·60	0·2743
0·80	0·2119
1·00	0·1587
1·20	0·1151
1·40	0·0808

Figure 2

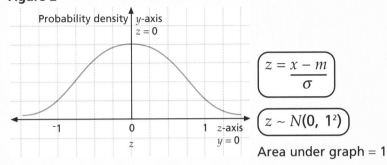

$$z = \frac{x - m}{\sigma}$$

$$z \sim N(0,\ 1^2)$$

Area under graph = 1

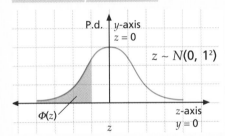

$z \sim N(0, 1^2)$

Figure 3

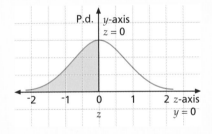

Figure 4

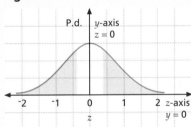

Figure 5

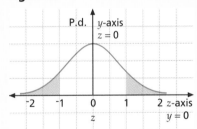

Key words   area under curve of probability density distribution $N(\mu, \sigma^2)$
probability density distribution   standard deviation (σ)   standard score
standardised score   variable   variance (σ^2)

Exercise bank

Plenary

👁   Discuss and sketch $N(0,1)$.

The normal curve

Handling Data

1 (a) Draw axes such that $^-10 \le x < 10$ and $^-10 \le y < 10$.

    (b) Draw rectangle ABCD such that the vertices are A(1, 10), B(3, 1), C(1, 2) and D(3, 2).

    (c) Translate ABCD to A'B'C'D' with vector $\begin{pmatrix} 4 \\ 0 \end{pmatrix}$.

    (d) Translate ABCD to A"B"C"D" with vector $\begin{pmatrix} ^-6 \\ 0 \end{pmatrix}$.

    (e) Translate ABCD to A'''B'''C'''D''' with vector $\begin{pmatrix} 2 \\ 5 \end{pmatrix}$.

    (f) Describe what happens to the area of rectangle ABCD under the translation $\begin{pmatrix} x \\ y \end{pmatrix}$.

    (g) Rectangle ABCD is stretched in the x-direction with scale factor 4. What will be the scale factor of the stretch in the y-direction if the area of ABCD does not change?

2 Study the four normal curves below. For each curve answer these questions.

    (a) What is the value of μ?

    (b) What is the value of σ?

    (c) What are the x values of the points of inflection?

(i) $x \sim N(0, 1^2)$

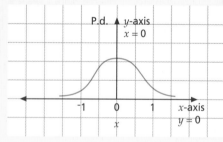

(ii) $x \sim N(1, 1^2)$

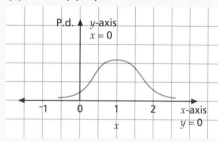

(iii) $x \sim N(0, \cdot 5^2)$

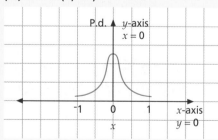

(iv) $x \sim N(1, \cdot 5^2)$

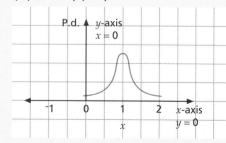

Challenging exercises

3 The standardised normal curve is defined by the function $N(0, 1)$.

Sketch the graphs of the normal curves below.

(a) $N(2, 1)$ (b) $N(-3, 1)$ (c) $N(25, 1)$
(d) $N(0, 4)$ (e) $N(0, 16)$ (f) $N(0, 2·25)$
(g) $N(1, 9)$ (h) $N(4, 4)$ (i) $N(1·5, 2·5)$

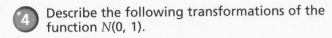

4 Describe the following transformations of the function $N(0, 1)$.

(a) $N(k, 1)$ (b) $N(0, p)$

5 What is the area under a standardised normal curve?

Problem-solving exercises

Use the table in Demonstration 2 for the following questions.

Figure 1

6 Study the normal curve $N(0, 1^2)$ in Figure 1.
(a) What is the area under the complete curve?
(b) What is the area coloured yellow?
(c) What is the area under the curve for $z < 0$?
(d) What is the area under the curve for $0 < z < 1$?
(e) What is the area under the curve for $z > 1$?
(f) What is the area under the curve for $-1 < z < 0$?

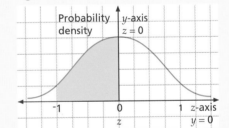

Figure 2

7 Study the normal curve $N(0, 1^2)$ in Figure 2.
(a) A Y9 student is selected at random from an English school. What is the probability that the student's standardised English score was $z < 0$?
(b) A Y9 student is selected at random from an English school. What is the probability that the student's standardised English score was $0 < z < 1$?
(c) A Y9 student is selected at random from an English school. What is the probability that the student's standardised English score was $z > 1$?
(d) A Y9 student is selected at random from an English school. What is the probability that the student's standardised English score was $-1 < z < 0$?

Standardised test scores in English for all Y9 students in all schools in England

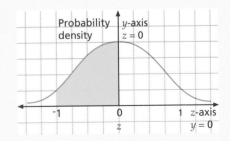

Homework

Suggest three populations that you would expect to be distributed normally.

Handling Data

1 All the students in a school recorded the time (in minutes) that it took them to get to school each day. The results are shown in the table on the right.

Time taken x minutes	Frequency $f(x)$	Cumulative frequency
$5 \leq x < 10$	74	
$10 \leq x < 15$	86	
$15 \leq x < 20$	120	
$20 \leq x < 25$	116	
$25 \leq x < 30$	84	
$30 \leq x < 35$	48	
$35 \leq x < 40$	22	
Total		

(a) What is the modal class?

(b) Draw a frequency diagram to represent this data.

(c) Draw a frequency polygon to represent this data.

(d) How many students took less than 20 minutes to get to school?

(e) Copy the table and complete the cumulative frequency column.

(f) Draw a cumulative frequency diagram to represent this data.

(g) Estimate the number of students who took between 12 and 18 minutes to get to school.

(h) Use the diagram to estimate Q_1 (the lower quartile), Q_2 (the median) and Q_3 (the upper quartile).

(i) Draw a box-and-whisker diagram to represent this data.

(j) Estimate the mean time taken to get to school.

(k) Discuss the merits of using the mode, median or mean as a measure of central tendency.

(l) Discuss the merits of using a frequency diagram, a frequency polygon, a cumulative frequency diagram and a box-and-whisker diagram to represent this data.

(m) When writing a report you are told to be efficient and concise, and not to use any redundant statistics. State which measure of central tendency and which diagram you would use to represent this data. Use your answers to (k) and (l) to help you give your reasons.

2 (a) The mean of a sample of six numbers is 4·5 and the mean of another set of eight numbers is 4·8. What is the mean of the combined sets of numbers? Give your answer to two decimal places.

(b) The mean of a set of numbers is 29·3. Each number in the set is increased by five. What is the mean of the new set of numbers?

(c) The mean of a set of numbers is 19·6. Each number in the set is increased by a multiple of 100. What is the mean of the new set of numbers?

(d) Each number, x, in a set of numbers is transformed to a number, y, using $y = 3x + 4$. Explain what effect this has on the value of the mean.

(e) There are thirty students in a class. The teacher says that 20 students had achieved an above-average mark for a test. Is this possible?

(f) A company with 85 employees says that the average annual salary is £25 400. What is the total of all the annual salaries for the year?

(g) Suggest two situations where the mean is not a useful measure of central tendency.

Letts I See Maths Book 3

3 (a) Copy and complete the table below.

Variable	13	16	21	22	23	25	27	29	x
Mean									$\bar{x}$
Deviation from the mean									$x - \bar{x}$
Square of deviation from the mean									$(x - \bar{x})^2$
Sum of squares of deviations from the mean									$\sum(x - \bar{x})^2$
Mean of squares of deviations from the mean (variance, S^2)									$\dfrac{\sum(x - \bar{x})^2}{n}$
Square root of mean of squares of deviations from the mean (standard deviation, S)									$\sqrt{\dfrac{\sum(x - \bar{x})^2}{n}}$

(b) Each value of the variable x is increased by 12 to give the following data set.

25	28	33	34	35	37	49	41

Calculate the mean and standard deviation for this data set.

(c) Each value of the variable x is increased by a multiple of 20 to give the following data set.

260	320	420	440	460	500	540	580

Calculate the mean and standard deviation for this data set.

(d) Write down a set of eight values of x with a standard deviation five times that of the original set in part (a).

4 The frequency table on the right gives the results of a PE test with marks out of ten.

(a) How many students took the test?

(b) Work out the mode, the median and the mean scores. (These are the measures of central tendency.)

(c) Calculate the standard deviation, S, for these marks. Give your answer to two decimal places.

(d) Draw a bar chart to represent the test results.

(e) Use the statistics you have calculated to help you describe the test results.

(f) Eighty students in a different school took the same test with the following results.

PE test marks

Mark x	Frequency $f(x)$
1	0
2	1
3	3
4	7
5	9
6	11
7	12
8	10
9	7
10	5

Mark x	1	2	3	4	5	6	7	8	9	10
Frequency $f(x)$	0	0	2	12	11	15	18	12	10	0

Compare the two sets of results using appropriate statistics.

Review of Handling Data

1 Here are the results of eight students' French and German tests.

French results								German results							
Mean mark $\bar{x} = 64$ for the year group								Mean mark $\bar{y} = 52$ for the year group							
Standard deviation $S_x = 5\cdot6$								Standard deviation $S_y = 10\cdot5$							
A	B	C	D	E	F	G	H	A	B	C	D	E	F	G	H
59	67	60	64	62	65	68	66	50	41	55	64	58	48	59	60
Deviation from the mean $(x - \bar{x})$								Deviation from the mean $(y - \bar{y})$							

(a) Copy the table and calculate the deviation from the mean for each mark.

(b) Use the formula $z = \frac{(x - \bar{x})}{S}$ to standardise each student's score. Give your answers to two decimal places (2 d.p.).

(c) Student D had a mark of 64 in each subject. Does this mean that she performed equally well in both subjects?

(d) Student A had a mark of 59 in French and a mark of 50 in German. In which test did he perform the best?

(e) Compare the test results for students B, C, E, F, G and H.

(f) Student G had a mark of 58 in English where the mean mark for the year group was 50 and the standard deviation was 8·2. She said that English was her worst subject. Was she correct?

(g) A student decided to use her test scores to help her decide which subjects to study in Y10. Explain why this might not be the best information to use.

2 In a DIY store, curtain rails are sorted according to their lengths. Jenny measured each stake, to the nearest centimetre, and recorded the results in a table.

Length x (in cm)	$90 \leq x < 110$	$110 \leq x < 120$	$120 \leq x < 125$	$125 \leq x < 135$	$135 \leq x < 150$
Frequency $f(x)$	42	65	120	50	20

(a) Work out the class width for each class interval.

(b) Draw a histogram to represent this data.

(c) What is the modal class for this set of data?

(d) Estimate the median and mean for this set of data.

(e) Draw a frequency polygon for this data.

(f) Discuss the merits of the diagrams and calculations you have made.

3 A card is selected from an ordinary pack of cards (no jokers). Write down the probability that the card is:

(a) the four of hearts

(b) a red queen

(c) an ace

(d) a number greater than four and less than eight.

Letts I See Maths **Book 3**

4 An ordinary die and a coin are thrown together. Draw a possibility space diagram to show all the possible outcomes. What is the probability that the outcome is:

(a) a head and a six

(b) a tail and an even number

(c) a head and a number less than four.

5 (a) The probability of an event happening is $\frac{3}{5}$. What is the probability that the event does not happen?

(b) Two events, A and B, are mutually exclusive. $P(A) = \frac{1}{3}$ and $P(B) = \frac{2}{5}$. What is the probability of $P(A \text{ or } B)$?

(c) A coloured counter is selected at random from a bag of counters and replaced. A second counter is selected in the same way. The probability of getting a blue counter for any selection is $\frac{2}{7}$. What is the probability of getting two blue counters in two selections?

(d) A coloured counter is selected from a bag of counters and not replaced. How does this affect the selection of a second counter?

6 Study the pie chart on the right.

(a) How many people took part in the survey?

(b) What is the most popular form of transport?

(c) What is the least popular form of transport?

(d) What proportion of the people surveyed travelled by bus?

(e) What percentage of people surveyed cycled to work?

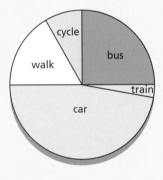

7 Study the cumulative frequency diagram on the right.

(a) What is the variable x?

(b) Does the variable x represent discrete or continuous data?

(c) What does the y-axis represent?

(d) Use the cumulative frequency diagram to estimate Q_1 (the lower quartile), Q_2 (the median) and Q_3 (the upper quartile) of the distribution.

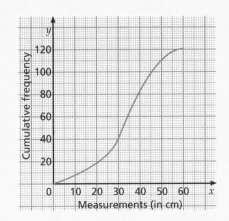

Introduction

Key Stage 3 National Strategy Framework for Teaching Mathematics

- Solve increasingly demanding problems and evaluate solutions; explore connections in mathematics across a range of contexts: number, algebra, shape, space and measures, and handling data; generate fuller solutions.

- Represent problems and synthesise information in algebraic, geometric or graphical form; move from one form to another to gain a different perspective of the problem.

- Solve substantial problems by breaking them into simpler tasks, using a range of different techniques, methods and resources, including ICT; use trial and improvement where a more efficient method is not obvious.

- Present a concise, reasoned argument, using symbols, diagrams, graphs and related explanatory text; give solutions to problems to an appropriate degree of accuracy, recognising limitations on the accuracy of data and measurements; give reasons for choice of presentation, explaining selected features and showing insight into the problem's structure.

- Suggest extensions to problems, conjecture and generalise; identify exceptional cases or counter-examples, explaining why; justify generalisations, arguments or solutions; pose extra constraints and investigate whether particular cases can be generalised further.

Helping you to solve problems using mathematics

1	Study the problem and read it very carefully.
2	Identify the information you need and make neat notes.
3	Decide whether to break down the problem into smaller steps or tasks.
4	Consider what mathematics you know that could apply to the problem. Can you use number and algebra? Can you use geometry or statistics?
5	Do you need to find out about some new mathematics to apply to the problem?
6	Can you use algebra right from the start?
7	Decide how to set out your solution: Do you need a table for results? Can you use diagrams and graphs to represent the problem? How much explanation do you need to write so that someone reading it will understand your solution?
8	Look for patterns. Make a conjecture. Test it with a new example. Can you make a general statement using words or algebra?
9	Go back to the original question. Have you answered it? Summarise your results.
10	Ask, 'What if …?'

Letts I See Maths **Book 3**

Example

Problem: Pythagoras' theorem states that: 'The square on the hypotenuse of a right-angled triangle is equal to the sum of the squares on the other two sides.'

- Will this rule work if the shape on the sides of the triangle is not a square?

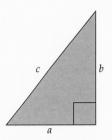

Prompts:	Solution:
1 What is given?	Pythagoras' theorem: $c^2 = a^2 + b^2$.
2 Interpret the question.	Will this rule work for different shapes on the sides of a triangle? I will try triangles, rectangles, regular polygons and parts of a circle.
3 How will you start?	I will start with a semi-circle because the radius is related to the lengths of the sides of the triangle.
4 What are you trying to find out? It is about area. I know that area of a semi-circle $= \frac{1}{2}\pi r^2$.	**To prove:** area of C = area of A + area of B **LHS:** Area of C $= \frac{1}{2}\pi$ radius^2 $= \frac{1}{2}\pi\left(\frac{c}{2}\right)^2$ $\qquad = \frac{1}{2}\pi\frac{c^2}{4} \qquad = \frac{1}{8}\pi c^2$
5 Use algebraic logic. Does LHS = RHS? What do you know?	**RHS:** Area of A + area of B $= \frac{1}{2}\pi\left(\frac{a}{2}\right)^2 + \frac{1}{2}\pi\left(\frac{b}{2}\right)^2$ $\qquad = \frac{1}{8}\pi a^2 + \frac{1}{8}\pi b^2$ $\qquad = \frac{1}{8}\pi(a^2 + b^2)$
6 Use what you are given.	I know that $c^2 = a^2 + b^2$ (Pythagoras' theorem). Therefore: $\frac{1}{8}\pi(a^2 + b^2) = \frac{1}{8}\pi c^2$ Therefore: LHS = RHS
7 Go back to the question.	The rule works for semi-circles.
8 Ask further questions	Now that I know the rule works for semi-circles, I will try triangles. I will start with the special case of equilateral triangles.

Using and Applying

Using maths to investigate

Goals

By the end of this lesson you will:

- 👁 know that, in a complex problem you break the task down

- 👁 know how to work systematically

- 👁 know how to use a range of efficient methods, techniques and resources

- 👁 know how to make a conjecture and test it

- 👁 know how to make a generalisation.

Starter

1 Partition the following numbers into thousands, hundreds, tens, units, tenths, hundredths etc.

(a) 365   (b) 4972   (c) 1405   (d) 2 600 370

(e) 24·6   (f) 9·78   (g) ab (h) abc

Demonstration

Question:
Write down a 3-digit number. Reverse the digits. Subtract the smaller number from the larger number. Reverse the digits. Add the two numbers. What do you notice? Can you prove your result? Are there similar results with 2-digit numbers? With 4-digit numbers? Extend to other bases.

Solution:
- I will start with the number: 234

       Reverse   432   Subtract

$$\begin{array}{r} 432 \\ -\ 234 \\ \hline 198 \end{array}$$

       Reverse   891   Add

$$\begin{array}{r} +\ 891 \\ \hline 1089 \end{array}$$

Answer: 1089

- Try a different number: 672

       Reverse   276   Subtract

$$\begin{array}{r} 672 \\ -\ 276 \\ \hline 396 \end{array}$$

       Reverse   693   Add

$$\begin{array}{r} +\ 693 \\ \hline 1089 \end{array}$$

Answer: 1089

Conjecture: I predict that the answer will always be 1089.

Check: Chose 926.

$$\begin{array}{r} 926 \\ -\ 629 \\ \hline 297 \\ +\ 792 \\ \hline 1089 \end{array}$$

It seems to work.

What if all or some of the digits are the same?

- Choose 333.   Answer 0.   Does not work.
- Choose 414.   Answer 0.   Does not work.
- Choose 662.   Answer 1089.   It does work.

Generalisation:

- Let the number be abc, with $a > c$.

		$\overset{a-1}{\cancel{a}}$	$\overset{9+b}{\cancel{b}}$	$\overset{10+c}{\cancel{c}}$
Subtract	$-$	c	b	a
		$(a-1-c)$	9	$(10+c-a)$
Add	$+$	$(10+c-a)$	9	$(a-1-c)$
		10	8	9

> Since $a > c$ I have to 'borrow' in order to subtract.

This proves, that provided $a > c$, the answer will always be 1089.

Extension: Try two digits.

- Choose 63.

Reverse	36	Subtract	$-\;\frac{63}{36}$
			27
Reverse	72	Add	$+\;\frac{72}{}$
			99

- Choose 82.

Reverse	28	Subtract	$-\;\frac{82}{28}$
			54
Reverse	45	Add	$+\;\frac{45}{}$
			99

Conjecture: The answer will always be 99.

Try 4 digits.

Choose 4321, reverse and subtract: 3087, reverse and add: 10 890. The answers are all multiples of 99. I will investigate further ... .

Key words   conjecture   generalise   partition   predict

Exercise bank ☞

Plenary

- What is a conjecture?

- Why do a test?

- Are examples and tests sufficient to prove something?

- What is a generalisation?

- Can you predict the answer in the problem above for 5-digit numbers? For 6-digits? For n-digits?

Letts I See Maths Book 3

Using and Applying

Using maths to investigate

1 Chains

$$7 \longrightarrow 22 \longrightarrow 11 \longrightarrow 34 \longrightarrow 17 \longrightarrow \ldots$$

Rules: (i) If a number is even, divide by 2. (ii) if a number is odd, multiply by 3 and add 1.

(a) Continue the chain above. What happens?
(b) Start with a different number and investigate.
(c) Change the rules and investigate.

2 Another number chain

$$12 \longrightarrow 5 \longrightarrow 25 \longrightarrow 29 \longrightarrow 85 \longrightarrow \ldots$$

Rule: Square each digit and add. For example, $12 \longrightarrow 1^2 + 2^2 = 1 + 4 = 5$

(a) Continue the chain above. What happens?
(b) Start with different numbers and investigate.
(c) Present your results in a diagram.
(d) What happens if you change the rule to 'cube each digit and add'?

3 Pascal's triangle

```
              1
          1       1
       1     2       1
     1     3     3       1
   1    ...   ...    ...     1
```

(a) Copy Pascal's triangle and write down the next three rows.
(b) Add the numbers in each row. What do you notice?
(c) Look at the numbers in the diagonal row beginning 1, 3, 6, 10, … .
   (i)   What will be the next three numbers in the sequence?
   (ii)   What will be the nth term of the sequence?
   (iii) Can you justify your answer?
(d) Look at these bands in Pascal's triangle

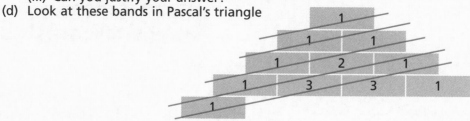

   (i)   Add the numbers in each band and write down the sequence. Write down the next five consecutive terms of the sequence and describe the term-to-term rule.
   (ii) This sequence is called the Fibonaccii sequence. Find out more about it.

(e) Extension: Multiply out the brackets below and see if you can find a connection with Pascal's triangle.
$(x + 1)$, $(x + 1)^2$, $(x + 1)^3$, …
Use Pascal's triangle to help you work out $(x + 1)^4$, $(x + 1)^5$ etc.

4 Modulo arithmetic (clock arithmetic)

Modulo 3

Modulo 5

Modulo 7

(a) Complete the following equations.

Mod 3
$0 + 1 = 1$
$1 + 1 = 2$
$2 + 1 = 0$
$2 + 2 =$

Mod 5
$0 + 2 =$
$2 + 3 =$
$1 + 4 =$
$3 + 4 =$

Mod 7
$2 + 3 =$
$3 + 5 =$
$4 + 6 =$
$6 + 6 =$

(b) Draw diagrams and write your own sums for modulo 6 and modulo 8.

(c) Now try these questions and explain how you work out the answers.

(i) $4 + 7 \pmod 9$

(ii) $5 \times 7 \pmod 8$

(iii) $2^5 \pmod 3$

(d) Investigate different operations in modulo arithmetic.

5

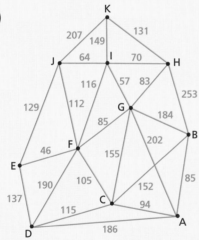

A cable has to be laid so that every town in the network in the diagram is connected either directly or through another town.

(a) Find the length of the shortest cable required to connect all the towns.

(b) Write an algorithm to find the shortest distance to connect places in a network.

6 On April 1st David agreed to do the housework for his parents. He said that he wanted 1p for the first day, 2p for the second day, 4p for the third day, 8p for the fourth day and so on.

(a) How much does he want on the thirtieth day?

(b) Investigate how much he would get altogether for the month of April. What about for a whole year?

(c) Was this an April Fools' joke?

Letts I See Maths **Book 3**

Goals

By the end of this lesson you will be able to answer questions like this:

👁 The area of the right-angled triangle ABC is 345 cm² and BC = 15 cm.
Calculate the length of AC.

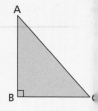

Starter

1 Construct the following angles using a straight edge and a pair of compasses.

(a) 90°   (b) 60°   (c) 45°   (d) 15°   (e) 75°

Use Pythagoras' theorem to work out the lengths marked with letters.

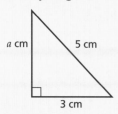

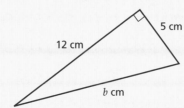

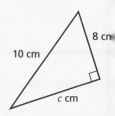

Demonstration 1

Question: ABCD is a square of side 12 cm.
Is triangle AMN right-angled?

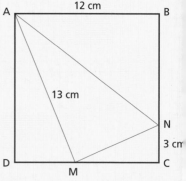

Solution:
Clue 1:   If △AMN is right-angled, its sides will obey
Pythagoras' theorem. Calculate the lengths of its sides.

Clue 2:   BC = 12 cm, BN = (12 − 3) cm. Use Pythagoras' theorem
on right-angled triangle ABN.

△ABN $AB^2 + BN^2 = AN^2$
              $12^2 + 9^2 = AN^2$ AN = 15 cm

MN is needed. First, use △ADM to calculate DM and then MC.

△ADM $AD^2 + DM^2 = AM^2$
              $12^2 + DM^2 = 13^2$ DM = 5 cm

△MCN $MC^2 + NC^2 = MN^2$
              $7^2 + 3^2 = MN^2$ MN = $\sqrt{58}$ cm

Check: △AMN $AM^2 + MN^2$. Does this equal AN^2?
                            $169 + 58 \leq 227$ >   225

Answer: No. The triangle is not right-angled. It is an obtuse-angled triangle.

Using and Applying

Demonstration 2

Question: Five circular cakes, each with radius 2·5 cm, are packed in a box like this.
What is the length of the box?

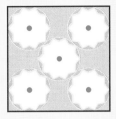

Solution:

Clue 1:

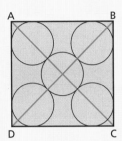

The box has a square base.
The diagonal of the box is three times the diameter of a cake.
Diameter of each cake $= 2 \times 2\cdot5$ cm
$\qquad\qquad\qquad\qquad = 5$ cm
Diagonal $= \quad 3 \times 5$ cm $= 15$ cm

Clue 2: $\triangle ABC$ is a right-angled isosceles triangle.
Let $AB = BC = x$.

Using Pythagoras' theorem:
$$AB^2 + BC^2 = AC^2$$
$$x^2 + x^2 = 15^2$$
$$2x^2 = 15^2$$
$$x^2 = \frac{15^2}{2}$$
$$x = \frac{15}{\sqrt{2}}$$

Answer: The length of the box is 10·6 cm, to 1 d.p.

> **Key words**   construct   Pythagoras' theorem

Exercise bank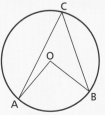

Plenary

◉ Go back to the Goals and calculate length AC.

◉ Explain how you would construct an angle of 52° using only a straight edge and a pair of compasses.

◉ State Pythagoras' theorem.

◉ Look at the diagrams below and make statements about the angles shown.

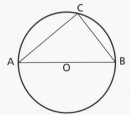

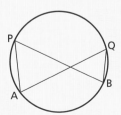

Working like a detective

Exercises

1 Use a ball (a tennis ball, for example).

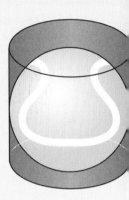

(a) Make a cylinder with base diameter and height exactly the same as the diameter of the ball.

(b) Make a cone with base diameter and height exactly the same as the diameter of the ball.

(c) How many conesful of rice will exactly fill the cylinder?

(d) Remove the rice and put the ball in the cylinder. How many conesful of rice are needed to fill the space around the ball?

(e) Determine a formula for the volume of the cone.

(f) Determine a formula for the volume of a sphere.

2 Design a container to hold four tennis balls. Consider features such as the most practical, the least volume, the most economical to make, and so on.

3 The sphere on the right has radius $R = 8$ cm.

A slice is cut off the sphere through P such that $P\hat{O}B = 60°$.

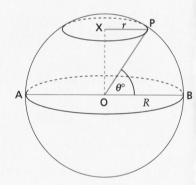

(a) Calculate the radius, r, of the circle through P.

(b) Calculate the area of the circle with radius r.

(c) Write an expression, in terms of R and θ, for the radius of a circle when a slice is cut from a sphere of radius R, at an angle θ to the diameter.

4 $\triangle ABC$ is any triangle and h is the length of the perpendicular from B to AC.

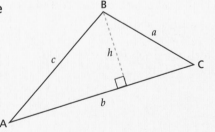

(a) Use the diagram to show that $\frac{a}{\sin A} = \frac{c}{\sin C}$.

(b) Draw a different perpendicular and show that $\frac{a}{\sin A} = \frac{b}{\sin B}$.

Using and Applying

5 Sector AOB is cut from a circle with radius r and $A\hat{O}B = \theta°$.

The sector is used to make a cone with base radius R.

(a) Write an expression for R in terms of r and θ.

(b) Determine an expression for the height of the cone, VX, and a formula for the volume of the cone.

(c) Determine an expression for the total surface area of the cone.

(d) If $r = 6$ cm and $\theta = 120°$, calculate the volume and surface area of the cone.

6 Seven bars are fitted at equal distances in a semi-circular archway. The width of the base of the arch is 4·8 m.

Calculate the total length of the bars, to the nearest centimetre.

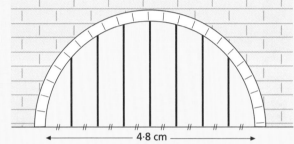

7 A regular octagon with side of 3 cm is cut from a square piece of card.

What is the length of the side of the square, to the nearest millimetre?

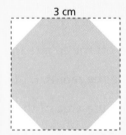

8 Two circles, with radii R and r, just touch one another as shown in the diagram. The length d is the horizontal distance between their centres, O and O'.

(a) Show that $d^2 = 4Rr$.

(b) Calculate d when $R = 16$ cm and $r = 4$ cm.

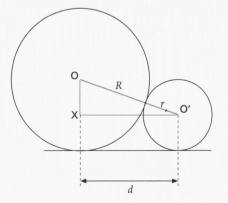

Conducting an enquiry

Goals

By the end of this lesson you will be able to answer questions such as these:

- 👁 Give an outline of the four-point plan for conducting a statistical enquiry.
- 👁 Describe how you would select a representative sample.
- 👁 Describe how you would write a questionnaire.
- 👁 Describe different ways of representing data.
- 👁 Describe the key points for communicating results.

Starter

1. Discuss how you would select a random sample of five people from your class.

2. Discuss how you would select a random sample of 50 heights stratified across year groups.

3. Discuss how you would allocate a quota sample of males and females in each year group.

Demonstration 1

A statistical enquiry: the four-point plan

1. Planning an enquiry
   - Read about your topic – and talk about it.
   - Decide what you want to find out. Focus on a manageable part. What is the hypothesis?
   - Decide on your variables, populations and samples.

2. Collecting data
   - Questionnaire?
   - Interview?
   - Existing data?
   - Observation?
   - Organising the work?

3. Representing data
   - Mean, median or mode?
   - Range?
   - Inter-quartile range?
   - Standard deviation?
   - Correlation?
   - Pie chart? Bar chart? Frequency diagram? Cumulative frequency diagram? Histogram? Normal curve? Box-and-whisker diagram? Scatter graph?

4. Communicating results
   - Original questions and hypothesis?
   - Audience?
   - Presentation?
   - Think carefully about the report.

Letts I See Maths Book 3

Using and Applying

Demonstration 2

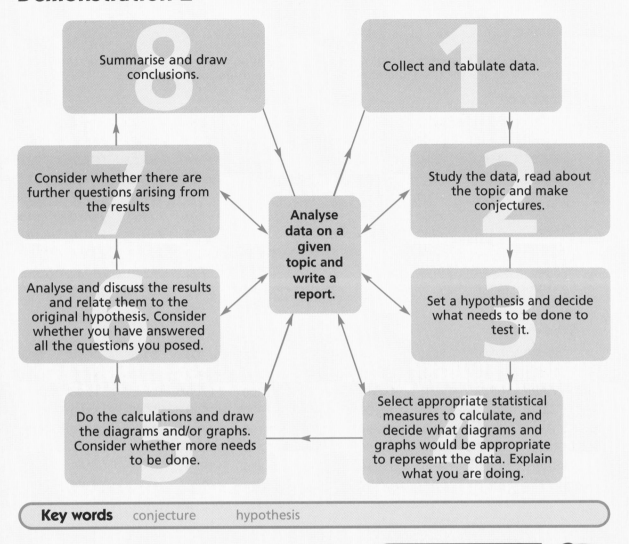

8 Summarise and draw conclusions.

1 Collect and tabulate data.

7 Consider whether there are further questions arising from the results

2 Study the data, read about the topic and make conjectures.

Analyse data on a given topic and write a report.

6 Analyse and discuss the results and relate them to the original hypothesis. Consider whether you have answered all the questions you posed.

3 Set a hypothesis and decide what needs to be done to test it.

5 Do the calculations and draw the diagrams and/or graphs. Consider whether more needs to be done.

4 Select appropriate statistical measures to calculate, and decide what diagrams and graphs would be appropriate to represent the data. Explain what you are doing.

Key words   conjecture   hypothesis

Exercise bank

Plenary

- ◎   Go back to the Goals and check that you can answer all of the questions
- ◎   Select an enquiry and plan what you have to do.
- ◎   Check that the data you have selected or intend to collect is representative of the subject of your enquiry.
- ◎   Discuss whether the statistical techniques, diagrams and graphs you have chosen to use are appropriate.
- ◎   Conduct your enquiry and write a report.

 I See Maths **Book 3**

Using and Applying

Conducting an enquiry

Exercises

 Enquiry 1

The salaries, in euros, of the employees of three companies are given below. Use statistical techniques to analyse these salaries and compare the three companies.

Company A

5320	5320	5320	6250	6250	6250	6250	7460	7460	7460
7460	7460	8240	8240	8240	8240	8240	8240	8960	8960
8960	8960	8960	8960	8960	9320	9320	9320	9320	9320
9320	9320	9320	10230	10230	10230	10230	10230	10230	10230
10230	10230	11700	11700	11700	11700	11700	11700	12750	12750
12750	12750	13480	13480	13480	15170	15170	20450	21430	21430
21430	22460	22460	22460	22460	22460	23470	23470	23470	23470
23470	23470	25220	25220	25220	25220	25220	25220	25220	27140
27140	27140	27140	27140	27140	27140	27140	29130	29130	29130
29130	29130	29130	29130	32480	32480	32480	32480	32480	49650

Company B

6140	6140	7240	7240	7240	8100	8100	8100	8100	8920
8920	8920	8920	8920	9740	9740	9740	9740	9740	10510
10510	10510	10510	10510	10510	11200	11200	11200	11200	11200
11200	11200	11900	11900	11900	11900	11900	11900	11900	11900
12750	12750	12750	12750	12750	12750	12750	12750	12750	13480
13480	13480	13480	13480	13480	13480	13480	15170	15170	15170
15170	15170	15170	15170	16830	16830	16830	16830	16830	16830
16830	18930	18930	18930	18930	18930	18930	21300	21300	21300
21300	21300	24630	24630	24630	24630	27510	27510	27510	27510
32450	32450	32450	37890	37890	37890	43210	43210	56230	69870

Company C

4460	4460	4460	4460	4460	4460	4460	5160	5160	5160
5580	5580	5580	5580	5580	5580	5580	5580	5580	6450
6450	6450	6450	6450	6450	6450	6450	6450	7320	7320
7320	7320	7320	7320	7320	7320	8140	8140	8140	8140
9170	9170	9170	9980	9980	9980	9980	9980	9980	9980
10980	10980	10980	10980	10980	10980	10980	11700	11700	11700
11700	11700	11700	12560	12560	12560	12560	12560	12560	13480
13480	13480	13480	13480	17650	17650	17650	17650	17650	19560
19560	19560	19560	29650	29650	29650	29650	37960	37960	37960
47850	47850	47850	50610	50610	56320	63820	77520	89950	98960

Using and Applying

Enquiry 2

The results, in percentages, of end-of-year assessments for 9H are shown below. Use statistical techniques to analyse Alison's results.

Alison: Art 92%; English 65%; D&T 56%; French 49%, Geography 73%, History 77%, Maths 62%, PE 84%, Science 69%

Art

58	58	60	60	65	68	69	71	72	73
75	75	77	78	82	84	85	85	87	89
90	92	92	92	93	94	95	95	95	96

English

42	47	50	52	52	54	55	55	55	58
60	60	60	62	62	62	63	64	64	65
65	65	68	70	70	70	73	74	75	75

Design and Technology

32	32	32	34	34	36	38	42	42	42
44	44	46	46	48	50	50	52	52	52
54	54	56	56	56	57	58	60	75	80

French

22	28	30	32	36	36	40	40	42	45
45	45	46	46	47	48	48	48	49	50
50	52	53	55	56	56	58	60	62	65

Geography

60	60	61	62	62	62	65	66	66	68
69	70	70	72	73	73	74	74	76	78
80	80	82	84	84	84	86	87	88	90

History

65	65	65	65	66	68	68	68	70	70
74	76	77	77	78	78	80	80	80	82
82	82	84	84	86	86	88	88	88	90

Maths

20	36	38	40	45	48	50	52	54	56
58	58	60	60	62	62	62	66	68	71
73	75	75	78	78	80	85	88	92	100

PE

54	54	55	55	56	56	58	59	60	60
62	65	65	66	68	68	70	70	75	78
84	84	85	85	85	86	86	87	88	88

Science

18	29	37	42	50	58	60	62	65	65
66	68	68	69	70	70	72	72	72	75
75	80	82	85	86	88	88	90	96	98

Letts I See Maths Book 3

Maths across the curriculum

Goals

When you have completed this lesson you will be able to answer questions such as these:

👁 What is the force of gravity, on the earth, of an object of mass 6·7 kg?

👁 What is the pressure on the ground exerted by this object?

👁 What is the pressure on the ground exerted by this object?

6·7 kg | 10 cm

5 cm

cylinder

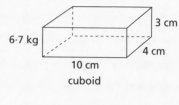

3 cm

6·7 kg

10 cm   4 cm

cuboid

Starter

1 On the earth, 1 kg experiences a force of gravity of 10 N. What force of gravity is experienced by these masses?

(a) 4 kg   (b) 1·5 kg   (c) 100 g   (d) 20 g   (e) 150 g   (f) 1 tonne

2 How many square metres are the areas of these rectangles?

(a) 1 m by 1 m
(d) 100 cm by 100 cm
(g) 1 cm by 1 cm

(b) 1 m by 3 m
(e) 100 cm by 50 cm

(c) 6 m by 2 m
(f) 100 cm by 10 cm

3 What is each of these areas in square metres?

(a) 100 000 cm²   (b) 200 000 cm²   (c) 100 cm²   (d) 250 cm²   (e) 125 cm²

Demonstration 1

Figure 1

Mass = 56 kg

Force on
ground = 560 N

125 cm² 125 cm²

250 cm²
= ·025 m²

Pressure = $\frac{560\,N}{·025\,m^2}$

Pressure = 22 400 N/m²
Pressure = 22 400 N m⁻²
Pressure = 22 400 pascal
Pressure = 22 400 Pa

Figure 2

Mass = 56 kg

Force on
ground = 560 N

125 cm²

125 cm²
= ·0125 m²

Pressure = $\frac{560\,N}{·0125\,m^2}$

Pressure = 44 800 N/m²
Pressure = 44 800 N m⁻²
Pressure = 44 800 pascal
Pressure = 44 800 Pa

Letts I See Maths **Book 3**

Demonstration 2

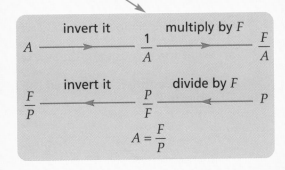

$$\text{Pressure} = \frac{\text{force}}{\text{area}} \qquad P = \frac{F}{A}$$

$F \xrightarrow{\quad \text{divide by } A \quad} \frac{F}{A}$

$PA \xleftarrow{\quad \text{multiply by } A \quad} P$

$$F = PA$$

$A \xrightarrow{\quad \text{invert it} \quad} \frac{1}{A} \xrightarrow{\quad \text{multiply by } F \quad} \frac{F}{A}$

$\frac{F}{P} \xleftarrow{\quad \text{invert it} \quad} \frac{P}{F} \xleftarrow{\quad \text{divide by } F \quad} P$

$$A = \frac{F}{P}$$

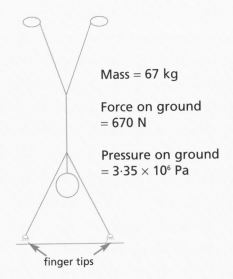

Mass = 67 kg

Force on ground
= 670 N

Pressure on ground
= 3·35 × 10⁶ Pa

finger tips

We can work out the area in contact with the ground:

$$A = \frac{F}{P}$$

$$A = \frac{670\,\text{N}}{3 \cdot 35 \times 10^6\,\text{Pa}}$$

$$= \frac{670}{335000000}\,\text{m}^2$$

$$= \cdot 0002\,\text{m}^2$$

$$= 2\,\text{cm}^2$$

Each finger has an area of 1 cm² in contact with the ground, assuming one finger of each hand is on the ground.

Key words   force   force of gravity   kilogram   newton   N/m²   N m⁻²

mass   Pa   pascal   pressure

Exercise bank 👉

Plenary

◉ Estimate the area of the blade of an ice skate that is in contact with the ice when a skater is on one foot.

◉ Calculate the pressure on the ice if the person in Demonstration 1, Figure 2, is skating.

◉ Discuss the questions in the Goals.

Maths across the curriculum

Exercise Bank

Essential exercises

1 What force of gravity, on the earth, is experienced by these masses?

(a) 7 kg   (b) 86·5 kg   (c) 500g   (d) 10 g   (e) 5 tonnes

2 All of the solids below have a mass of 2 kg.

(a) What force does each shape exert on the ground?

(b) What pressure is exerted on the ground by each object when it rests on the face indicated?

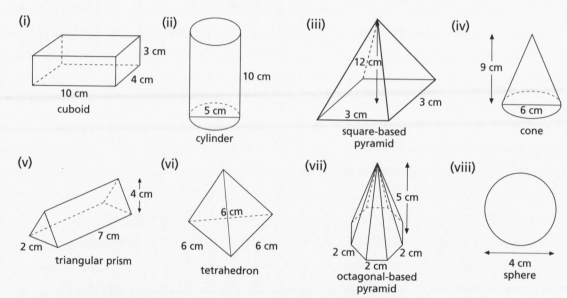

(i) cuboid — 3 cm, 4 cm, 10 cm
(ii) cylinder — 10 cm, 5 cm
(iii) square-based pyramid — 12 cm, 3 cm, 3 cm
(iv) cone — 9 cm, 6 cm
(v) triangular prism — 4 cm, 7 cm, 2 cm
(vi) tetrahedron — 6 cm, 6 cm, 6 cm
(vii) octagonal-based pyramid — 5 cm, 2 cm, 2 cm, 2 cm
(viii) sphere — 4 cm

3 Mass can be measured in kilograms (kg) or grams (g). Density can be measured in kilograms per metre cubed (kg/m^3) or grams per centimetre cubed (g/cm^3).

(a) Which is the larger unit, $1 \ kg/m^3$ or $1 \ g/cm^3$?

(b) The density of air under ordinary conditions is about $1 \cdot 2 \ kg/m^3$.

(i) What is the mass of air in a room that measures 4 m by 5 m by 2·5 m?

(ii) What is the mass of air in the room where you are?

(iii) How does the mass of air in your room compare with the average mass of an adult male of 72 kg?

(c) If 1 g of water has a volume of $1 cm^3$, what is its density in:

(i) g/cm^3

(ii) kg/m^3

Using and Applying

Letts I See Maths **Book 3**

Maths across the curriculum

Challenging exercise

4 Ayten made aluminium paperweights in the shape of a cone like this. The diameter of the base is 4 cm and the perpendicular height is 5 cm. Aluminium has a density of about 2·7 g/cm³.

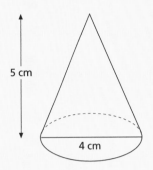

5 cm

4 cm

(a) What is the mass of the aluminium cone?

(b) What force is exerted on the ground by the cone?

(c) What pressure is exerted on the ground by the cone when it rests on its circular base?

(d) What pressure is exerted by twelve cones when they are packed in a box, all resting on their circular faces?

(e) Discuss the effect on the pressure when the cones are packed with half of them inverted.

Problem-solving exercise

5 Select one of the investigations below and write a report to present to the class.

(a) What is your density?

(b) Design a paperweight and consider the effect on density, force and pressure when you use different materials.

(c) A ceramic Victorian bath sits on four legs made like the feet of a lion. Consider the effect of filling the bath with water.

(d) Modern skis are much smaller than those made 10–15 years ago. Investigate.

(e) Car tyres have recommended pressures for different conditions. Investigate.

Using and Applying

Preparing for tests

Goals

When you have completed this lesson you will:

- 👁 know how to do mental-arithmetic tests
- 👁 know how to do non-calculator tests.

Mental-arithmetic test

- You will need a pencil and pen. You must *not* use a calculator.
- Each question will be read twice.
- Try to work out the answer to the question in your head. You may jot down workings if this helps.

Test – Lower tier

For this group of questions, you have 5 seconds to work out each answer and write it down.

(1) What number do you need to add to seventy-three to make one hundred?
(2) How many sides has an octagon?
(3) What number multiplied by eight equals fifty-six?
(4) What is one-fifth of twenty?
(5) Write down the number that is seven greater than negative three.

For the next group of questions, you have 10 seconds to work out each answer and write it down.

(6) How many seconds are there in five minutes?
(7) The time now is eleven hundred hours. School finishes at 1530. How much time is there before school finishes?
(8) Four tins of soup cost two pounds. How much would six tins of soup cost?
(9) Look at the hexagon. What is its perimeter?

(10) Look at the expression $3x + 2x$. Which expression below has the same value as this expression?
     5      $32x$ $5x$ $6x$
(11) Look at this equation: $y = 5x + 3$. When x equals four, what is the value of y?
(12) Look at this diagram. What is the size of the angle labelled x?
(13) Multiply three point six by one hundred.
(14) What is the next prime number after twenty-nine?
(15) What is twenty per cent of five hundred pounds?

For the next group of questions, you have 15 seconds to work out each answer and write it down.

(16) In a survey, Lucy asked some students how many hours they spent exercising each week. The bar chart shows the results. How many students were in the survey?
(17) A packet of crisps costs thirty-two pence. I buy two packets of crisps. How much change do I get from a pound?
(18) What fraction of a metre is twenty-five centimetres?
(19) I am thinking of two numbers whose sum is fifteen. One number is half the other. What are my two numbers?
(20) Subtract two-thirds from five-sixths.

Letts I See Maths Book 3

- You may need pencil, pen, ruler, protractor and a pair of compasses.
- You have 50 minutes to do the test. Do not waste time on questions that you cannot do. Make a note and come back to them if you have time at the end.
- Read the questions carefully and underline any information you want to remember.
- Show *all* your workings neatly.

Example 1

> **Bike rental**
> £20 deposit
> £1.75 per half hour

How much does it cost to rent a bike for 3 hours?

Answer:

Deposit = £20   Time = 3 hours = 6 half hours

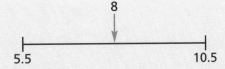

$$\begin{array}{r} £1.75 \\ \times\ 6 \\ \hline £10{\cdot}50 \end{array}$$

> You may get marks for your method even if your answer is wrong.

Total cost = £20 + £10·50 = £30·50

Example 2

The number 8 is halfway between 5·5 and 10·5.

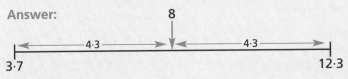

Question:

The number 8 is halfway between 3·7 and ...?

Answer:

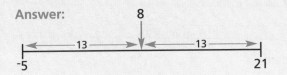

The number 8 is halfway between 3·7 and 12·3.

Question:

The number 8 is halfway between ⁻5 and ...?

Answer:

8

├── 13 ──→├←── 13 ──→┤
-5   21

The number 8 is halfway between ⁻5 and 21.

Tests 👉

Plenary

- Identify the questions in the mental-arithmetic test that you could not do and set yourself targets for improvement.

- Mark the questions in Tests A1, A2 and A3, and do corrections.

Test A1 levels 3 and 4

Calculator not allowed

1 (a) Add together 274 and 397.   (b) Subtract 268 from 504.

(c) Multiply 78 by 4.   (d) Divide 138 by 6.

2 Starkey School's first hockey and football teams play in the School's Division. The table shows how many matches the teams won, lost or drew over five years.

	Win	Lose	Draw
Hockey	35	15	10
Football	45	30	25

The football team played more matches than the hockey team. How many more?

3 Fill in the missing numbers labelled with letters on the function machines below.

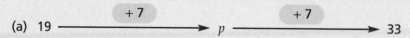

(a) 19 —— +7 ——→ p —— +7 ——→ 33

(b) 27 —— +9 ——→ q —— +9 ——→ r

(c) s —— +8 ——→ t —— +8 ——→ 73

(d) 45 —— +u ——→ v —— +u ——→ 79

4 Which of the following expressions are correct?

(a) $9 + 7 = 7 + 9$ (b) $9 - 7 = 7 - 9$ (c) $9 \times 7 = 7 \times 9$ (d) $9 \div 7 = 7 \div 9$

5 (a) What is the perimeter of the rectangle on the right?

(b) What is the area of the rectangle on the right?

5 cm
4 cm

6 Use +, −, × or ÷ to make each calculation correct.

(a) 7 ... 3 = 12 ... 2   (b) 3 ... 6 = 23 ... 5   (c) 16 ... 2 = 3 ... 5

7 Name the triangles below using the following names.

acute-angled   obtuse-angled   right-angled

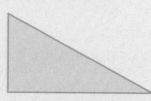

Letts I See Maths **Book 3**

National Curriculum Tests

8 (a) Write down all the whole number factors of 24.

(b) Write down the prime factors of 24.

(c) Write the number 24 as a product of its prime factors.

9 What single multiplication changes the first number into the second number in each of the questions below?

(a) 5 ⟶ 20   (b) 4 ⟶ 10   (c) 12 ⟶ 6

10 (a) Zara's height is 1·34 m. Jack is 0·12 m taller than Zara. What is Jack's height?

(b) Vera's height is 1·52 m. Frank is 0·13 m shorter than Vera. What is Frank's height?

(c) Emma's height is 1·68 m. What is Emma's height, in centimetres?

11 The sixty-five times table is on the right.

Use the table to help you to complete the following statements.

(a) $65 \times 5 =$

(b) $585 \div 65 =$

(c) $65 \times 7 =$

(d) $195 \div 65 =$

(e) $65 \times 50 =$

(f) At the School Fayre each go on the lucky dip cost 65 pence. Five hundred people had a go. How much money did they collect?

$65 \times 0 = \quad 0$
$65 \times 1 = \quad 65$
$65 \times 2 = 130$
$65 \times 3 = 195$
$65 \times 4 = 260$
$65 \times 5 = 325$
$65 \times 6 = 390$
$65 \times 7 = 455$
$65 \times 8 = 520$
$65 \times 9 = 585$

12 Which of the numbers below is the correct answer to this calculation: $8 - 3 \times 2$?

(a) 10   (b) 18   (c) 2

13 Put brackets in the expression below to make the equation correct.

$7 + 3 \times 8 - 5 = 30$

14 (a) The temperature when I go to bed at 10 p.m. is 3°C. Overnight the temperature drops by 7°C. What is the temperature in the morning?

(b) How many degrees is a drop from ⁻9°C to ⁻17°C ?

Letts I See Maths Book 3

Test A2 levels 5 and 6

Calculator not allowed

1 This is a multiplication grid. It is used to work out 65×27.

Use the grid to complete the following questions.

×	20	7	
60	1200	420	1620
5	100	35	135
			1755

(a) $60 \times 27 =$

(b) $135 \div 65 =$

(c) $65 \times 27 =$

(d) $1755 \div 65 =$

(e) At the School Fayre, Martin charged people 27 pence for a go at skittles. An hour before the end of the Fayre he had collected £17·55. How many people had a go at skittles?

(f) Write the number 1755 to the nearest thousand.

2 (a) How many goes were recorded for the game of pick-a-stick?

(b) Which was the most popular game?

(c) What was the total number of goes recorded?

(d) (i) What fraction of the total number of goes was recorded for roll-a-penny?

(ii) Write this as a percentage.

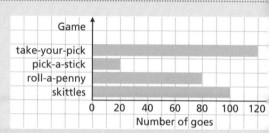

3 The octagon on the right is drawn on a centimetre-square grid. Which of the following statements is correct?

(a) The perimeter of the octagon is less than 8 cm.

(b) The perimeter of the octagon is exactly 8 cm.

(c) The perimeter of the octagon is more than 8 cm.

4 (a) What is the probability of scoring a five when rolling a die?

(b) What is the probability of selecting a red queen when you select a card at random from an ordinary set of playing cards with no jokers?

(c) What is the probability of getting two heads when you throw two coins?

5 Look at this table. Use the information in the table to write in words the meaning of each equation below.

(a) $r = 32$

(b) $r = 2p$

(c) $p + q = 37$

(d) $\frac{p + q + r}{3} = 23$

	Age in years
Rashid	p
Mark	q
Hannah	r

6 When $x = 7$, work out the values of the expressions below.

(a) $6x + 9$

(b) $5x - 14$

(c) $3x^2$

(d) $2x^2 - x$

Letts I See Maths **Book 3**

National Curriculum Tests

7 Solve the following equations.

(a) $3y + 7 = 19$ (b) $5x - 2 = 28$ (c) $3x + 2 = 2x + 7$

8 Complete the following equations.

(a) $^-3 + {^-4} =$ (b) $^-8 + 4 =$ (c) $^-9 - {^-5} =$ (d) $6 - {^-4} =$

9 (a) A sale offers an 8% discount. Work out the sale price of a pair of trainers costing £65 before the sale.

(b) The sale price of a DVD player is £243. If the discount was 10%, what was the original price of the DVD player?

10 (a) Draw the graphs of $y = 2x + 3$ and $y = 4x - 1$.

(b) Write down the coordinates where the two lines intersect.

(c) Explain why $y = 2x + 3$ and $y = 2x - 6$ cannot intersect.

(d) What is the gradient of the line $y = 7x - 9$?

11 Write down the next three consecutive terms of the following number sequences.

nth term	Sequence
$4n + 5$	9, 13, 17, ...
$3n - 6$	$^-3$, 0, 3, ...
$n^2 - 1$	0, 3, 8, ...
$2^n + 1$	3, 5, 9, ...

12 Work out the size of the angle marked $x°$, and give reasons for your answer.

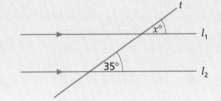

13 Which two numbers have a mean of 28 and a range of 8?

14 Simplify the following expressions.

(a) $2 \times 2 \times 2 \times 2 \times 5 \times 5$ (b) $x \times x \times x \times x \times y \times y \times y \times y$

Calculator not allowed

 1 In a bag there are four blue counters, seven red counters, nine green counters and three yellow counters.

(a) What is the probability that, if I select a counter at random, I will get a green counter?

(b) What is the probability of selecting a counter that is not green?

(c) What is the probability of selecting a counter that is black?

2 Simplify the following expressions.

(a) $2^5 \times 2^8 \times 2^7$

(b) $x^4 \times x^5 \times y^6 \times y^{11}$

3 Rearrange the formulae below to make the letters in square brackets the subjects.

(a) $s = 3(p + q)$ $[p]$

(b) $d = 5(a - b)$ $[b]$

4 (a) What is the equation of the locus of all the points that are the same distance from the points $(3, 2)$ and $(-5, 2)$?

(b) Write down the equations of the two lines that represent the locus of all the points that are the same distance from both the x-axis and the y-axis.

(c) Use a ruler and a pair of compasses to construct the perpendicular bisector of a line segment, AB = 6 cm.

(d) Construct the bisector of an angle of size 70°.

5 On a grid show the region satisfying the following inequalities.

$x + y < 10$, $x \geq 0$, $y \geq 0$

6

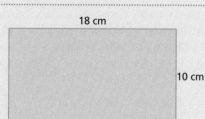

12 cm
8 cm
18 cm
10 cm

(a) Explain why these two rectangles are not mathematically similar.

(b) If you want the second rectangle to be mathematically similar to the first with the width 18 cm, what would be the height?

Letts I See Maths Book 3

7 (a) Work out the volume of a prism with a cross-section that is a regular hexagon of side 4 cm. (Leave your answer in surd form.)

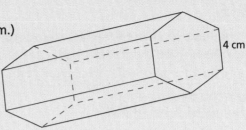

4 cm

(b) Work out the volume of a square-based pyramid with perpendicular height 8 cm and square base of side 5 cm.

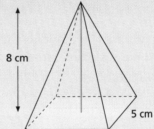

8 cm

5 cm

8 Write the following numbers in standard index form.

(a) 1 567 000   (b) 0·000 37

9 The two rectangles below have the same area.

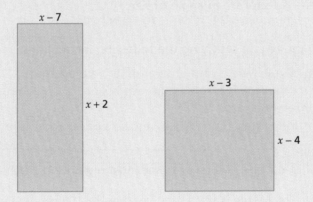

$x - 7$

$x + 2$

$x - 3$

$x - 4$

Use an algebraic method to find the value of x. You must show your working.

10 I mix a tin of paint with blue and white paint in the ratio 5 : 3. I use half the tin and then fill it with white paint. Now what is the ratio of blue to white paint in the tin?

Show your working.

Preparing for tests

Goals

When you have completed this lesson you will:

- 👁 know how to do mental-arithmetic tests
- 👁 know how to do calculator-allowed tests.

Mental-arithmetic test

- You will need a pencil and pen. You must *not* use a calculator.
- Each question will be read twice.
- Try to work out the answer to the question in your head. You may jot down workings if this helps.

Test – Higher tier

For this group of questions, you have 5 seconds to work out each answer and write it down.

(1) How many seconds are there in two and a quarter minutes?

(2) How many faces has a square-based pyramid?

(3) Look at the equation $y = 2x - 7$. When x equals five, what is the value of y?

(4) Write the ratio nine to fifteen in its simplest form.

(5) In a group of twenty-eight students, twenty-one are boys. What percentage of the group is boys?

For the next group of questions, you have 10 seconds to work out each answer and write it down.

(6) Write down the lowest common multiple of three and seven.

(7) The term-to-term rule in a sequence is 'subtract six'. If the first term is one, what are the next two consecutive terms?

(8) If the probability that it will rain tomorrow is 0·7, what is the probability that it will not rain?

(9) What is half of three hundred and thirty-two?

(10) Forty per cent of a number is 24. What is the number?

(11) Look at the expression $2x^3$. What is the value of the expression when x equals four?

(12) What is the sum of the interior angles of a pentagon?

(13) Multiply four x by five x. Write your answer in its simplest form.

(14) The nth term of a sequence is given by the expression $\frac{n(n+1)}{2}$. What is the seventh term?

(15) What is half of three-quarters?

(16) A solid shape has four faces, four vertices and six edges. What is its name?

For the next group of questions, you have 15 seconds to work out each answer and write it down.

(17) The perimeter of a rectangle is thirty-two centimetres. One side has length ten centimetres. What is the length of the other side?

(18) How many hours are there in four days?

(19) Increase £28 by ten per cent.

(20) A right-angled triangle has a hypotenuse of ten centimetres and one side of six centimetres. Work out the length of the third side.

(21) The angles of a triangle are given as x, $2x$, and $3x$. What are the sizes of the three angles?

(22) Work out the value of three squared multiplied by two to the power five.

Letts I See Maths Book 3

Calculator paper

- You may need pencil, pen, ruler, protractor, a pair of compasses and a calculator.

- You have 50 minutes to do the test. Do not waste time on questions that you cannot do. Make a note and come back to them if you have time at the end.

- Read the questions carefully and underline any information you want to remember.

- Show *all* your workings neatly.

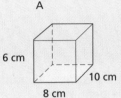
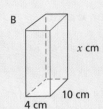

Example 1
The drawing shows two cuboids that have the same volume.

(a) What is the volume of cuboid A?

(b) Work out the value of the length marked x.

Answer:
(a) Volume of cuboid = lwh = $(8 \times 10 \times 6)$ cm³ = 480 cm³

> Even though you are using a calculator write down what you are doing.

(b) Volume of cuboid A = Volume of cuboid B
$$480 \text{ cm}^3 = (4 \times 10 \times x) \text{ cm}^3$$
$$480 \text{ cm}^3 = 40x \text{ cm}^3$$
$$x \text{ cm} = 12 \text{ cm}$$

Example 2
The diagram shows a square and a circle. The circle touches the edges of the square. What percentage of the diagram is shaded? (Use $\pi \approx 3.14$.)

Answer:
Area of circle   = 4π cm²
Area of square = 16 cm²

Use $\pi \approx 3.14$.

$$\frac{\text{Area of circle}}{\text{Area of square}} = \frac{4\pi}{16}$$
$$= \frac{\pi}{4}$$
$$\approx 3.14 \div 4$$

> First you need to know what proportion of the diagram is shaded.
>
> The shaded area is a circle.
>
> Write this as a fraction of the total area, which is a square.
>
> Use your calculator to divide 3·14 by 4, and then multiply by 100 to get the percentage.

The percentage of the diagram shaded is approximately 78·5%.

Plenary

- Identify the questions in the mental-arithmetic test that you could not do and set yourself targets for improvement.

- Mark the questions in Tests B1, B2 and B3, and do corrections.

- Write down the maths you are good at doing. Write down the maths you find difficult. Go back and do exercises from the book to help you with questions you find difficult.

Test B1 levels 3 and 4

Calculator allowed

1 Write down the answers.

(a) Add 327 to 649, then subtract 162.

(b) Multiply 427 by 17, then add 952.

(c) Add 103 to half of 936.

(d) How much less than 2005 is 48×19?

2 (a) A shop has 284 loaves of bread in the morning. By mid-day there are 74 loaves of bread left. How many loaves of bread have been sold?

(b) A gardener plants six rows of eight cabbages. How many cabbages did he plant?

(c) In a class the teacher says, 'Put the cups into groups of three.' There are nine groups of three and two cups left over. How many cups are there altogether?

3 (a) What is the total cost of a ham and cheese pizza, a cheese and pineapple pizza, a cola and a coffee?

Pizza Menu		Drinks	
Tomato and cheese	£6·35	Cola	90p
Ham and cheese	£7·40	Tea	£1·25
Cheese and mushroom	£7·65	Coffee	£1·85
Cheese and pineapple	£7·50		

(b) What change would you get from a £20 note?

(c) Nick has a £10 note. How much more does he need to buy a cheese and mushroom pizza and two cups of coffee?

4 Fill in the missing numbers.

(a) $805 - ... = 537$ (b) $... - 236 = 672$ (c) $67 \times ... = 2345$

(d) $6148 = ... + 96$ (e) $... \div 17 = 23$ (f) $510 \div ... = 30$

5 (a) How many people travelled by bus?

(b) How many people were in the survey altogether?

(c) What fraction of people travelled by car?

(d) What percentage of people travelled by bike?

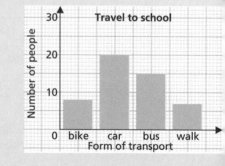

Letts I See Maths **Book 3**

6 Name the following shapes.

(a) The shape has four straight sides and is closed.

(b) The shape has four straight sides and is closed. It has two pairs of opposite sides equal and parallel.

(c) The shape has four straight sides and is closed. It has four right angles.

(d)

Fill in the gaps in the sentences below.

(i) The shape has … straight sides.

(ii) It has … pairs of parallel lines.

(iii) … sides are the same length.

(iv) The shape is a … .

7 (a) A coach can seat a maximum of 42 people. How many coaches would be needed to transport 384 people?

(b) The coach company charges £12·50 for every seat that is used and £3·50 for any seat left empty. Work out the total cost of hiring the coaches for the 384 people in part (a).

8 (a) What is the probability of getting the number 5 when I throw a die?

(b) If I get a 5 on the first throw of a die, what is the probability of getting a 5 on the second throw? Explain your answer.

(c) I throw the die six times. Is it certain that I will get at least one 5? Explain your answer.

9 Look at the four diagrams A, B, C and D.

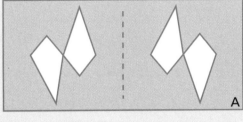

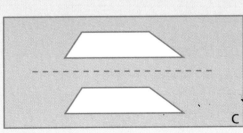

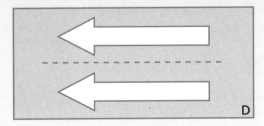

Write the letter of every diagram where the figure shows reflective symmetry in the dotted mirror line.

National Curriculum Tests

Test B2 levels 5 and 6

Calculator allowed

1   (a)   The rule to get to the next number in the number chain is **multiply by 2·4 then subtract 1·5**.

Fill in the two missing numbers in the number chain.

( ) ⟶ (10·5) ⟶ (23·7) ⟶ (55·38) ⟶ ( )

(b)   This number chain has a different rule.

(3·5) ⟶ (14) ⟶ (56) ⟶ (224) ⟶ (896)

Write down what the rule might be.

---

2   Tins are placed in rows of six, tightly in a box. Each tin has a diameter of 6·78 cm.

(a)   What is the length of one row?

(b)   The width of the box is 27·12 cm. How many tins can be placed in one layer in the box?

(c)   A total of 120 tins are to be placed in the box. How many layers of tins will there be?

(d)   The mass of each tin is 325 grams and the box has a mass of 400 grams. What is the total mass of the box of tins? Write your answer in kilograms.

---

3   Model aeroplanes are made using a scale such that 1 cm of the model represents 250 cm in real life.

(a)   The length of the model aeroplane is 8·25 cm. What is the length of the aeroplane in real life?

(b)   The length of a different aeroplane in real life is 26 m. What is the length of its model?

---

4   The probability that a component being made by a machine is faulty is 0·094.

(a)   What is the probability that a component will not be faulty?

(b)   Estimate how many faulty components there will be when the machine makes one thousand components?

---

5   Simplify these expressions.

(a) $3x + 9x + 11$ (b) $7x + 4y + 14x - 3y$ (c) $5a + 7b - 8a$

---

6   (a)   Work out $\frac{14}{15}$ of 555.   (b)   Work out 3·4% of 960.

---

7   (a)   Work out the volume of a cuboid with dimensions:

length = 17 cm, width = 12 cm and height = 29 cm.

(b)   The volume of a cube is 274·625 cm³. What is the length of its edges?

Letts **I See Maths** Book 3

National Curriculum Tests

8 Multiply out the brackets in each of the following expressions and write each answer in its simplest form.

(a) $5(2x + 3) + 9$ (b) $3(4x - 2) + 5(x + 4)$

9 Students in a school voted between two different school uniforms, Type A and Type B.

There were 279 students altogether. Two-thirds of the students were girls. One-third of the girls voted for Type B uniform. Altogether, 152 students voted for Type A uniform.

(a) Complete the two-way table.

	Boys	Girls	Total
Type A			
Type B			
Total			

(b) What percentage of boys chose Type A uniform? (Give your answer to one decimal place.)

10 A shape ABCDE is enlarged with linear scale factor 3·8 to become shape A′B′C′D′E′.

(a) If line AB = 9 cm, what is the length of line A′B′?

(b) What is the linear scale factor of enlargement from A′B′C′D′E′ to ABCDE? Give your answer to three significant figures.

11 The volume of a sphere is given by the formula $V = \frac{4}{3}\pi r^3$ where r is the radius of the sphere.

(a) Calculate the volume of a sphere with radius 2·5 cm. (Use $\pi \approx 3\cdot14$.) Give your answer to three significant figures.

(b) The volume of a sphere is given as 972π. What is its radius?

12 (a) Prices in a shop are increased by 2·5% in March and by a further 1·5% in April. What is the overall percentage increase?

(b) Prices are increased by x% in June and decreased by x% in July. Is the overall effect on prices:
(i) an increase (ii) a decrease (iii) no change?

13 A group of people have a mean age of 32 years and 4 months, and a range in age of 10 years and 2 months.

(a) What will be the mean age and the range in age of the same group of people exactly two years later?

(b) A new member joins the group at this time. Will the average age be increased by:
(i) more than a year (ii) exactly one year (iii) less than a year?

Calculator allowed

1 (a) Which calculation below gives the answer to the question,

'What is 320 increased by 4·5%?'

(i) 320×0.45 (ii) 320×0.045 (iii) 320×1.045 (iv) 320×1.45

(b) What single multiplication will decrease a quantity by 17%?

(c) What single multiplication will have the effect of increasing a quantity by 5% followed by a further increase of 5%?

2 (a) (i) Rewrite the equation $3y - 6x = 15$ in the form $y = ax + b$.

(ii) Write down the gradient of the graph of this equation.

(iii) What are the coordinates of the point where this graph intersects with the y-axis?

(b) (i) Draw the graphs of $y = 2x + 1$ and $y = 5x - 3$ on the same axes.

(ii) Write down the coordinates of the intersection of the two graphs.

(iii) Explain why this point gives the solution of $2x + 1 = 5x - 3$.

3 (a) How far did Tom travel on his journey?

(b) How long did Tom take to complete his journey?

(c) What was Tom's average speed on his journey?

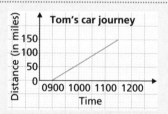

4 A box contains cards with one question on each card. There are four categories of questions. Each category has some easy and some difficult questions. The table shows the probability of selecting a card at random from the box.

Category	Difficult	Easy
sport	0·15	0·2
music	0·05	0·1
citizenship	0·1	0·15
health	0·2	0·05

Cards are drawn at random from the box.

(a) What is the probability it will be a citizenship question?

(b) What is the probability it will be a difficult question?

(c) There are 200 cards in the box. How many of these are health questions?

Letts I See Maths Book 3

National Curriculum Tests

5 (a) Plot the points A(2, 2), B(5, 2) and C(5, 6), and join them to form the triangle ABC.

(b) Calculate the length of the line AC.

(c) Find the coordinates of the midpoint of the line AC.

(d) Reflect triangle ABC in the line $y = x$ to form triangle A'B'C'.

---

6 (a) Draw triangle ABC with angle ABC a right angle. BC is labelled x, AC is labelled 12 and angle BAC = 42°.

Calculate the value of x.

(b) Draw triangle PQR with angle PQR a right angle. PQ is labelled 7, PR is labelled 15 and angle PRQ is y.

Calculate the value of angle y.

---

7 Simplify the expressions below.

(a) $\dfrac{x^4 y^3}{x^2 y}$

(b) $\dfrac{x^9 y^5 - x^3 y^7}{x^4 y^8}$

(c) $\dfrac{x^2 - y^2}{x + y}$

---

8 The diagram shows a prism with a cross-section that is a regular hexagon of side 4 cm.

(a) Calculate the area of the cross-section.

(b) Calculate the total surface area of the prism.

(c) Calculate the volume of the prism.

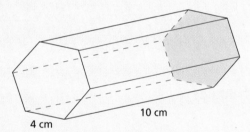

10 cm

4 cm

---

9 The diagram shows a square-based pyramid with height 12 cm and square base of side 5 cm.

(a) Calculate the volume of the pyramid.

(b) Calculate the length of the slant edge VA.

(c) Calculate the total surface area of the pyramid.

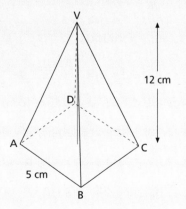

12 cm

5 cm

Glossary

additive inverse

The number which gives the identity when added to the original number.
For example: $3 + {}^-3 = 0$, so the additive inverse of 3 is ${}^-3$.

adjacent to ...

The same as 'next to ...'.
For example:
The angles $a°$ and $b°$ are adjacent to each other.

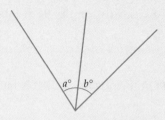

The integers 6 and 7 are adjacent to each other.

alternate angles

The lines l_1 and l_2 are parallel. The angles $c°$ and $d°$, formed by the line T as it crosses both lines, are equal and are called 'alternate angles'.

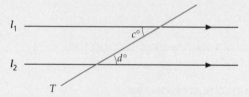

altitude

The vertical height of an object. The perpendicular distance from the vertex to the base of a geometrical figure or solid.

angle

An angle is a measure of turn as the object AB turns onto the image AC.

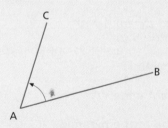

approximation

Find an expression for some quantity, accurate to a specified degree.
For example:
$57 \approx 60$ to the nearest 10
$\pi \approx 3 \cdot 14$ to 2 decimal places

Letts I See Maths Book 3

arc	Part of a curve.
	When using a pair of compasses, you might be asked to 'draw arcs' like those below.

arc

arithmetic sequence	A sequence of numbers where the difference between successive terms is constant. If a is the first term of the sequence and d is the common difference then the sequence is a, $a + d$, $a + 2d$, $a + 3d$, … .
	An arithmetic series is a string of terms obtained by adding the terms of an arithmetic sequence.
assumed mean	A number chosen to be close to the mean in order to make the calculation of the actual mean simpler to perform.
average	A way of summarising the variable in a set of data. There are three different types of average: the mean, mode and median.
axis, axes	A defined line such as an axis of reflection.
	A pair of rectangular axes is used to define a grid for drawing graphs.
axis of reflection	The line in which an object is reflected to produce an image. It is sometimes referred to as the 'mirror line' or a 'line of symmetry'.
bar chart	A diagram showing frequency by the height of columns.
bearing	Directions given by the amount of turn clockwise from north (measured in degrees).
bias	Not giving a fair outcome.
binomial factors	A binomial expression is one that contains just two terms.
	For example:
	$3x + 4y$ is a binomial expression.
	When the expression is seen in a product, it is a binomial factor.
	For example:
	$(3x + 4y)(2x − 6)$ has two binomial factors.
bisect	Divide into two equal parts.
bi-variate distribution	A distribution of two variables.

Glossary

box-and-whisker diagram (sometimes called a 'box plot')	A diagram depicting the five-point summary of a set of data: the lowest value; the lower quartile; the median; the upper quartile; the highest value. (See also quartiles.)

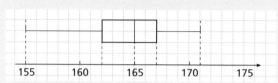

chord	A straight line joining two points on the circumference of a circle.
circle	A set of points that are equidistant from a single point (the centre).
circumcentre	The point of intersection of the perpendicular bisectors of the three sides of a triangle giving the centre of a circle that passes through each vertex of the triangle.
circumference	The distance around the outside of a circle.
circumscribe	To draw a shape that touches, but does not intersect, another geometrical shape.
coefficient	A numerical or constant factor of an algebraic term. The coefficient of x in the term $5x$ is 5. The coefficient of y in the term $3xy$ is $3x$.
commutative	Giving the same result whatever the order: $a * b = b * a$. Addition and multiplication are commutative. Subtraction and division are not commutative.
complementary angle	Either of two angles whose sum is 90°.
congruent	Identical in size and shape.
conjecture	A prediction based on results.
consecutive	Following one another without interruption. For example: 3, 4, 5, 6 are consecutive whole numbers.
construct	Use given measurements to draw accurately using geometrical instruments.
continuous data	Data that has been found by measuring.

Letts I See Maths Book 3

coordinates	A set of numbers defining a point. For example: (x, y) or $(3, 2)$
correlation	The extent to which variables are related.
corresponding angles	The lines l_1 and l_2 are parallel. The angles $e°$ and $f°$, formed by the line T as it crosses both lines, are equal and are called 'corresponding angles'.

cross-section	The plane surface made by cutting a solid.
cube	A solid with six identical square faces. OR The instruction to multiply a number by itself three times. For example: $5^3 = 5 \times 5 \times 5 = 125$
cuboid	A solid with six rectangular faces. A cube is a special kind of cuboid.
cube root	The number which when multiplied by itself and by itself again gives the given result. E.g. The cube root of 64 is 4 $(4 \times 4 \times 4 = 64)$. This is written as: $\sqrt[3]{64} = 4$ or $64^{\frac{1}{3}} = 4$.
cyclic quadrilateral	A quadrilateral with all of its vertices on the circumference of a circle.
data	Information that has been measured or counted.
data set	A collection of data.
decimal fraction	A fraction whose denominator is a power of ten. Decimal fractions can be written, for example, as $\frac{6}{10}$ or 0.6 or $\frac{72}{100}$ or $.72$.
denomination	A unit of measure such as pounds sterling, metres, litres, miles, fifths, hundredths, etc.
denominator	The number denoting the size of a fraction. For example: In the number $\frac{3}{5}$, the denominator 5 tells you that the denomination is fifths.

Glossary

diameter	A chord that passes through the centre of a circle.
difference	Used in mathematics specifically to mean the positive result of subtracting one number from another.
discount	To deduct an amount or percentage from a price.
discrete data	Data that has been found by counting.
distributed	Spread over.
distributive law	For example: $k(a + b) = ka + kb$ $\qquad$ $k(a - b) = ka - kb$ $6 \times 54 = 6 \times 50 + 6 \times 4$ $\qquad$ $6 \times 19 = 6 \times 20 - 6 \times 1$
equally likely	Events that have an equal chance of occurring.
equilateral triangle	A triangle that has all sides equal. The angles all equal 60°.
expected frequency (f_e)	The number of times you would expect something to occur, based on its properties or features. i.e. based on theoretical probability.
experimental frequency (f_o)	The number of times something occurs, based on experimental or observed results.
experimental probability (P_e)	A measure of probability that is calculated from a set of experimental data. For example: A set of data is collected about the weather and this is used to predict the probability of future weather patterns.
explicit	Used in mathematics to describe information that is given or can easily be seen.
expression	A collection of algebraic terms. Each of the following is an expression: $5x \qquad 2x + 3y - 4 \qquad 2 \times 3 + 5 \times 8$
exterior angle	An angle outside a shape formed by extending a line segment.

factor	A number that divides exactly into another number. For example: 5 is a factor of 20, x is a factor of $3xy$.
factorise	Write as the product of factors. For example: One way of factorising 12 is $12 = 3 \times 4$. The string of terms $3yz + 6ay$ can be factorised by writing $3y(z + 2a)$.
favourable outcomes	In a set of possible outcomes, those that satisfy the criteria. For example: If I am looking for even numbers in the set of numbers, 1, 2, 3, 4 and 5, then the favourable outcomes are 2 and 4. Two of the outcomes are favourable.
finite decimal	A number with an exact number of decimal places. For example: 0·5 or 4·362
formula (pl: formulae)	A way of expressing a rule using letters to denote quantities. For example: The formula for the area of a rectangle is lw, where l is the length and w the width.
frequency	In any set of data, the number of times a variable occurs is called its frequency. (It is how frequently the variable occurs.)
frequency diagram	A diagram representing grouped continuous data in columns.
frequency polygon	The shape that is the result of joining with straight lines the mid-points of the tops of bars representing continuous data.
frequency table	A table of events showing the number of times each event occurs.
function	A relationship between two sets of numbers. A mapping of one set of numbers onto another.
geometric sequence	A sequence of numbers where the ratio between successive terms is constant. If a is the first term of the sequence and r is the common ratio, then the sequence is $a, ar, ar^2, ar^3, \dots$. A geometric series is a string of terms obtained by adding the terms of a geometric sequence.
gradient	The steepness of a line.

Letts **I See Maths** Book 3

Glossary

highest common factor (HCF)	The largest number that divides exactly into each of a set of numbers. For example: 6 is the HCF of 18, 30, 42.
hypotenuse	The longest side of a right-angled triangle.
hypothesis	A predictive statement based on observation, experiments or theory.
identity element	When doing addition or subtraction of numbers, adding or subtracting zero has no effect: $3 + 0 = 3$ and $3 - 0 = 3$. Zero is the identity element for addition and subtraction. When doing multiplication or division of numbers, multiplication or division by the number one has no effect: $3 \times 1 = 3$ and $3 \div 1 = 3$. One is the identity element for multiplication and division.
image	The result of any mathematical operation. For example: If 5 (the object) undergoes the operation 'add 2', the result of this is 7, the image of 5. If $\triangle ABC$ is translated to a new position and is labelled $\triangle A'B'C'$, then $\triangle A'B'C'$ is the image of the object $\triangle ABC$.
implicit	Used in mathematics to mean information that can be deduced about something. For example: An isosceles triangle has two equal sides and two equal angles. The radii of a circle are equal. Multiplication is commutative.
incentre	The point of intersection of the three angle bisectors of the angles of a triangle that is the centre of a circle that touches the three sides of the triangle.
included angle	The angle between two given sides.
included side	A side between two given angles.

independent events	Events A and B are said to be independent if the occurrence of event A does not alter the probability of event B occurring, and vice versa.
index (pl: indices)	The value of the power to which a number is raised. For example: in 4^7, the index is 7. The number 7 is also called the 'exponent'.
infinite ∞	Uncountable. For example, there is an infinite number of fractions between a quarter and a half.
infinite decimal	A number with a never-ending number of decimal places. When there is a repeated pattern in the decimals they are called **recurring decimals**, e.g. $\frac{2}{11}$ as a decimal is 0·18181818 …and this is written as 0·1̇8̇. When there is no pattern in the decimals they are called **irrational** numbers, e.g. π.
inscribed	A shape that is totally inside another geometrical shape. The shapes touch but do not intersect.
integer	A positive or negative whole number.
intercept	A point at which two figures intersect. The y-intercept is the name given to the point where a straight line cuts the y-axis.
interior angle	An angle inside a closed shape. Any of the angles inside the triangle is an interior angle.
inter-quartile range	The difference between the values of the lower and upper quartiles of a set of data.
inverse operation	An operation that has an opposite or contrary effect. For example: Subtracting 3 has the opposite effect to adding 3. Dividing by 3 has the opposite effect of multiplying by 3. Rotating a shape 90° clockwise about a given point has the opposite effect of rotating the shape anti-clockwise about the given point. Finding the inverse cosine ($\cos^{-1}$) has the opposite effect of finding the cosine.

Glossary

inversely proportional	One set of numbers related to the reciprocal of another set of numbers with a constant scale factor. $y \propto \frac{1}{x}$ and $y = \frac{k}{x}$ (where k is a constant)
irrational	See 'infinite decimal'.
like terms	Algebraic terms containing the same letters such as $2ab$ and $7ab$ or $5x^2y$ and $8x^2y$.
linear	The word 'linear' implies a 'line'. In most cases in maths, it implies a straight line. A linear graph is a straight-line graph. A linear equation is one that implies a straight-line graph. The linear scale factor refers to the lengths of lines (not, for instance, the area).
locus (pl: loci)	A set of points determined by specified conditions.
mean	The average calculated by working out the total and dividing by the number of objects. For example: The mean of 3, 5, 2, 8 and 7 is $x = \frac{25}{5} = 5$.
median	The average calculated by placing the values of the variable in a set of data in order of size and working out the middle value. If the set contains an even number of values, the median is halfway between the two middle values.
modal class	The class of values of the variable in a set of data with the greatest frequency.
mode	The value of the variable in a set of data that occurs most frequently.
multiplicative inverse	The number which gives the identity when multiplied by the original number. For example: $\frac{2}{3} \times \frac{3}{2} = 1$, so the multiplicative inverse of $\frac{2}{3}$ is $\frac{3}{2}$. $5 \times \frac{1}{5} = 1$, so the multiplicative inverse of 5 is $\frac{1}{5}$.
mutually exclusive events	The single incident 'rolling a die' has many outcomes. Two events such as 'rolling a die and getting a 4' and 'rolling a die and getting a 5' cannot happen in a single incident. The two events are mutually exclusive. The single incident 'rolling a die' has many outcomes. Two events like 'rolling a die and getting a 4' and 'rolling a die and getting an even number' can happen in a single incident. The two events are not mutually exclusive.

negative number	For every positive number there exists a negative number such that their sum is zero. For example: $3 + {}^-3 = 0$ $\qquad 2{\cdot}5 + {}^-2{\cdot}5 = 0$ $\qquad 99 + {}^-99 = 0$ $\qquad x + {}^-x = 0$
numerator	The number denoting how many fractions of the given denomination there are. For example: In the number $\frac{3}{5}$, the numerator 3 tells you that there are three of those things called fifths.
observed frequency (f_o)	The number of times an event occurs in an experiment.
parallel lines	Lines that are always the same distance apart. Parallel lines never meet. Parallel lines point in the same direction.
percentage	'Compared to one hundred.'
perimeter	The distance all the way around a shape.
perpendicular	A line that is at right angles to another line.
perpendicular bisector	The line that cuts another line in half and is at right angles to that line.
π (pi)	An irrational number that relates the circumference and diameter of a circle: $C = \pi d$. Common approximations for π are: $\pi \approx \frac{22}{7}$, $\pi \approx 3$, $\pi \approx 3{\cdot}1$ and $\pi \approx 3{\cdot}14$.
population	The overall set of data from which a sample is taken.
possibility space	All the possible outcomes of an event or successive events.
possible outcomes	An example would be, when rolling a die, all the possible outcomes are 1, 2, 3, 4, 5 and 6.
prefix (e.g. mill- centi- deci- deca- hecto- kilo-)	The first part of a word used to describe the size of the unit being used.
prime	A number with only two factors, 1 and itself.
prime factor	A factor that is also a prime number.

Glossary

prism	A solid with a regular cross-section.
probability	An estimate of how frequently something will happen based on theory or experiment.
product	The result of multiplication.
oportional	One set of numbers relating to another set of numbers with a constant scale factor.
quartiles	Any data set has three quartiles: the first quartile (Q_1); the second quartile (Q_2); and the third quartile (Q_3). They are summary statistics. They are calculated by listing the data set, from the lowest value to the highest value, and separating it into four quarters of equal frequency. The three values of the variable at the boundaries are called the quartiles. The second quartile (Q_2) is also called the median.
quota sample	A way of selecting a representative sample by choosing sub-samples of a given size from particular groups. For example: Selecting a fixed number of people from given age groups.
quotient	The result of a division.
radius (pl: radii)	The distance from the centre to the circumference of a circle.
random sample	A sample taken from a population using a system or method to avoid bias.
range	The difference between the largest and smallest values in a set of data.
ratio	The comparison of quantities.
rational number	A number that can be expressed as a vulgar fraction.
recurring decimal	See 'infinite decimal'.
regular	Used in mathematics to denote a polygon with all its sides equal and all its angles equal.
relative frequency	The number of times an event occurs relative to the total number of trials.

rombus	A quadrilateral with four equal sides.
rotational symmetry	A property of a shape as a result of turning about some point. For example: A rectangle has rotational symmetry of order 2 because it can turn 180° and 360° about its centre and fit exactly into its original shape.
sample	A selection of the variable of a specified population.
sample space	An alternative name for a possibility space.
scale factor	The number used to multiply a quantity.
scalene triangle	A triangle with no equal sides.
scatter diagram (or scattergraph)	A diagram used to represent bi-variate data.
sector	A part of a circle bounded by two radii and an arc.
segment	A part of a circle bounded by a chord and an arc.
sequence	Something that is placed in order. For example: This is a sequence of numbers: 3, 6, 9, 12.
shear	The transformation of a shape such that all points at a distance from a given line move parallel to that line. The greater the distance from the given line the further the points will move.
significant figures	The word 'significant' means 'important'. The number 2354 has four significant figures. We do not always need such a high level of accuracy. An approximate value would be 2000 (to one significant figure – 1 sig. fig.) or 2400 (to 2 sig. figs.) or 2350 (to 3 sig. figs.). Not all figures are significant. For example: The number 0.007 23 has three significant figures. The zeros in front of the 7 merely indicate place value and are not significant.

Letts I See Maths Book 3

Glossary

similar	Geometrical shapes with identical angles and corresponding sides in the same ratio.
simplify	Write in a less complicated form. For example: In algebra, the string of terms, $3y + 2a + 2y$, has the same value as $5y + 2a$, but $5y + 2a$ is simpler. In fractions, the number $\frac{28}{70}$ has the same value as $\frac{14}{35}$ and $\frac{2}{5}$, but the number $\frac{2}{5}$ is its simplest form.
simultaneous solution	A solution that provides answers to more than one problem at the same instant.
solution	Used in algebra to refer to the specific value or values of a variable that satisfy an equation. For example: The solution of $x + 2 = 5$ is $x = 3$. 'Solve this equation' means 'state its solution(s)'. In an equation such as $x + 2 = 5$, the value of x is implicit. The solution $x = 3$ is explicit.
square	A quadrilateral with four equal sides and four right angles. OR An instruction to multiply a number by itself. For example: $3^2 = 3 \times 3 = 9$
square root	The number that was squared to produce the given number. For example: $\sqrt{25} = \pm 5$.
square-based pyramid	A 3D shape with a square base reducing to a vertex above the base.
standard index form	Expressing a number in the form $a \times 10^n$ where $1 \leq a < 10$, and n is any integer.
stratified sample	Selecting a sample from a population by first dividing the population into status groups and then taking a random sample from each group.
successive	Following another without interruption.
supplementary angle	Either of two angles that have a sum of 180°.
surd	The number $\sqrt{2}$ is a surd: it is expressed using a square root sign and its value is an infinite decimal (it is an irrational number). This means that $\sqrt{4}$ is not a surd (because the value, 2, is rational). The expression $\sqrt{4}$ is known as a radical.

term	A single number or letter, or the product or quotient of numbers and/or letters.
theoretical expected frequency (f_e)	The number of times you would expect an event to occur based on its properties.
theoretical probability (P)	Probability that is calculated using implicit information. For example: A coin has two faces and one of them is a head. The probability of getting a head when you spin a coin is therefore considered to be $\frac{1}{2}$.
transformation	A change according to some rule.
translation	A transformation that moves an object from one position to another without turning, reflecting or enlarging.
transversal	A line that crosses other lines.
trapezium	A quadrilateral with at least one pair of parallel sides.
trial	When an event is recorded it is called a trial.
unbiased	When any possible outcome is equally likely to occur.
variable	Having a range of possible values.
vector	A pair of numbers $\begin{pmatrix} x \\ y \end{pmatrix}$ describing a translation.
velocity	The rate of change of the position of an object in a particular direction.
vertex (pl: vertices)	The point where straight lines meet.
vertically opposite angles	

Published by Letts Educational
The Chiswick Centre
414 Chiswick High Road
London W4 5TF
✆ 020 89963333
✆ 020 87428390
✉ mail@lettsed.co.uk
🌐 www.letts-education.com

Letts Educational is part of the Granada Learning Group. Granada
Learning is a division of Granada plc.

© Sue Jennings and Richard Dunne 2003

First published 2003

ISBN 184 085 6947

The authors assert the moral right to be identified as the authors of
this work.

All rights reserved. No part of this publication may be reproduced,
stored in a retrieval system, or transmitted in any form or by any
means, electronic, mechanical, photocopying, recording or
otherwise, without either the prior permission of the Publisher or a
licence permitting restricted copying in the United Kingdom issued
by the Copyright Licensing Agency Ltd, 90 Tottenham Court Road,
London W1P 9HE. This book is sold subject to the condition that it
shall not by way of trade or otherwise be lent, hired out or
otherwise circulated without the publisher's prior consent.

British Library Cataloguing in Publication Data
A catalogue record for this book is available from the British Library.

Acknowledgements
Commissioned by Helen Clark
Project management by Vicky Butt
Designed and edited by Topics · The Creative Partnership, Exeter
Cartoons by Jim Peacock
Printed and bound in the UK by Ashford Colour Press